KU-660-818

by Carrick Publishing,
Road, Ayr, KA7 2AY
79
ished 1985
ght Carrick Publishing 1985

reserved. No part of this publication may be reproduced, stored in
system, or transmitted, in any form or by any means, electroni
al, photocopying, recording or otherwise, without the prior permissio
Publishing.

great care has been taken to ensure the accuracy of entries, th
do not assume, and hereby disclaim, any liability to any party for an
amage caused by errors or omissions in The Scottish Companion,
uch errors or omissions result from negligence, accident or any othe

Great Britain by
owe Ltd.
am

THE SCOTTISH COMPANION

THE SCOTTISH C

First Edition 1

Published
28 Miller
0292 266
First pub
© Copyr

All rights
retrieval
mechanic
of Carric

*Although
publisher
loss or
whether
cause.*

Printed in
Antony R
Chippenh

Carrick Publishing

WE PUT NORTH SCOTLAND IN THE PICTURE

Broadcasting experience, local knowledge and continued investment in advanced technology enable Grampian Television to provide a wide-ranging programme service to over 1.28 million people from Fife to Shetland.

GRAMPIAN TELEVISION

STUDIOS: Queen's Cross, Aberdeen 0224 646464
Albany House, Dundee 0382 739363
Huntly Street, Inverness 0463 242624

OFFICES: Manor Place, Edinburgh 031 226 3926
Glasshouse Street, London 01 439 3141

ROYAL HIGHLAND EXHIBITION CENTRE

Every Facility you need to make your event a success.

The Exhibition Hall is situated in the Royal Highland Showground at Ingliston, just west of Edinburgh. It offers 6,000 sq. metres (64,590 sq. feet) of custom designed accommodation for exhibitions, conferences and events, with an additional 8,000 sq. metres of covered exhibition space adjacent.

For further information write: Reservations Manager, Royal Highland Exhibition Centre, P.O. Box 1, Ingliston, Newbridge, Midlothian, or Tel 031-333 3036/2444.

The ideal place for exhibitions, conferences and events –large and small– indoor and outdoor– all seasons.

- Adjacent to Edinburgh Airport.
- Centrally situated, 10km (6½ miles) from Edinburgh Haymarket railway station and less than an hour by motorway from Glasgow, Stirling, Perth and Dundee.
- Generous catering facilities.
- Parking for 20,000 cars.
- 40 Hectares (100 acres) fully-serviced and landscaped outdoor exhibition area.

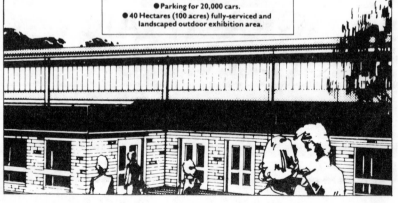

CONTENTS

ScotRail
serving a nation.

ScotRail plays a vital role in the transport needs of the nation.

Fast, frequent services carry commuters to and from work, housewives on shopping trips, families on holidays and leisure outings. For the travelling business executive smooth InterCity trains link all the major cities in Scotland and throughout the U.K.

Railfreight carries the country's produce — both day and night — with Speedlink services providing the important connection between manufacturer and consumer, while Rail Express Parcels offer the fastest, most frequent same day parcels service in the mainland.

ScotRail has more than 16,000 employees waiting to serve you. Contact them at:—
Head Office:
Buchanan House,
58 Port Dundas Road,
Glasgow G4 0HG
(Telephone: 041-332 9811)
or stations and offices throughout the country.

ScotRail

FOREWORD

by Kenneth Roy, Editor *The Scottish Companion*
Welcome to the first edition of *The Scottish Companion* – which we intend to make an annual work of reference devoted to all things Scottish. If, by the end of 1985, users of the book are pausing to wonder how they managed without *The Scottish Companion*, we will have succeeded in our aim.

It is a curious fact that such a comprehensive guide to the public life of Scotland has not been attempted before. Certainly, there are well-established directories devoted to specific aspects of Scottish affairs, local government and the law, for example. But these are consciously narrow in range, and in any case primarily intended for specialists. *The Scottish Companion* seeks to encourage the many different Scotlands to co-exist within its pages. It strives to be all-encompassing, as informative on the Scottish theatre as it is on the Scottish banks. Here, the reader will find learned societies jostling with major industries, tourist boards with judicial tribunals, further education colleges with regiments.

In another respect, *The Scottish Companion* also fulfils a distinctive role among reference books about Scotland. It addresses itself to the general reader as well as to those with a professional interest in the organisations and institutions listed. Readers who consult the book with a view to leisure interests or educational opportunities will find it just as ready a source of information as those who use it mainly as a practical guide to who does what in today's Scotland.

We list about 1,000 bodies of all shapes, sizes, and sorts. Many were selected by virtue of their positions of importance in the life of Scotland; some – particularly so in the case of sports governing bodies – were included as representative of a sphere of activity; and we also invited some organisations regional or local in scope, such as enterprise trusts and chambers of commerce. We drew a line before local branches of national bodies.

Entries are arranged from A to Z. We considered a system of classification, but in view of the many difficulties, settled for a straightforward alphabetical sequence, supported by a broadly-based classified index.

Most entries have been compiled with the active co-operation of the organisations concerned, and we wish to thank all those who took the time and trouble to complete our questionnaire. Without them, there would have been no book! More than three-quarters of those circulated responded – a gratifying display of confidence in an unknown quantity. As for the rest, some verified a basic entry compiled by our own staff, while others could not be traced or ignored our repeated requests for information and were therefore reluctantly omitted. Three organisations confessed themselves unwilling to co-operate; they have been entered as nil returns.

We would be pleased to hear of, or from, any organisation inadvertently omitted, in time to make amends for the 1986 edition, preparations for which will begin in the late summer. Indeed, any helpful suggestions from readers would be much appreciated. We aim to make the book not only a reliable companion, but a friendly one.

LOTHIAN REGIONAL COUNCIL

Napier College EDINBURGH

DEGREE COURSES (CNAA)

Full-time: BA Accounting
           BSc Applied Chemistry (Hons/Ord)
           BSc Biological Sciences
           BA Business Studies
           BA Catering and Accommodation Studies
           BA Commerce (Hons/Ord)
           BSc Communication and Electronic Engineering

BSc Computing and Data Processing
BSc Energy Engineering
BSc Industrial Design (Technology)
BA Photographic Studies
BSc Science with Industrial Studies (Hons/Ord)
BEng Technology with Industrial Studies (Hons/Ord)
BEng Transportation Engineering

Part-time: BA Business Studies, BSc Life Sciences
           BSc Quantity Surveying

HIGHER NATIONAL DIPLOMA/HIGHER DIPLOMA COURSES

Accounting	Business Studies	Electrical and Electronic	Legal Studies
Applied Physics with	Business Studies with	Engineering	Music
Electronics	Languages	Engineering (Mechanical/	Printing Administration and
Applicable Mathematics	Chemistry	Production)	Production
Biology	Civil Engineering	Hotel, Catering and	Secretarial Studies
Book and Periodical	Communication Studies	Institutional Management	Secretarial Studies and
Publishing	Computer Studies	Interior Design	Languages
Building	Computer Data Processing	Journalism Studies	

PROFESSIONAL/POST GRADUATE COURSES

Accounting (ACA/ICMA)	European Marketing and Languages	Personnel Management
MSc Biology of Water	(CNAA)	Systems Analysis and Design
Management	Graduate Secretaries	Transportation Engineering (Part-time)
Careers Guidance (Diploma)	Industrial Administration (DIA)	Transportation Planning in
Chemistry (GRSC)	Management (DMS) (CNAA) (Part-time)	Developing Countries

FOR INFORMATION WRITE TO:

        ACADEMIC REGISTRAR (ADMISSIONS)
        NAPIER COLLEGE, SIGHTHILL COURT, EDINBURGH EH11 4BN. 031 453 6111

YOUR SECOND CHANCE

Stay and Study at Newbattle Abbey, Scotland's Adult Residential College.
One and two-year courses with choice of subjects from:

Logic : Economics : Trade Union Studies
History : Government : English Literature
Sociology : Philosophy : Political Theory
French : General Studies

During vacations there are short courses in leisure interests and activities
Further details from

The Secretary,
NEWBATTLE ABBEY COLLEGE
Dalkeith, Midlothian, EH22 3LL
Tel. 031-683 1921

EXPLANATORY NOTES

i. Arrangement of entries

Common prefixes, such as **Scottish** or **Society of** are placed at the end of the entry title, e.g. **Churches Council, Scottish.** Entries are arranged in strict alphabetical order, according to the alphabetical sequence of the entire entry title, e.g. **Law Commission, Scottish** is followed by **Lawn Tennis Association, Scottish,** which is in turn followed by **Law Reporting, Scottish Council of.**

ii. Structure of entries

In a typical entry, the name of the organisation is given in bold, followed in parenthesis by its year of foundation, its Headquarters (or only) address and telephone number, its principal office-bearers and staff, and a description of its objectives and functions.

iii. Structure of index

A comprehensive index is provided in which all entries are classified under at least one subject heading. For ease of reference, most prominent organisations can be found in more than one classification, e.g. Rowett Research Institute appears under **Agriculture and Fisheries** as well as under **Research Institutes.**

UNIVERSITY OF GLASGOW

One of the largest universities in Britain, teaching and
researching in over 130 subjects, Glasgow University is
further developing its links with industry and with the
community at large, and welcomes enquiries about its
services to business, industry and the professions.

- Consultancies and R & D Joint Ventures
  Patent Licensing and Science Park
- Training and Updating Courses
  Science and Technology, Management, Languages
- Purpose-built Kelvin Conference Centre
  Residential and Non-Residential Facilities

For further information contact:

University of Glasgow
Glasgow G12 8QQ

Tel: 041-339-8855

Industrial Liaison	Ext. 7199
Education and Training	Ext. 394
Conferences and Accommodation	Ext. 7385

A

Aberdeen and District Milk Marketing Board (1934), Twin Spires, Bucksburn, Aberdeen, AB2 9NR. T.-0224 696371. Chairman: I. Marr; Vice Chairman: W.J. Ferguson. Managing Director and Secretary to the Board: R.C. Naylor; Marketing Director: I. Owen. Established by the authority of the Agriculture Marketing Act for the organised marketing of milk.

Aberdeen-Angus Cattle Society (1879), Pedigree House, 6 King's Place, Perth, PH2 8AD. T.-0738 582477. Secretary: Robert Anderson. To maintain unimpaired the purity of the breed, and promote the breeding of Aberdeen-Angus.

Aberdeen Chamber of Commerce (1877), 15 Union Terrace, Aberdeen AB9 1HF. T.- 0224 641222. President: Charles P. Skene. Chief Executive: Derek G. Marnoch. Promotion of business interests.

Aberdeen College of Commerce (1959), Holburn Street, Aberdeen, AB9 2YT. T.-0224 572811. Principal: J.M. Ferguson; Deputy Principal: W.G. Eady. College of further education with the following teaching departments: accounting and legal studies; business studies; English and communication studies; general studies; language studies; mathematics, science and computing studies; office administration studies; secretarial studies.

Aberdeen College of Education (1958), Hilton Place, Aberdeen, AB9 1FA. T.-0224 42341. Chairman: W.B. Anderson, O.B.E. Principal: D.A. Adams. The primary function of the College is the training of teachers, both pre-service and in-service. It also trains youth and community workers.

Aberdeen District Council (1974), Town House, Aberdeen, AB9 1AQ. T.-0224 642121. Lord Provost: H.E. Rae; Members: D. Clyne, A.J. Forrest, R. Gallagher, N.B. Lindsay, A.P. MacLean, B. Fenwick, B.M. Mearns, Freda Mutch, G. Urquhart, A.C. Collie, R. Slater, C.H. Clevitt, J. Ewen, R.H. Thomson, Margaret Farquhar, C.W. Devine, J.A. Donaldson, B.S. Morrison, R. Clark, R. Hutcheon, P.J. Woodward-Nutt, Jillian Wisely, Agnes Keay, N. Cooney, J.M. Low, Elizabeth Henry, Elizabeth Kelly, R.A. Robertson, D.B. Walley, E.S. Massie, J. Sim, R.R. Webster, G.C. Adams, W.J. Fraser, B. Rattray, Janetta Anderson, F. McCallum, D.C. Davidson, N.L. Bonney, R.G. Milne, R.D.I. Anderson, M.C. Hastie, D.P. Durward, T. Paine, M.K. Savidge, M.J. Sheehan, J. Wyness, Catherine Nikodem, Margaret Havergal. Town Clerk and Chief Executive: John M. Wilson; Director of Law and Administration: J.J.K. Smith; City Chamberlain: George G. Niven; Director of Planning and Building Control: Albert Allen; Director of Housing: Trevor Muir; Director of Cleansing: D.S. Stephen; Director of Environmental Health: R.P. Findlay; Director of Personnel and Management Services: F.T. Dohan; Director of Art Gallery and Museums: I.

McKenzie Smith; Director of Leisure and Recreation: D. Welch; City Librarian: P. Grant; Director of Building and Works: D.A. Macdonald; Director of Development and Tourism: G.E. Henry; City Architect: Ian A. Ferguson; Director of Estates: A.J. MacColl. District Council. Population of District: 212,000.

Aberdeen Fish Curers' and Merchants' Association Ltd. (1944), South Esplanade West, Aberdeen. T.- 897744. Chairman: J. Kelly; Vice Chairman: G. Cumming. Chief Executive and Secretary: R.H. Milne. Trade association representing 170 members; also operates a box factory, stores department, filling station, and accountancy service to members.

Aberdeen Harbour Board (1960), Harbour Office, 16 Regent Quay, Aberdeen, AB9 1SS. Chairman: G.M. Lawrence. General Manager: J.R. Turner; Secretary: J.R. Scott; Harbour Master: Captain B. Atkinson. Major Scottish port with extensive modern facilities for handling cargo of all types: international passenger terminal; largest fish market in Scotland; largest and principal offshore support harbour in Europe.

Aberdeen Technical College, Gallowgate, Aberdeen, AB9 1DN. T.-0224 640366. Principal: Andrew M. Bole. College of further education.

Aberdeen, University of (1495), Regent Walk, Aberdeen, AB9 1FX. T.-0224 40241. Chancellor: Rt. Hon. The Lord Polwarth, T.D.; Vice Chancellor and Principal: George P. McNicol; Vice Principals: Professor Hamish M. Keir, Professor James C. Laidlaw; Secretary: William M. Bradley. University Court: (ex officio) The Rector, The Principal, Professor Hamish M. Keir; (Chancellor's Assessor) Calum A. MacLeod; Rector's Assessor; (co-opted) Andrew G. MacEwen, Richard T. Ellis, O.B.E., Roger J.C. Fleming, O.B.E., T.D., J.P., William Kemp, M.B.E., James C. Laidlaw; (Assessor nominated by Grampian Regional Council) John Sorrie; (Assessor nominated by Aberdeen District Council) William J. Fraser, J.P.; (Assessors elected by General Council) Harold M.R. Watt, J.P., Sheila E. Ritchie, Elizabeth Garrett, Alexander L. Stalker, T.D.; (Assessors elected by Senatus) Roy D. Weir, Anthony S. Milton, Robert S. Moore, Edward M. Patterson, James G. Roberts, Henry R. Sefton.
Senatus Academicus: Professorial Members holding established Chairs: Professors H.M. Keir, J.C. Laidlaw, J.D. Hargreaves, J.D. Nisbet, O.B.E., R.H. Thomson, F.W. Bealey, E.M. Patterson, M. Gaskin, D.F.C., J.R. Mallard, P.H. Ramsey, D.F. Kerridge, R.E. Henderson, M.C. Meston, C. Chadwick, R.D. Weir, P.L. Payne, F.W. Robertson, A.S. Douglas, R.A.S. Barbour, M.C., G.D. MacCormack, G.M. Dunnet, A. Martin, C.H. Gimingham, R.P. Draper, E.A. Salzen, A.G.M. Campbell, P.E. Brown, W. Walker, A.S. Milton, F. Lyall, A.J. Whiteman, M.F. Morley, P.N. Love, C.B.E., E.J. Clegg, R.S. Moore, A.R. MacLeary, J.B. Torrance, J.R. Smith, G.W. Ashcroft, G. Rochford, G.A. Lodge, J.R. Hubbuck, J.F.D. Greenhalgh, G.S.S. Yule, J.R. Cameron, T.H. Pennington, P. Wilkinson, W. Ritchie, W. Mordue, S.R. Reid, W. Johnstone, G.V. Marr, J.W. Parsons, I.H. Marshall, F. Walker, H.G. Miller, J.V. Forrester, P.J. Sloane, C. Kidd, G.F. Bass.
For 267 years there were two separate universities in Aberdeen, each with its own statutory rights and degree-granting privileges. The first, King's College, was founded in Old Aberdeen under a papal bull in 1495. The second, Marischal College, was founded in New Aberdeen under a charter dated 1593. The two colleges remained rival institutions until 1860, when a royal ordinance united them. Today, there are five Faculties within the University

of Aberdeen: Arts and Social Sciences; Science; Divinity; Law; and Medicine. The University has about 5,500 students.

Aberdeen, University of, Department of Adult Education and Extra Mural Studies, Kings College, Aberdeen, AB9 2UB. T.-0224 40241. Director: William D. Brooker. Established to make available the expertise within the University to the community in general, in Grampian and Highland Regions, the Western Isles, Orkney and Shetland. Offices in Inverness and Thurso deal with the northern areas.

Academy of Music and Drama, Royal Scottish, St. George's Place, Glasgow, G2 1BS. T.-041-332 4101. Chairman, Board of Governors: J. Ainslie Millar, T.D. Principal: Philip Ledger; Registrar: T.W.M. Gourdie. The Academy offers specialist education in music and drama at tertiary level. Degree courses in both music and drama are validated by the University of Glasgow; postgraduate courses in music are also available. Part-time courses in music and drama for children of school age.

Academy, Royal Scottish (1826), The Mound, Edinburgh, EH2 2EL. T.-031-225 6671. President: H. Anthony Wheeler, O.B.E. Secretary: Robert R. Steedman; Treasurer: William J.L. Baillie; Members of Council: John Houston, David McClure, Gordon Cameron, Frances Walker, Elizabeth Blackadder, Sir Robin Philipson. Administrative Secretary: F.K.B. Murdoch, C.V.O., M.B.E., T.D. Art Gallery.

Accident Prevention Council, Scottish (1930), 41 South West Thistle Street Lane, Edinburgh, EH2 1EW. T.-031-226 6856. Chairman: Councillor J. Jennings (Strathclyde). Secretary to the Council: A.F. Dryburgh. To co-ordinate and stimulate the work of accident prevention by the constituent local authorities and by all other organisations with an interest in accident prevention in Scotland. The Council's objectives are achieved through three main Standing Committees: Road Safety; Home Safety; and Water Safety. The secretariat for the Council is provided by the Royal Society for the Prevention of Accidents.

Actuaries in Scotland, Faculty of (1856), 23 St. Andrew Square, Edinburgh, EH2 1AQ. T.-031-557 1575. President, Council: Alexander Denis Shedden; Hon. Treasurer: Alistair Neill; Hon. Secretary: William McCorkindale; Hon. Secretary: William Proudfoot. Secretary: William Wallace Mair. Professional body concerned with the education and training of actuaries, in the setting of professional standards in the business of life assurance and in consulting practice.

Adoption Association, Scottish (1923), 69 Dublin Street, Edinburgh, EH3 6NS. T.-031-556 2070. Chairman: Lady Cowie; Acting Vice Chairman: Dr R. Scott; Treasurer: R.A.L. Finlay; Medical Adviser: Dr N. Johnston; Fund Raising Chairman: Mrs R. Plumb. Senior Social Worker: Mrs E.M. Thornton; Social Workers: Mrs S. McGuire, Mrs P. Keen. Voluntary organisation whose aim is to find loving and secure adoptive homes for young children unable to remain with their natural parents. The Association provides counselling for unmarried or separated parents to enable them to decide whether or not to place their child for adoption; fostering for a few weeks before placement when requested by the natural mother; support for mothers who decide to keep their babies; counselling for childless couples; and information and preparation for prospective adopters, both in groups and individually. Its work in arranging adoption placements involves visits to adoptive homes and undertaking the necessary legal work. The Association co-operates with local authority social work departments and other voluntary agencies.

Adult Basic Education Unit, Scottish (1980), Atholl House, 2 Canning Street, Edinburgh, EH3 8EG. T.-031-229 2433. Chairman: Professor Lalage Bown. Director: Pablo Foster; National Field Consultants: Dona Williams, Alicia Bruce, Brendan Donovan, Jeana Papamichael. Provides support for regional adult basic education schemes, voluntary organisations, and any agency with a potential for providing adult basic education. Offers training, materials, and programme development.

Adult Education, Scottish Institute of (1949), 30 Rutland Square, Edinburgh, EH1 2BW. T.-031-229 0331; 031-229 0311. President: Dr Ethel Gray, C.B.E.; Honorary Fellows: N. Dees, T.E.M. Landsborough; Hon. Life Member: Vernon Smith. Director: Dr Elisabeth Gerver; Administrative Assistant: Celia Carson. National membership organisation which aims to advance education among adults, and to co-ordinate the efforts of organisations, institutions, and individuals in attaining that aim. It brings together full-time, part-time, and volunteer workers from all the different sectors and levels of adult education. The Institute promotes the discussion of policy and practice, encourages new ideas and ventures, offers a variety of information services, and plays an active role in international adult and continuing education.

Advisory Conciliation and Arbitration Service (1976), Franborough House, 123-157 Bothwell Street, Glasgow, G2 7JR. T.-041-204 2677. Director, Scotland: Matt Cochran. To help workers, their representatives, and employers resolve trade disputes and improve their industrial relations generally.

Advocates, Faculty of, Advocates' Library, Parliament House, Edinburgh, EH1 1RF. T.-031-226 5071. Dean of Faculty: W.D. Prosser, Q.C.; Vice Dean of Faculty: J.A. Cameron, Q.C.; Treasurer of Faculty: A.C.M. Johnston, Q.C.; Keeper of the Library: J.T. Cameron, Q.C.; Clerk of Faculty: N.M.P. Morrison, Advocate. Librarian: J.A. Sibbald.
Professional body to which all persons practising before the Supreme Courts of Scotland and holding the office of Advocate must belong. The Faculty is responsible for the qualification, training, and discipline of Advocates and provides services for them, including a copyright law library. The exact date of the establishment of the Faculty is unknown, but Advocates were known to exist before 1532.

Age Concern Scotland (1943), 33 Castle Street, Edinburgh, EH2 3DN. T.-031-225 5001. Chairman: Dr Jack Kane, O.B.E.; Vice Chairmen: Marjorie McInnes, O.B.E., Very Rev. Dr R. Leonard Small, C.B.E.; Treasurer: Thomas R. Moffat; Law Agent: Brenda Rennie. Director: Mary Marshall; Assistant Director (Administration and Finance): Edith MacKenzie; Assistant Director (Development): Averil Osborn. Borders Development Officer: Ann Ferguson, 31 Queen's Croft, Kelso, Roxburghshire (T.-0573 23339); Grampian Development Officer: Sandra Thomas, c/o Centre for the Deaf, Smithfield Road, Aberdeen (T.-0224 40404); Strathclyde Project Co-ordinator: Charles Ferrier, 657 Edgefauld Road, Glasgow, G21 (T.-041-558 1511); Tayside Development Officer: Ian Borthwick, 3 Stirling Terrace, Dundee (T.-0382 25729).
The Scottish Old People's Welfare Committee was formed in 1943, and became known as Age Concern Scotland in 1974. Its aim is to improve services for older people and campaign on their behalf. It supports a network of more than 200 local groups which provide practical services, and acts as a

centre of information and social advocacy on subjects related to the welfare of older people.

Agricultural Arbiters' Association, Scottish (1925), 10 Dublin Street, Edinburgh, EH1 3PR. T.-031-556 2993. President: John F. Seed; Vice President: G.K. Robertson. Secretary: Kenneth M. Campbell. Professional body for agricultural arbiters or valuers.

Agricultural Benevolent Institution, Royal Scottish (1897), Ingliston, Newbridge, Midlothian EH28 8NB. T.-031-333 1023. Chairman, Board of Directors: David C. Marshall, V.R.D.; Vice Chairman: John M. Stevenson. Secretary: Kenneth M. Campbell; Organising Secretary: Miss M. Ritchie Hay. Founded to commemorate Queen Victoria's Diamond Jubilee. The Institution is the only national organisation in Scotland which assists aged or infirm farmers or their dependents who are in needy circumstances. Last year, the total given in payments and grants was more than £66,000. Income is derived solely from voluntary contributions and bequests.

Agricultural Consultative Panel, Scottish (1963), c/o Department of Agriculture and Fisheries for Scotland, Chesser House, 500 Gorgie Road, Edinburgh, EH11 3AW. T.-031-443 4020, Ext. 2531. Chairman: D.G. Mackay; Secretary: J.M. Stephen. Originally the Winter Keep Consultative Panel. Advises on certain cases of dispute between the Department and farmers, and expresses views on other agricultural matters.

Agricultural Development Council, Scottish (1977), Department of Agriculture and Fisheries for Scotland, Chesser House, 500 Gorgie Road, Edinburgh, EH11 3AW. T.-031-443 4020. Chairman: A.S. Macdonald; Vice Chairman: J.T. Harle; Members: J.A. Brown, H. Crawford, J. Elliot jnr., W.L. Forrest, D. Goldie, J. Kinloch, A. Logan, M. Mackie jnr., A.R.J.D. Millwe, W.W. Peat, A. Taylor jnr., K. Chalmers Watson, F.B. Young.

The Council's remit is to keep under review the research and development needs of the Scottish farming industry; to assess annually programmes of development work undertaken in Scotland; to keep under review the translation of research and development results into commercial practice; and to advise the Secretary of State for Scotland on matters falling within its remit. Members are representative of a wide range of experience and knowledge of the development needs of Scottish farming. The Council is serviced by staff of the Department of Agriculture and Fisheries for Scotland.

Agricultural Engineering, Scottish Institute of (1946), Bush Estate, Penicuik, Midlothian, EH26 OPH. T.-031-445 2147. Scottish Committee: Chairman: Professor J.S. Hall; Members: J.M. Stevenson, J.M.M. Imlay, D. Haydn-Jones, Professor T.D. Patten, Professor G.A. Lodge, J. Kinloch, H. Crawford, P.J. Perkins. Director: Dr P.J. Blight; Head, Agricultural Department: Dr B.D. Soane; Head, Engineering Department: Dr D.P. Haughey; Head, Instrumentation Department: Dr R. Parks; Secretary: A.M. Macpherson. The Institute is one of seven agricultural research institutes financed by the Department of Agriculture and Fisheries for Scotland. It is concerned with research into agricultural engineering. Liaison is maintained with the Scottish colleges of agriculture and other research institutes.

Agricultural Industries PLC, Scottish (1928), 25 Ravelston Terrace, Edinburgh, EH4 3ET. T.-031-332 2481. Chairman: B. Appleton; Managing Director: Q. Brown. Manufacturers and suppliers of fertilisers, seeds, agrichemicals, animal health products, animal feeding stuffs. S.A.I. has an oil subsidiary which services offshore oil activities, a horticultural subsidiary, and an agricultural computer firm. Turnover (1984): £126m.

Agricultural Organisation Society, Scottish (1905), Claremont House, 18/19 Claremont Crescent, Edinburgh, EH7 4JW. T.-031-556 6574. President: R.N.L. Malcolm; Vice President: A.R. Manson. Chief Executive/Secretary: E. Rainy Brown; Finance Officer: J.Y. Donnan. Central body in Scotland for the promotion, development, and representation of agricultural co-operation. Management services are provided to both established co-operatives and groups in process of formation.

Agricultural Training Board (1966), 13 Marshall Place, Perth, PH2 8AH. T.-0738 31481. Scottish Members: M.R. Burnett, J.A. Kilgour, D. Rose. Scottish Regional Training Adviser: I.D. Dewar; Senior Training Advisers: J. Kelly (South Scotland), J.D.S. Birkbeck (North Scotland); Scottish Regional Administrative Officer: J.S. Mathers. Provides training on a national basis for persons engaged in agriculture and horticulture. Training takes the form of short on-farm craft courses, supervisory and management skills courses, and financial management courses covering the whole range of enterprises. Most training is carried out through producer-orientated training groups, of which there are 130 in Scotland.

Agricultural Wages Board, Scottish, Chesser House, 500 Gorgie Road, Edinburgh, EH1 3AW. Chairman: R.A. Bennett, Q.C. Secretary: D.A. Fantom. Concerned primarily with determining minimum rates of wages and conditions of employment for agricultural workers in Scotland. Employers and workers are represented on the Board along with independent members appointed by the Secretary of State for Scotland.

Agriculture and Fisheries for Scotland, Department of, Chesser House, 500 Gorgie Road, Edinburgh. T.-031-443 4020. Secretary: L.P. Hamilton. Private Secretary: John Henderson.
Responsible for the promotion of the agriculture and fishing industries in Scotland; advice on the formulation of U.K. and E.E.C. agricultural and fisheries policy; implementation of schemes for capital assistance to agriculture and horticulture, the provision of livestock and crops, and provision of finance for educational, advisory, and resarch services; liaison with the Crofters' Commission; and consideration of proposals for the use of agricultural land for non-agricultural purposes. It advises ministers on all aspects of international and domestic policy, including E.E.C. questions relating to the fishing industry.

Alcoholism, Scottish Council on (1973), 147 Blythswood Street, Glasgow, G2 4EN. T.-041-333 9677. Chairman: Rt. Hon. The Earl of Minto, M.B.E., J.P. Executive Director: D.T. Allsop. Autonomous national body dealing with problems of alcohol abuse. It seeks to establish, co-ordinate, service, and help to sustain a national network of affiliated local Councils, increase public knowledge of alcohol abuse, and promote the prevention, early diagnosis, and treatment of alcohol related problems.

Ambulance Service, Scottish, Maitland Street, Glasgow, G4 0HX. T.-041-332 6001. Director: D.J. Buckley.

Ancestry Research Society, Scots (1945), 3 Albany Street, Edinburgh, EH1 3PY. T.-031-556 4220. Chairman: Professor J. MacQueen. Administrator: Mrs B.L. Walker. Assists persons of Scottish blood to trace facts about their ancestors in Scotland. It has investigated more than 50,000 inquiries from people of Scottish descent both at home and overseas.

Ancient and Historical Monuments of Scotland, Royal Commission on the (1908), 54 Melville Street, Edinburgh, EH3 7HF. T.-031-225 5994. Chairman: Rt. Hon. The Earl of Wemyss and March, K.T., J.P.; Members: Professor K.H. Jackson, Professor A.A.M. Duncan, Professor J.D. Dunbar-Nasmith, C.B.E., Professor R.J. Cramp, H.M. Colvin, C.B.E., Professor L. Alcock, Professor G. Jobey, D.S.O., Professor J. Butt. Secretary: J.G. Dunbar; Investigators: Miss M.M. Brown, I. Fisher, G.D. Hay, A. MacLaren, G.S. Maxwell, Dr J.N.G. Ritchie, G.P. Stell, J.B. Stevenson; Curator, National Monuments Record of Scotland: Miss C.H. Cruft; Head of Photographic Section: G.B. Quick; Head of Drawing Office: I.G. Scott; Head of General Office: Miss C.N.C. Bowie.
Appointed to make an inventory of the ancient and historical monuments of Scotland and to specify those that seem most worthy of preservation. It also has a responsibility to record monuments threatened with destruction, including a statutory duty to record historic buildings for which Listed Building Consent for demolition has been granted. The National Monuments Record of Scotland, a branch of the Commission, contains an extensive collection of pictorial and documentary material relating to Scottish ancient monuments and historic buildings and is open daily for public reference.

Ancient Monuments Board for Scotland, 3-11 Melville Street, Edinburgh, EH3 7QD. T.-031-226 2570. (Nil Return).

An Comunn Gaidhealach (1891), 109 Church Street, Inverness. T.-0463 231226. President: N. McKechnie. Administrative Officer: Norman J. Macpherson; Education Officer: Colin Spencer. Exists for the promotion of Gaelic language, literature, music, the arts, and Highland studies.

Anglers' Association, Scottish. Secretary and Treasurer: David Mackay, Glen Earn, Humbie Bridge, Newton Mearns, Glasgow. T.-041-639 2599.

Angus District Council (1974), County Buildings, Forfar, DD8 3LG. T.-0307 65101. Provost: Andrew Welsh; Depute Provost: Brian Milne; Members: Alexander King, Clive Meldrum, Helen Cargill, Sheena Welsh, Kenneth Hirstwood, John Gray, Anne Thomson, George Suttie, George Norrie, Michael Weir, Robert Wright, Ruth Dundas, David F. Myles, William Roberton, Andrew Thomson, William Phillips, Isobel McLellan, M.B.E., Alex. Buchan, John Thomson. Chief Executive: W.S. McCulloch; Director of Administration and Legal Services: John S. Richardson; Director of Finance: Harry C. Nicoll, T.D.; Director of Technical Services: George C. Macphee; Director of Planning: William Ferguson; Director of Environmental Health: Leslie A. Cameron; Director of Housing: George Deans; Director of Parks, Recreation and Tourism: Samuel Reid; Director of Libraries and Museums: Gavin N. Drummond. District Council. Population of District: 93,000.

Angus Technical College, Keptie Road, Arbroath DD11 3EA. T.-0241 72056. Principal: J.W. Wilson. College of further education.

Animal Breeding Research Organisation, A.F.R.C. (1945), West Mains Road, Edinburgh, EH9 3JQ. T.-031-667 6901. Director: Dr R.B. Land; Secretary: J.A. Glen; Research Leaders: Dr R. Lathe, Dr C. Smith, Dr R.L. Spooner, Dr St. C.S. Taylor, R. Thompson, Dr A.J. Webb, Dr G. Wiener. The Organisation is concerned with biological research relevant to the improvement of farm livestock. While based on the science campus of the University of Edinburgh, it is made up of farms in England and Scotland and the Dryden Laboratory at Roslin, Midlothian.

Animal Diseases Research Association (1920), Moredun Institute, 408 Gilmerton Road, Edinburgh, EH17 7JH. T.-031-664 3262. President: J. Stobo; Vice President: G.B.R. Gray. Scientific Director: Dr W.B. Martin; Secretary: F.B. Coutts. Investigation into diseases affecting farm animals, particularly sheep and cattle.

Annandale and Eskdale District Council (1974), District Council Chambers, High Street, Annan, DG12 6AQ. T.-046 12 3311. Convener: Richard G. Greenhow; Vice Convener: Pearson Cameron; Members: Jane Stevenson, G.M. Flitcroft, T. Gates, D.G. Mundell, R.J. Brodie, W.H. Grieve, G. Willacy, J. Rae, J.W. Bruce, Margaret Wilson, W.A. Rutherford, Janette Richardson, S. Adams, F. Park. Chief Executive: John A. Whitecross. Director of Finance: William J. Davidson; Director of Environmental Health: Thomas Finlayson; Director of Technical Services: Ian Smith. District Council. Population of District: 35,000.

Anniesland College, Hatfield Drive, Glasgow, G12 OYE. T.-041-339 6851. Principal: William Morris. College of further education.

Anti-Common Market Council, Scottish (1976), 35 East Claremont Street, Edinburgh, EH7 4HT. T.-031-556 1890. President: Lord MacLeod of Fuinary; Chairman: T. Graham Salmon; Secretary: Iain McGregor. Pressure group seeking complete withdrawal from the E.E.C. and European Parliament.

Antiquaries of Scotland, Society of (1780), National Museum of Antiquities of Scotland, Queen Street, Edinburgh, EH2 1JD. T.-031-557 3550. Hon. Secretary: Dr T.F. Watkins; Hon. Treasurer: R.J. Mercer; Assistant Secretary: Miss A.S. Henshall; Assistant Treasurer: Mrs R.A. Meldrum. The study of the antiquities and history of Scotland, more especially by means of archaeological research.

Antiquities of Scotland, National Museum of (1781), 1 Queen Street, Edinburgh. T.-031-557 3550. Chairman, Board of Trustees: Ivor R. Guild; Members: W.F. Cormack, Rev. G.M. Dilworth, The Hon. Caroline Douglas-Home, Lady Grimond of Firth, J.S. Morris, R.G.W. Prescott, Professor V.B. Proudfoot, W.G.A. Shepherd, J.M. Urquhart, C.B.E., Professor A.F. Walls, S.M. Maxwell, Professor D.W. Harding, Professor L. Alcock, L.J. Masters, R.W. Munro, Rev. D. Shaw, A.A. Woodham, Professor G.W.S. Barrow, Professor M.C. Meston, Professor D.E.R. Watt, Professor F. Willett. Director: Alexander Fenton; Deputy Keeper: Dr D.V. Clarke; Assistant Keepers: D.H. Caldwell, D.H.G. Cheape, G.C. Sprott, Miss M.K.S. Bryden; Higher Executive: Miss D. Slee.
Collects, researches, conserves, and displays Scotland's heritage from prehistoric times to the present day. Its collections range from objects of outstanding beauty and importance to everyday items, from medieval town life to the rural life of yesterday. Its areas of display are in the main museum in Queen Street, Edinburgh, the York Buildings galleries which house special summer exhibitions, and the Scottish Agricultural Museum at Ingliston.

Anti-Vivisection Society, Scottish (1876), 121 West Regent Street, Glasgow, G2 2SD. T.-041-221 2300. President: James Scott. Organising Secretary: John F. Robins. Animal rights group campaigning against experiments on living animals, specifically against the quarter of a million vivisections carried out in Scotland each year.

Arbitrators (Arbiters), Chartered Institute of, Scottish Branch. Hon. Secretary and Treasurer: J.C. Dietrichsen, Pannell Kerr Forster, 44 Wellington Street, Glasgow G2 6RL.

The Scottish Companion 21

Archaeology, Council for British, Scotland (1946), c/o National Museum of Antiquities, Queen Street, Edinburgh, EH2 1JD. T.-041-334 1134. President: Mrs E. Proudfoot; Secretary: Miss H. Adamson. Protection of all kinds of archaeological material and stimulation of informed interest in the past through publications, conferences, and a summer school.

Archery Association, Scottish. Secretary: N. Naismith, 38 Castle Avenue, Edinburgh, EHR 7LB. T.-031-334 4486.

Architects in Scotland, Royal Incorporation of (1916), 15 Rutland Square, Edinburgh, EH1 2BE. T.-031-229 7205. President: J.D. Richards, C.B.E.; Past President: A.S. Matheson; Chapter Presidents: N.W. Paterson, A.L.M. MacDonald, J.D. Spencely, D.J. Leslie, G. Reynolds, A. Ferguson. Secretary and Treasurer: Charles McKean. Professional body for chartered architects in Scotland, with a membership of 2,600. It publishes journals and books, arranges lectures and exhibitions, and provides technical advice.

Architects, Surveyors, and Building Contractors in Scotland, Joint Standing Committee, 7 Manor Place, Edinburgh, EH3 7DN. T.-031-225 7078. Provides a medium whereby questions affecting the building industry in Scotland can be discussed, and a means of concerting action within the industry. Bodies represented are the Royal Incorporation of Architects in Scotland, the Royal Institution of Chartered Surveyors (Scottish Branch), the Scottish Building Employers' Federation, the Scottish and Northern Ireland Plumbing Employers' Federation, the Electrical Contractors Association of Scotland, the Scottish Decorators Federation, the Association of Consulting Engineers, the Scottish Board of the Federation of Associations of Specialists and Sub-Contractors, and the Heating and Ventilating Contractors Association.

Argyll and Bute District Council (1974), Kilmory, Lochgilphead, Argyll, PA31 8RT. T.-0546 2127. Chairman: Douglas C. Currie; Vice Chairman: W.R. Hunter; Councillors: George McMillan, John J. McIntyre, Douglas Robertson, Robert Currie, Neil McArthur, Donald MacMillan, Robin Malcolm, Allan Macaskill, Donald McKerrell, Archibald Fletcher, Ian Smyth, Noel M. Faccenda, John Sharples, John Wilson, Alexander MacArthur, Donald McPhail, D.D. Johnston, James McMillan, R.R. Reid, J.S. Bradley, Arthur Allan, John Thomson, J.R. Walsh, Peter Menzies. Chief Executive: Michael A.J. Gossip; Director of Administration: J.A. McLellan; Director of Finance: G.M. Stewart; Director of Planning: M.R. Oliver; Director of Architectural Services: T.A. Paterson; Director of Housing: R.J. Couper; Director of Environmental Health: J. Smart; Director of Tourism, Leisure and Recreation: J.E. Moran. District Council. Population of district: 64,000.

Argyll and Clyde Health Board (1974), Gilmour House, Gilmour Street, Paisley, PA1 1DU. T.-041-887 0131. Chairman: J. Ryan; Members: A.H. Brabender, J.P., J. Campbell, L. Capaldi, J. Cattanach, Mrs E.M. Cockburn, O.B.E., Dr R. Erskine, J.E. Fyfe, J.H. Gillougley, I.D.F. Halligan, Mrs J.C. Le Roux, Dr S.G. McAlpine, N.S. MacCallum, J. McCorkindale, Miss P. McGowan, Miss M. MacLeod, Dr J. Moffat, R.R. Reid, E.T.F. Spence, T.A. Stewart, Miss A.A. Thomson. Secretary: A.K. Skirving; Chief Administrative Medical Officer: Dr A.A. Reid; Chief Area Nursing Officer: Miss M.A. Sommerville; Treasurer: I.C. Smith. Provision of health service in an area of 452,000 people.

Argyll and Sutherland Highlanders, Regimental Headquarters (1881), The Castle, Stirling. T.-Stirling 75165. Regimental Secretary: Lt. Col. G.P. Wood, M.C.

Army Headquarters, Scotland, Craigie Hall, near Edinburgh. T.-031-336 1761. General Officer Commanding the Army in Scotland: Lt. General Sir Alexander Boswell, K.C.B., C.B.E.

Arran Tourist Board, Isle of, Tourist Information Centre, Brodick Pier, Brodick, Isle of Arran. T.-0770 2140. Chairman: John Forgie. Area Tourist Officer: Jill M. Gardiner. Promotion of tourism on the Isle of Arran.

Arts Club, Scottish (1874), 24 Rutland Square, Edinburgh. T.-031-229 8157. President: R.S. Renton; Vice President (Professional): T.A. Sharp; Vice President (Lay): A.N. Smith; Hon. Treasurer: D.M. Webster; Hon. Secretary: W.B. Logan; Hon. Architect: C.E. Hunter. To promote the interests of the arts in general, and social intercourse amongst its members.

Arts Council, Scottish (1946), 19 Charlotte Square, Edinburgh. T.-031-226 6051. Chairman: Gerald Elliot; Vice Chairman: James Logan; Members: Mollie Abbott, C.B.E., Christopher Allan, William Cunningham, Peter Evans, Roderick Graham, Brian Ivory, Andrew Johnstone, Joan Knight, Joan Lingard, Robert Logan, Jan McDonald, Colin MacInnes, Colin MacLean, Alexander Moffat, Alexander Orr, Donald Pack, C.B.E., Willis Pickard, Stewart Sanderson, Ann Turner Thomson. Director: Timothy Mason; Deputy Director: Harry McCann; Music Director: Christie Duncan; Drama and Dance Director: Robert Palmer; Touring Director: Anthony Wraight; Art Director: Lindsay Gordon; Literature Director: Walter Cairns; Combined Arts Director: John Murphy.
The Scottish Arts Council is one of the principal channels for Government funding of the arts in Scotland. It forms part of the Arts Council of Great Britain. Its objects are: to develop and improve the knowledge, understanding and practice of the arts; to increase the accessibility of the arts to the public; and to advise and co-operate with local authorities and other bodies on any matters concerned with these objects. S.A.C. grant, 1984: £11.879m.

Assessors' Association, Scottish (1975). Secretary: John L.S. McDonald, Scott House, Sprouston Road, Newtown St. Boswells. T.-0835 23388. To encourage the exchange of ideas among the membership about their statutory duties, and to promote uniformity in operating the provisions of the Valuation and Registration Acts.

ASSET Ltd. (1981), 21 Green Street, Saltcoats, Ayrshire. T.-0294 602515/6. Chairman: Douglas C. Muirhead. Chief Executive: Douglas H. Martyn. ASSET is a joint private/public sector initiative established to combat the considerable unemployment problem in North Ayrshire by helping new businesses to become established and by assisting existing companies to expand within the Ardrossan, Saltcoats and Stevenston area. Since ASSET was set up in May, 1981, 200 new businesses or company expansions have been made possible with the Trust's assistance.

Associated Scottish Life Offices (1841), 23 St. Andrew Square, Edinburgh, EH2 1AQ. T.-031-556 7171. Chairman, General Purposes Committee: W.M. Morrison; Deputy Chairman: C.M. Cavaye; Members: W. Proudfoot, J.M. MacHarg, J.M. Souness, G.D. Gwilt, A. Scobbie, D.D. McKinnon, D.A. Berridge. Secretary: G.C. Train. The advancement of the business of life assurance with special reference to the interests of Scottish offices – by promoting uniformity of practice among the offices in matters of general administration, by watching over all legislative measures bearing upon life assurance with a view to joint action in regard to them, and by affording opportunities for consultation and co-operation on all matters affecting the common interests of the offices.

Astronomical Society of Edinburgh (1924), City Observatory, Calton Hill, Edinburgh, EH7 5AA. T.-031-556 4365. President: Dr David Gavine; Secretary: Iain Neil; Treasurer: John Rostron. Observatory Director: James Shepherd; Assistant Director: Duncan Waldron. Exists to promote interest in astronomy in the Edinburgh area. Meetings, public exhibitions.

Athletic Association, Scottish Amateur. General Secretary: J.D. Fairgrieve, 16 Royal Crescent, Glasgow, G3 7SL. T.-041-332 5144.

Autistic Children, Scottish Society for (1968), Room 2, 2nd Floor, 12 Picardy Place, Edinburgh, EH1 3JT. T.-031-557 0474. Chairman: Ruth Hampton; Vice Chairman: A.R. Critchley. General Secretary: Mrs I.M. Watson. To educate and care for children and adults diagnosed as autistic or with severe communication problems.

Auto Cycle Union, Scottish. Secretary: T. Arnott Moffat, Kippilaw, Longridge Road, Whitburn, West Lothian, EH47 OLG. T.-0501 42663.

Automobile Association, The (1905), Fanum House, Erskine Harbour, Erskine, PA8 6AT. T.-041-812 0144. Director, Scotland and Northern Ireland: H.E.H. Murphy; Regional Managers: P.C. Smith (Road Services), C.R. Paton (Travel Services), J. Mason (Membership Services), B. Thorne (Administration). World's largest motoring organisation, providing a comprehensive service to members.

Automobile Club, Royal Scottish (1899), 11 Blythswood Square, Glasgow, G2 4AG. T.-041-221 3850. Chairman, General Committee: N.L. Campbell. Chief Executive: H. Dewar; Assistant Secretary: Jonathan C. Lord. To promote, encourage, and develop automobilism in Scotland.

Aviemore and Spey Valley Tourist Organisation (1969), Tourist Information Centre, Main Road, Aviemore, PH22 1PP. T.-0479 810363. Chairman: Major W. Dunlop. Area Tourist Officer and Secretary: M.W. Lowson. Promotion of tourism.

Ayr Chamber of Commerce (1949), Royal Bank Buildings, 28 Sandgate, Ayr, KA7 1BS. T.-Ayr 265004. President: Ewen G. McHarg. Secretary and Treasurer: Forsyth Brash, T.D. Promotion of commercial and manufacturing interests in Ayr and South Ayrshire.

Ayr College, Dam Park, Ayr, KA8 OEU. T.-0202 265184. Chairman, College Council: R. Conway. Principal: Robert McKinney; Registrar: A. Smith. College of further education.

Ayr Locality Enterprise Resource Trust (1983), 88 Green Street, Ayr, KA8 8BG. T.-0292 264181. Chairman: W.J. Barr; Secretary: W.J.M. Mowat. Chief Executive: D.M. Troup. To mobilise private business interests and resources in an effort to expand or protect existing employment and promote the creation of new jobs in Kyle and Carrick. The Trust works in collaboration with local and other public authorities. About 40 new businesses have been created to date.

Ayrshire and Arran Health Board (1974), 1A Hunter's Avenue, Ayr. T.-0292 281821. Chairman: W.S. Fyfe; Members: J. Cahill, Dr J.H. Cameron, Mrs C.L. Hutchison, Dr J. Morrow, Mrs C.R. Murray, G.M. Pettitt, I.B. Valentine, Mrs S. Wilson, Dr W.M. Wilson, Mrs M.M. Bicker, Mrs A. Dunbar, P. Hunter, Mrs N.M. Lambie, F.J. McCaffery, Mrs M. Macdonald, W.S. McConnell, D. McMillan, B.A. Murphy, D. Shankland, Dr J.P. Wiltshire. Secretary: M.S. Abbott; Treasurer: J. Dishington; Chief Administrative Medical Officer: Dr J.P. Wall; Chief Area Nursing Officer: C.R. Mackie. Provision of health service.

Ayrshire and Burns Country Tourist Board (1982), 39 Sandgate, Ayr. T.-0292 284196. Tourist Officer: Jack Wild. Responsible for the promotion and marketing of the Kyle and Carrick District.

Ayrshire Archaeological and Natural History Society (1947), 1 Portmark Avenue, Ayr, KA7 4DD. T.-0292 42077. President: Ronald W. Brash; Hon. Secretary: George E. Sleight. The antiquities, history, and natural history of Ayrshire. Lectures, excursions, publications.

Ayrshire Cattle Society (1877), 1 Racecourse Road, Ayr. T.-0292 267123. President: Brian T. King; President-Elect: John Weaver. General Secretary: Stuart Thomson. To promote and help improve the Ayrshire dairy cow. The Society is responsible for the pedigree registration, progeny test selection, and type classification of stock. Its own company – Cattle Services (Ayr) Ltd. – suplies semen from Ayrshire bulls and livestock for use at home and abroad.

Ayrshire Valleys Tourist Board (1982), P.O. Box 13, Civic Centre, Kilmarnock, KA1 1BY. T.-0563 21140, Ext. 320. Tourist Officer: James McK. Wilson. To promote the areas of Cumnock and Doon Valley District Council and Kilmarnock and Loudoun District Council.

B

Badenoch and Strathspey District Council (1974), Courthouse, 36 High Street, Kingussie, Inverness-shire. T.-Kingussie 555. Chairman: J.A. McCook; Members: A. Gordon, Marie B. Anderson, D. MacKellar, Elizabeth Main, A.K.L. McWilliam, W.M. McKenna, J.L. Wainford, T.R. Wade, D.S. Sinclair, G.A.D. Chalmer. Chief Executive: H.G. McCulloch; Director of Finance: T.M. Robertson; Director of Environmental Health, Technical Services, and Housing: W.G. Walters. District Council. Population of District: 9,900.

Badminton Union, Scottish, 40 Bogmoor Place, Glasgow, G51 4TQ. T.-041-445 1218. President: David Gow; Hon. Secretary: Neil Cameron. Administrator: Anne Smillie; Coaching Director: Allan Campbell. To foster and encourage badminton in Scotland; organises annual Scottish championships and selects Scottish international teams.

Ballet, The Scottish (1969), 261 West Princes Street, Glasgow, G4 9EE. T.-041-331 2931. President: Robin Duff. Chairman, Board of Directors: Roy H. Thomson; Vice Chairman, Sir Norman Macfarlane; Secretary: John Gray; Members: Russell Brown, Alex. Clark, The Countess of Dalkeith, Professor J.V.G.A. Durnin, Leon Fontaine, Dr Michael Kelly, Rt. Hon. The Earl of Rosebery, Alexander Stone. Artistic Director: Peter Darrell, C.B.E.; General Administrator: Robin Anderson.
Scotland's national dance company. Repertoire embraces full-scale productions with orchestra of the classics and commissioned works as well as a wide range of works by contemporary choreographers. The company also makes provision for medium and small-scale touring throughout the country and abroad. The Scottish Ballet's commitment to education in the broadest sense is demonstrated in the work of the full-time educational unit, Steps Out. Vocational dance training is catered for by The Dance School of Scotland.

Ballroom Dancers Association, Scottish Amateur. Secretary: Helen Bradley, 37 Tanzieknowe Drive, Cambuslang, Glasgow, G72 8RG. T.-041-641 5073.

Banff and Buchan College of Further Education, Argyll Road, Fraserburgh, AB4 5RF. T.-0346 25777. Principal: James M. Crawford.

Banff and Buchan District Council (1974), St. Leonard's, Sandyhill Road, Banff, AB4 1BH. T.-Banff 2521. Convener: Norman Cowie; Vice Convener: John B. Gordon; Members: Robert C. Bremner, Gilbert Buchan, Samuel Coull, Sally M. Cowley, William R. Cruickshank, James Ingram, Duncan D. Knox, Donald J. Mackinnon, Stuart B. Mair, Sydney Mair, Joseph R. Mitchell, Brian L. Munro, James M. Reid, Douglas Swanson, James M. Taylor, Brian Topping. Director of Administration and Legal Services: Ronald W.

Jackson; Director of Finance: Daniel Urquhart; Director, Planning and Development: Peter Suttie; Director of Environmental Health: Douglas H. Miller; Director of Technical Services: Edward Blackwood; Director of Housing and Property: Brian J. Watson; Director of Leisure and Recreation: Gilbert K. Carling. District Council. Population of District: 83,000.

Banff and Buchan Tourist Board (1983), Collie Lodge, Banff, AB4 1AU. T.-Banff 2789/2419. Chairman: S. Mair; Vice-Chairman: F.C.D. Lees. Tourism Manager: David M.H. Du Boulay. To promote and develop tourism in the area.

Bank Employers, Federation of Scottish (1970), 19 Rutland Square, Edinburgh, EH1 2BB. T.-031-229 8766. Director: Miss A.E. Miller.

Bankers in Scotland, Institute of (1875), 20 Rutland Square, Edinburgh, EH1 2DE. T.-031-229 9869. Secretary-General: Brian McKenna; Director of Studies: A. Evan Williams. To improve the qualifications of those engaged in banking in Scotland and to raise their status and influence. Membership totals 10,800. The Institute's main activities are examinations for trainee bankers; publications on banking practice; *The Scottish Bankers Magazine*; and courses and lectures for qualified members.

Bank of Scotland (1695), The Mound, Edinburgh, EH1 1YZ. T.-031-229 2555. Governor: Sir Thomas N. Risk; Deputy Governor: Rt. Hon. Lord Balfour of Burleigh; Ordinary Directors: W. Birkbeck, Rt. Hon. Lord Clydesmuir, K.T., C.B., M.B.E., T.D., Sir William B. Duncan, C.B.E., J.G.S. Gammell, M.B.E., Sir William J. Lithgow, Bt., J.A. Lumsden, M.B.E., T.D., Duncan J. MacLeod, D.B. Pattullo, Sir Richard T. Pease, Bt., A.M. Pelham Burn, Rt. Hon. Lord Polwarth, T.D., W.F. Robertson, M.F. Strachan, C.B.E. Treasurer and General Manager: D.B. Pattullo; Secretary: H.K. Young; Joint General Managers: R.L. Cromar, A.T. Gibson, T. Bennie, J.M. Young; Divisional General Managers: J.R. Browning, R. Smith, A.J.R. Thomson, P.A. Burt.
Bank of Scotland offers a complete banking service to personal and corporate customers through its 500 branches in Scotland. This includes all types of business financing normally associated with a joint stock bank, international business including export financing and oil and energy financing, as well as all types of currency transactions. The Personal Financial Services Division provides investment, trustee, registrar, tax, estate planning, and insurance services.

Baptist Union of Scotland (1869), 14 Aytoun Road, Glasgow, G41 5RT. T.-041-423 6169. Hon. President: James Bernard; Hon. Vice President: Rev. A.T. Peck; General Secretary: Rev. P.H. Barbour. The Baptist Union of Scotland is a fellowship of 160 churches with a total membership of 14,600. It has Departments of Mission, Church Life, and Publications, and publishes a monthly magazine, *The Scottish Baptist*. Its annual Assembly takes place in October.

Barmulloch College (1964), 186 Rye Road, Glasgow, G21 3JY. T.-041-558 9071. Chairman, College Council: R.W. Wait; Vice Chairman: D. Watson. Principal: D.M. Brown; Depute Principal: T.B. Wilson; Registrar: G. McGroarty. Community college providing a wide range of part-time and full-time courses.

Barony Agricultural College, Parkgate, Dumfries, DG1 3NE. T.-0387 86251. Principal: D. Rose.

Baroque Ensemble, Scottish (1969), 34-40 South Clerk Street, Edinburgh, EH8 9PS. T.-031-667 3074. Chairman: Lt. Gen. Sir Derek Lang, K.C.B., D.S.O., M.C. Artistic Director: Leonard Friedman; Acting Administrator: Michael Chibbett. Formed by the violinist Leonard Friedman, the Scotish Baroque Ensemble is recognised as one of the five main national music bodies in Scotland. Following the tradition of the Baroque period, it performs without a conductor. Its repertoire, though solidly based on Baroque music, includes string compositions of all periods, played on modern instruments. It promotes concerts and accepts engagements throughout Scotland and has toured extensively abroad.

Basketball Association, Scottish (1947), 8 Frederick Street, Edinburgh, EH2 2HB. T.-031-225 7143. Chairman: W.B. McGuinness. Technical Director: K.D.A. Johnston. Responsible for the development, promotion, and control of basketball in Scotland.

Bathgate Area Support for Enterprise, 19 North Bridge Street, Bathgate, West Lothian. T.-0506 634024. Director: Michael J. Fass. Enterprise agency.

BBC Radio Highland (1976), Broadcasting House, 7 Culduthel Road, Inverness, IV2 4AD. T.-0463 221711. Manager: Martin Macdonald; Acting Senior Producer: Douglas McRoberts. A regional VHF radio station, broadcasting to the Highlands, the Western Isles, and parts of Grampian and Argyll, producing news and current affairs and magazine programmes in English and Gaelic. Local programmes broadcast over the largest regional radio area of any station in Britain. The station contributes in both languages to Radio Scotland and to network programmes.

BBC Radio Orkney (1977), Castle Street, Kirkwall, Orkney. T.-0856 3939. Senior Producer: Howie Firth. Community radio station, one of the first two established by the BBC in Scotland. Broadcasts twice daily with local news, information, interviews, features, and music, as well as programmes for local schools. Amongst its community activities, it operates an Orkney Sound Archive, and assists with the organisation of the Orkney Traditional Folk Festival.

BBC Radio Solway (1983), Elmbank, Lovers Walk, Dumfries, DG1 1NZ. T.-0387 68008/9. Senior Producer: Iain J. McConnell. Community radio station serving the Dumfries and Galloway Region. Provides the community with local news, views, and weather information, broadcasting for a total of one hour and 10 minutes daily.

BBC Radio Shetland, Brentham House, Harbour Street, Lerwick, ZE1 OLR. T.-0595 4751. Community radio station.

BBC Radio Tweed (1983), Municipal Buildings, High Street, Selkirk, TD7 4BU. T.-0750 21884. Senior Producer/Presenter: Caroline Adam. Community radio station, broadcasting programmes of local interest throughout Borders Region, and supplying local information, news, reports, and programmes to Radio Scotland.

BBC Scotland, Broadcasting House, Queen Margaret Drive, Glasgow, G12 8DG. T.-041-339 8844. Broadcasting House, Queen Street, Edinburgh, EH2 1JF. T.-031-225 3131. Controller, Scotland: Patrick Chalmers; Head of Radio, Scotland: Stan Taylor; Head of Television, Scotland: James Hunter; Head of Production Resources and Engineering, Scotland: Donald Brodie; Head of Administration, Scotland: Stephen Ansell; Head of Finance, Scotland: Bryan Mitchell; Secretary and Head of Information, Scotland:

John McCormick; Head of Drama, Television, Scotland: Roderick Graham; Managing Editor, News and Current Affairs, Television: George Sinclair; Head of Educational Broadcasting, Scotland: Gordon Menzies; Head of Religious Programmes, Scotland: Ian Mackenzie; Head of Music, Scotland: Martin Dalby; Head of Sports Unit, Scotland: Malcolm Kellard.

BBC Scottish Symphony Orchestra (1960), Queen Margaret Drive, Glasgow. T.-041-339 8844. Head of Music, Scotland: Martin Dalby; Orchestral Manager: Trevor Green.

Bearsden and Milngavie District Council (1974), Municipal Buildings, Boclair, Bearsden, G61 2TQ. T.-041-942 2262. Provost: R.W. Robinson; Members: Renate Boyd, Barbara Waterfield, E. Gotts, D.B. McGarry, D. Sillars, A. Mongredien, I.J. Miller, J. Santos, Joan Cameron. Chief Executive and Director of Administration and Legal Services: A.R. Rae; Director of Finance: J.M. Hornby; Director of Technical Services: W.W. Dudgeon. District Council. Population of District: 39,000.

Beef Shorthorn Cattle Society, Pedigree House, 6 King's Place, Perth, PH2 8AD. T.-Perth 23471. President: J.H. Dewhurst; Vice President: W. Anderson. Secretary: Barbara M. McDonald. Breed society to further and promote the breeding and marketing of beef shorthorn cattle.

Bell & Sons plc, Arthur (1825), Cherrybank, Perth, PH2 ONG. T.-0738 21111. Chairman and Managing Director: Raymond Miquel, C.B.E. Scotch whisky distillers. Turnover (1984): £246m.

Berwickshire District Council (1974), District Council Offices, 8 Newtown Street, Duns, TD11 3DU. T.-0361 82600. Chairman: J. Evans; Members: J. Finlay, J. Aitchison, D.K. Swan, G.B. Millican, A. Elizabeth Wilson, P.J. Redpath, W. Smith, J. Guthrie, Fiona Sutherland, J. Nairn, Ms. M. Burns-Greig. Chief Executive: R.A. Christie; Director of Finance: D.W. Dewar; Director of Housing: W.J. Fennell; Director of Environmental Services: N.C. Rhind. District Council. Population of District: 18,000.

Bible Society of Scotland, National (1809), 7 Hampton Terrace, Edinburgh, EH12 5XU. T.-031-337 9701. Chairman: Rev. D. Nicol; General Secretary: Rev. Fergus Macdonald. To provide Bibles, New Testaments, and shorter portions of the Scriptures to people worldwide; to promote the distribution and use of the Bible in Scotland.

Billiards Association and Control Council, Scottish. Hon. Secretary: Stuart Ramsden, 83 Morven Road, Bearsden, Glasgow. T.- 041-942 8064.

Blackface Sheep Breeders Association (1905), 4 Alloway Park, Ayr, KA7 2AW. T.-0292 264295. Exists to promote the interests of the blackface breed in particular and the sheep industry in general.

Black Watch, The, Regimental Headquarters, Balhousie Castle, Hay Street, Perth, PH1 5HR. T.-Perth 21281, Ext. 30. Regimental Secretary: Colonel (Rd.) The Hon. W.D. Arbuthnott, M.B.E. Headquarters and Regimental Museum.

Blood Transfusion Service, Glasgow and West of Scotland (1939), 80 St Vincent Street, Glasgow, G2 5UA. T.-041-226 4111. Regional Director: Dr Ruthven Mitchell; Organising Secretary: Ian Armour, T.D. A division of the Common Services Agency of the Scottish Home and Health Department. Responsible for the collection, processing, storage and distribution of blood and blood products throughout Glasgow and the West of Scotland. More than 3,500 voluntary donations are required every week to supply hospitals in the area.

Blood Transfusion Service, Scottish, Headquarters Unit, Ellens Glen Road, Edinburgh, EH17 7QT. T.-031-664 2317. National Medical Director: Dr J.D. Cash.

Borderline Theatre Company (1974), 92 Montgomery Street, Irvine, KA12 8PW. T.-0294 79648. Chairman: Jim Wyper. Artistic Director: Morag Fullarton; Administrator: Edward Jackson. Professional touring theatre company which has commissioned many new works, including plays by Billy Connolly, John Byrne, Alex. Norton, Tom McGrath, and Liz Lochhead. At least half of the company's work in any one year is devised and performed for young people. The company tours extensively throughout Scotland, taking popular theatre to a wide range of audience.

Borders College of Further Education (1984), Thorniedean, Melrose Road, Galashiels, TD1 2AF. T.-0896 57755. Principal: R. Campbell-Pearson; Depute Principal: Dr A. Brown; Assistant Principals: J. Allan, R. Brown, R. McDonald, N. McLeish, D. Sharp. Variety of educational provision in the following areas: health, catering, science, tourism, leisure, mechanical, electrical and electronic engineering, motor vehicle, textiles, knitwear, business and industrial studies, secretarial, computing, information technology, distribution, general education, and special needs.

Borders Health Board (1974), Huntlyburn, Melrose, Roxburghshire, TD6 9BP. T.-Melrose 2662. Chairman: J. Gibb; Vice Chairman: A.C. Purves; Convener, Finance Committee: A. Pat Dorward; Convener, Primary Care Committee: P.S. Elliot; Convener, Works and Buildings Committee: R.A. Stewart; Members: Dr W.B. Aitken, R.W. Jack, Mary Millican, Florence Nisbet, Mrs E.G. Reid, A.G. Rennie, Walter Scott, Mrs G.M.L. Shaw-Stewart, Dr S.A. Stephen, A.S. Watt. Secretary: D.A. Peters; Chief Administrative Medical Officer: Dr I.A. McDonald; Chief Area Nursing Officer: Miss M. Hillier; Treasurer: M.D. Murray; Chief Administrative Dental Officer: J.R. Wild; Chief Administrative Pharmaceutical Officer: W.R. Yuill. Provision of health service.

Borders Regional Council (1974), Regional Headquarters, Newtown St. Boswells, Melrose, TD6 OSA. T.-St. Boswells 23301. Convener: T. Hunter; Vice Convener: G.B.Dorward; Chairmen of Committees: Mrs F. Ballantyne (Education), W. Lamb (Planning and Development), A. Watt (Roads and Transportation), R.D. Birch (Social Work), D.R. Stewart (Water and Drainage); Members: J.M. Askew, Michaelle B. Burns-Greig, I. McIvor, Major N.P. Thomson, T.A. Burnham, Dr R.R. Hamilton, G.P. Turnbull, Betty B. Boyd, W. Douglas, W.F. Lamb, J.P. Boyle, Barbara D. Baker, A.J.C. Hewat, Pamela M.N. Stewart, L.G.W. Thomson. Chief Executive: K.J. Clark; Depute Chief Executive: R.A. MacAskill; Director of Finance: P. Jeary; Director of Architectural Services: D.A.S. Henry; Assessor: J.L.S. McDonald; Director of Education: J. McLean; Director of Planning and Development: D.P. Douglas; Director of Roads and Transportation: R.I. Hill; Director of Social Work: D.A. Macdonald; Director of Water and Drainage: R.W. Fraser. Regional Council. Population of Region: 100,000.

Borders Tourist Board, Scottish (1983), Municipal Buildings, High Street, Selkirk, TD7 4JX. T.-0750 20555. Director of Tourism: Michael Ambrose; Assistant Director of Tourism: Riddell Graham.

Botanic Garden, Royal, Inverleith Row, Edinburgh, EH3 5LR. T.-031-552 7171. Regius Keeper: Professor D.M. Henderson.

Boundary Commission for Scotland (1945), Room 226, St. Andrew's House, Edinburgh, EH1 3DE. T.-031-556 8501. Chairman: Rt. Hon. Bernard

Weatherill, M.P.; Deputy Chairman: The Hon. Lord Ross; Members: A.A.L. Evans, Professor U.A. Wannop. Secretary: A. Simmen. To review Parliamentary constituencies and European Assembly constituencies in Scotland.

Bowling Association, Scottish (1892), 50 Wellington Street, Glasgow, G2 6EF. T.-041-221 8999. Secretary and Treasurer: Peter Smith. To foster, safeguard, and control the game of bowls. The Association is responsible for organising the Scottish championships and selecting international teams.

Boxing Association, Scottish Amateur. Hon. General Secretary: W. Cowan, M.B.E., 60 St. Andrew's Gardens, Dalry, Ayrshire, KA24 4JZ. T.-Dalry 2478. National Coach: Dick McTaggart.

Boys' Brigade, The (1883), Scottish Headquarters, Boys' Brigade House, 168 Bath Street, Glasgow, G2 4TQ. T.-041-332 0936. Brigade President: Rt. Hon. The Earl of Thurso; Vice President and Chairman of Executive: Col. C.H.K. Corsar, O.B.E., T.D., J.P.; Treasurer: L. Boyle, C.B.E. Secretary for Scotland: Alexander C. McLaren. The advancement of Christ's Kingdom among boys and the promotion of habits of obedience, reverence, discipline, self-respect, and all that tends towards a true Christian manliness. Membership (aged 6 to 18) totals 130,000 in the U.K., of whom more than one third are located in Scotland.

Boys' Clubs of Scotland (1928), 53 George Street, Edinburgh, EH2 2HT. T.-031-226 7255. Chairman: David A. Blaikie; Vice Chairman: John A. Swanston. Chief Adviser and Secretary: Les Beaton; Field Officer: Neil Conn. Voluntary youth organisation whose stated aim is to promote the spiritual, mental, physical, and social well-being of boys and young men in Scotland. Its services to member clubs include comprehensive insurance cover, sporting competitions, development training, outdoor pursuits, international exchanges, video library and use of video equipment, drug abuse material for leaders, use of camping equipment, advice and support.

British Aerospace, Civil Division (1977), Prestwick Airport, Prestwick, Ayrshire, KA9 2RW. Divisional Director and General Manager: G.J. Curran; Divisional Directors: D. McConnell (Commercial), W. Agnew (Production), J. Larroucau (Technical); Divisional Secretary: J.W. Connell. British Aerospace Civil Division at Prestwick is an integral part of British Aerospace Aircraft Group. It is responsible for the design, development, production, sales and support of the Jetstream 31 Light Turboprop Transport Aircraft. Manufacture of wing/engine pylons for the BAE 146 Jetliner is also undertaken.

British Airports Authority, Scottish Airports Head Office, Glasgow Airport, 2 St. Andrew's Drive, Abbotsinch, Paisley. T.-041-887 1111. **Prestwick Airport.** T.-0202 79822. General Manager: George Giles. **Edinburgh Airport.** T.-031-333 1000. General Manager: Andrew Hamilton. **Glasgow Airport.** T.-041-887 1111. General Manager: Alan Proctor. **Aberdeen Airport.** T.-0224 722331. General Manager: Vernon Murphy.

British Council, The (1934). Scottish Offices: 3 Bruntsfield Crescent, Edinburgh. T.-031-447 4716. 6 Belmont Crescent, Glasgow. T.-041-339 8651. Representatives: N. Bissett (Edinburgh); A. Russell (Glasgow). To promote a wider knowledge of Britain and the English language abroad and to develop closer cultural relations with other countries.

British Industry, Confederation of, (Scotland) (1965), 5 Claremont Terrace, Glasgow, G3 7XT. T.-041-332 8661. Chairman: C.J. Risk, C.B.E.; Vice

Chairman: J.M. Little, C.B.E.; Members of Council: H.J. Arbuthnott, J.B. Ashworth, I. Barr, J.D.S. Bennett, J.J. Blanche, Sir Colin Campbell, G.R. Carter, I.R. Clark, C.B.E., J.L. Copland, G. Craig, J. Dean, J.G. Dunbar, J.A. Eddison, T. Forgie, D.D. Fraser, A.D. Garland, R. Garrick, Sir James Goold, I. Grant, C. Green, J. Grier, G.A. Haggart, D.F. Hardie, C.B.E., J.P., R.W. Hill, B.C. Hilton, J.N. Hornibrook, J. Howie, W.Y. Hughes, J.D.H. Hume, C.B.E., E. Innes, I.S. Irwin, C.B.E., T. Jaap, A. Johnston, T. Johnston, O.B.E., A. Joyce, R. Lander, A.L. Lindsay, W. Low, C.B.E., J.P., E.D. Mackie, C.S. Macphie, A.S.F. Mair, J.L. McGavigan, D.J. Miller, R.O.S. Miller, W.B. Miller, O.B.E., D.W. Mitchell, C.B.E., Dr D.A. Pattison, W.C.H. Phillips, N.J. Purvis, A.M. Rankin, I.W. Stewart, N.T. Sturrock, A. Wheeler, A.B. Wherry, I.C. Wood, C.B.E., M. York. Director, Scotland: John Davidson.
The CBI is an independent, non-party-political body financed entirely by industry and commerce, and represents all sectors of business. Member companies range in size from small local businesses to multinational corporations and nationalised industries. It is the voice of British business and exists primarily to make sure that Goverments of all political complexions, and the public at large, understand the importance of wealth creation and the needs, intentions, and problems of the business community. CBI Scotland exists to promote the interests of all sectors of Scottish business and ensures that Scottish interests are fully weighed in the determination of national policy.

British Legion, Scotland, Royal (1921), New Haig House, Logie Green Road, Edinburgh, EH7 4HR. T.-031-557 2782. President: Major The Earl Haig, O.B.E. Chairman: Dr J.F. Cameron; Vice Chairman: Major General Sir John Swinton, K.C.V.O., O.B.E. General Secretary: Brigadier R.W. Riddle, O.B.E. The Royal British Legion Scotland is a democratic, non-sectarian and non-political organisation of ex-servicemen and women. The aims of the organisation are comradeship, assistance to ex-servicemen and women in need and to their widows and dependents, and Remembrance.

British Linen Bank Ltd. (1746), P.O. Box 49, 4 Melville Street, Edinburgh, EH3 7NB. T.-031-226 4071. Governor: Sir Thomas N. Risk; Deputy Governor: Thomas W. Walker; Chief Executive: Ian F. Brown; Deputy Chief Executive: Ian Macpherson; Directors: J. Douglas Anderson, J. Edward Boyd, Andrew S.R. Davidson, Michael D. Heeley, Duncan J. MacLeod, M. Douglas McPhail, James E. Miller, Alexander D. Nicol, D. Bruce Pattullo, Eric F. Sanderson, Nigel M. Suess, Ian A. Watt, James M. Young. Assistant Directors: Brian Finlayson, David M. Graveson, John S. Hunter, James E. Kidd, Ian Kirkpatrick, John McCabe, Alan A. Murray, Peter H. Redhead, David J. Stobie, Duncan C. Thompson, Charles W. Young. Secretary: J.D. Watt. Merchant bank providing a full range of services including: corporate finance; investment; fund management; leasing; deposit facilities; term loans.

British Rail, Scottish Region, Buchanan House, 58 Port Dundas Road, Glasgow. T.-041-332 9811. General Manager: C.E.W. Green; Deputy General Manager: J.S. Cornell; Director of Public Affairs: J.S. Boyle; Passenger Business Manager: C.R. Leah; Regional Operations Manager: V. Chadwick; Regional Freight Manager: A.G. Davies. British Rail is one of the largest industries in Scotland with a staff of 16,000, and covers an area from Carlisle to Kyle and Lochalsh and from Berwick-upon-Tweed to Wick and Thurso, with 287 passenger stations. British Rail, Scotland, handles £91m. of passenger business and £37m. of freight. 1,800 trains run daily over a network of 1,700 route miles with 55m. passenger journeys annually.

British Telecom Scotland, Canning House, 19 Canning Street, Edinburgh, EH3 8TH. T.-031-229 2525. Director: A.B. Wherry; Controller Finance and Business Management: R.G. Vance; Controller Personnel and Industrial Relations: G.E. Griffiths; Controller Programming and Technology: J.M. Garbutt; Controller Service & Marketing: R.G. Fraser; General Managers: W.A. Furness (Aberdeen), E.J. Simpson (Dundee), D. Strachan (Edinburgh), J.W. Robb (Glasgow), D. Soutar (Scotland West). Provision of telecommunications.

Britoil plc (1982), 150 St. Vincent Street, Glasgow, G2 5LJ. T.-041-204 2525. Chairman: Sir Philip Shelbourne; Managing Directors: Ian R. Clark, G.M. Ford.

Building Contract Committee, Scottish (1965), 39 Castle Street, Edinburgh, EH2 3BH. T.-031-225 1200. Secretary: G.W. Burnet. The Committee's constituent bodies are: Royal Incorporation of Architects in Scotland; Scottish Building Employers Federation; Scottish Branch, Royal Institution of Chartered Surveyors; Committee of Associations of Specialist Engineering Contractors; C.O.S.L.A.; Federation of Associations of Specialists and Sub-Contractors, Scottish Branch; Association of Consulting Engineers, Scottish Group; C.B.I.; Association of Scottish Chambers of Commerce. The remit of the Committee from its constituent bodies is to prepare Forms of Contract for building work in Scotland and to amend or revise these from time to time as may be required; and generally to consider and advise upon other matters relating to building contracts in Scotland.

Building Employers' Federation, Scottish (1895), 13 Woodside Crescent, Glasgow, G3 7UP. T.-041-332 7144. Director: R.W. Campbell; Secretary: W.I. Barclay; North East Area Secretary: K.P. Thom, 154 Union Street, Aberdeen, AB1 1QT (T.-0224 643838); North West Area Secretary: J. Gilchrist, Albyn House, 37A Union Street, Inverness, IV1 1QA (T.-0463 237626); Western Area Secretary: J.E. Hay, 122 Wellington Street, Glasgow, G2 2XF (T.-041-332 0051); Eastern Area Secretary: J.T. Moore, 60A George Street, Edinburgh, EH2 2LR (T.-031-226 4907). Employers' organisation for the building industry in Scotland, recognised as such by central and local Government, trades unions, and the professions. The Federation is a membership organisation covering the whole of Scotland, and it is estimated that its members employ about 80% of the building workers in Scotland.

Building Standards Advisory Committee (1959), Scottish Development Department, Building Control Division, New St. Andrew's House, Edinburgh, EH1 3SZ. T.-031-556 8400, Ext. 5952. Chairman: T. Harley-Haddow, O.B.E.; Members: Miss J.E.M. Adams, A.C. Aitken, A.P. Goudie, J.H.R. Hampson, T. Henney, J.F. Hoey, R.S.G. Mann, W.H. Millar, D. Nicoll, M.B.E., John Richards, C.B.E., L.A. Warwicker, I. Wiseman, R.C. Young, H. Zegleman. The Committee advises the Secretary of State for Scotland in connection with his building control powers.

Burns Federation, The, (1885), Dick Institute, Elmbank Avenue, Kilmarnock, KA1 3BU. T.-0563 26401. President: John Inglis. Hon. Secretary: William A. Anderson. Promotion and encouragement of the work of Robert Burns.

Business Achievement Award Trust Ltd., Scottish (1981), P.O. Box 25, Edinburgh, EH3 6UD, or 10/11 North Leith Sands, Edinburgh, EH6 4ER. T.-031-556 3521. Chairman: Sandy Irvine Robertson; Trustees: David Birrell, David Bowes-Lyon, Jeremy Burnet, Michael Healy, Lewis Hynd, O.B.E. Selection Committee: Angus Grossart, Lewis Hynd, O.B.E.,

Douglas Macdonald, Sir Norman Macfarlane, James Miller, Roger Ridley-Thomas. The aim of the Award is to select a young business person in Scotland (under 35) who has shown outstanding achievement in business. It is believed that by identifying and praising such achievement, there will also be created a wider recognition of the importance of excellence and effort by younger people in Scotland.

Business Education Council, Scottish (1973), 22 Great King Street, Edinburgh, EH3 6QH. T.-031-557 4555. Chairman: Professor M.J. Baker, T.D.; Vice Chairmen: C.S. Hudson, D.S.O., Councillor J.F. McLean, James Milne. Chief Officer: Andrew F. Moore; Senior Assistant Chief Officers: Miss A.M. Reid, P. Burns; Assistant Chief Officers: R.T. Whiteside, G.B. Preston, D.T.G. Allan, C.C. Robertson; Examinations Officer: O.N. Dickson. Devises courses for business and related sectors of employment; assesses performance and attainments; awards certificates and diplomas. Courses leading to SCOTBEC qualifications are provided in most colleges of further education in Scotland and in some of the central institutions. SCOTBEC and SCOTEC (the Scottish Technical Education Council) have agreed to amalgamate to form a new Scottish Vocational Education Council.

Business in the Community, Scottish (1982), Eagle Star House, 25 St. Andrew Square, Edinburgh, EH2 1AF. T.-031-556 9761. Director: Graham T. Ross; Company Secretary and Treasurer: George M. Thomson. The aims of ScotBIC are to increase the involvement of business in the affairs (economic, environmental and social) of the areas where they are located. The organisation has played the major role in the creation of a network of enterprise trusts which seek to stimulate local economies through, inter alia, the provision of free advice to new and existing businesses. At the end of August 1984, 22 such trusts were in operation in Scotland, with a further 10 planned.

Business School, Scottish (1970), 79 St. George's Place, Glasgow, G2 1EU. T.-041-221 3124. Chairman of Council: Sir Monty Finniston; Secretary to Council: W.G. Edgar. Dean: Professor A.W.J. Thomson; Marketing Manager: W. Edgar. Consortium of the management education departments of four universities (Glasgow, Edinburgh, Strathclyde and Stirling). The School provides a range of educational and consultancy services in the management field to both the private and public sectors of Scottish industry, commerce, and administration.

Byre Theatre (1933), Abbey Street, St. Andrews, Fife, KY16 9LA. T.-St. Andrews 76288. Chairman: A.B. Paterson, M.B.E. Administrator: Jon Whatson; Artistic Director: Adrian Reynolds. Professional repertory theatre seating 145 whose season runs from April to October, with a special Christmas show in December/January. The theatre is open at other times of the year for visiting companies and amateurs.

C

Caithness District Council (1974), Council Offices, Market Square, Wick, KW1 4AB. T.-Wick 3761. Convener: John M. Young; Members: James H. Fry, Thomas W. Pollock, William S. Smith, Margaret Hinds, Anderson Murray, Rev. Alastair A. Roy, James W. Oag, George G. Fraser, John H. Green, David Allan Richard, William A. Mowat, Peter Sutherland, George C. Aitchison, George S. Gunn, Alastair I. MacDonald. Chief Executive: Alastair Beattie; Depute Chief Executive: Mrs J. M. Campbell; Director of Technical Services: M. Lunny; Director of Finance: R.L. Bruce; Director of Leisure and Recreation: R.G. MacPherson; Director of Environmental Health: R.G. Ferguson. District Council. Population of District: 27,000.

Caithness Tourist Board, Tourist Office, Whitechapel Road, Wick, Caithness. T.-0955 2596. Tourist Officer: Ted Simons.

Caledonian Curling Club, Royal (1838), 2 Coates Crescent, Edinburgh, EH3 7AN. T.-031-225 7083. President of Council: W. Sanderson. Secretary and Treasurer: J.M. Aitken. To unite curlers throughout the world into one brotherhood of the rink; administer all aspects of the game; organise all Scottish championships. There are 30,000 curlers in Scotland and 680 curling clubs.

Cambuslang College, 6 Glasgow Road, Cambuslang, Glasgow, G72 7BS. T.-041-641 6197. Principal: Nelson J. Wright. College of further education.

Campaign for Nuclear Disarmament, Scottish, 420 Sauchiehall Street, Glasgow, G2. T.-041-331 2878. Chairman: Keith Bovey; General Secretary: Margaret Morton. Administrators: Fiona Montgomery, Sheena Moreby. Pressure group campaigning for nuclear disarmament.

Campaign to Resist the Atomic Menace, Scottish (SCRAM) (1975), 11 Forth Street, Edinburgh, EH1 3LE. T.-031-557 4283. Collective (no officers). SCRAM's objectives are to inform the public of the issues in energy policy and defence policy.

Camping and Caravanning Club (Scottish Region). Secretary: Alan Strachan, 70 Douglas Road, Longniddry, East Lothian, EH32 OLJ. T.-0875 53292.

Camps Association, Scottish National (1947), 57 Melville Street, Edinburgh, EH3 7HL. T.-031-226 6391. Chairman: Allan F. Blacklaws, O.B.E. General Manager and Secretary: J.A. Dinwiddie. To provide in Scotland permanent camps for the social, physical, and mental training of children and young people. The Association's five outdoor centres/school camps are used each year by thousands of school children and youth groups.

Canoe Association, Scottish, 18 Ainslie Place, Edinburgh, EH3 6AU. T.-031-226 4401. General Secretary: R. Day; Administrator: Margaret Winter.

Carberry Tower (1963), Musselburgh, Midlothian, EH21 8PY. T.-031-665 3135. Warden: Rev. Paul C.J. Burgess; Assistant Warden: Rev. Ailsa McIntyre. Residential Centre of the Church of Scotland Department of Education. Runs short-term courses.

Cardonald College (1971), 690 Mosspark Drive, Glasgow, G52 3AY. T.-041-883 6151/4; 041-883 1119. Chairman of College Council: I.B. Smail. Principal: G.H. Barr, D.F.C.; Deputy Principal: R. Bailey; Registrar: C. Kelly. College of further education serving the south western district of Glasgow. Courses are offered in art and design; clothing manufacture and fashion; secretarial and business studies (including computing); building and construction, especially plumbing, domestic heating, and thermal insulation; engineering, especially electronics but including other skills; S.C.E. subjects; and pre-nursing courses.

Care and Resettlement of Offenders, Scottish Association for the, 53 George Street, Edinburgh, EH2 2EH. T.-031-226 4222. Director: John Phillips. Regional Schemes: Lothian, T.-031-668 1091; Strathclyde, T.-041-332 1763; Tayside, T.-0382 23445.

Carnegie United Kingdom Trust (1913), 80 New Row, Dunfermline, Fife, KY12 7EJ. Secretary and Treasurer: Geoffrey Lord. Charitable trust which supports innovatory schemes with national implications in arts, community services, and heritage interpretation run by voluntary organisations registered as charitable. Priority is given to national charitable bodies. Policy guidelines available from Trust office.

Catholic Archives, Scottish (1958), Columba House, 16 Drummond Place, Edinburgh, EH3 6PL. T.-031-556 3661. Keeper: Rev. G. Mark Dilworth. The primary purpose is to make available to scholars the records of the post-Reformation Roman Catholic Church in Scotland.

Celtic Society, Royal (1820), 49 Queen Street, Edinburgh, EH2 3NT. Chairman of Council: Rev. Dr Roderick Smith; Members: A.C. Macpherson, Iain MacLaren, E.S. Ogilvy, Rev. Ewen A. Maclean, J.M. Urquhart, C.B.E., K.M. Hay, B.E.M., Dr C.P. Lowther, Captain Hugh Macpherson, J.P., Col. J.J. Lamb, O.B.E., T.D., D.F. Stewart, Alan Hay. Secretary and Treasurer: J.G.S. Cameron. Maintaining and promoting interest in the history, traditions, language and arts of the Highlands and Western islands of Scotland.

Central College of Commerce, 300 Cathedral Street, Glasgow, G1 2TA. T.-041-552 3941. Principal: G.S. Barr.

Central Film Library, Scottish (1934), 74 Victoria Crescent Road, Glasgow, G12 9JN. T.-041-334 9314. Secretary: G. Berry. Distribution of educational and training material throughout the U.K.

Central Fire Brigades Advisory Council, Scottish (1947), Room 274, St. Andrew's House, Edinburgh, EH1 3DE. T.-031-556 8501, Ext. 2860. Chairman: W.K. Reid; Secretary: N.M. Keegan. Advises the Secretary of State for Scotland on Fire Service matters.

Central Regional Council (1974), Viewforth, Stirling, FK8 2ET. T.-0786 73111. Convener: J.F.G. Anderson, C.B.E., O.St.J., J.P.; Vice Convener: C. Snedden, O.B.E., J.P.; Members: J.G. Allan, W. Anderson, R. Ball, M.C. Barr, Mrs E.S. Brodie, C. Brown, H. Brown, J.P., D. Bryson, P.M. Burt, S. Conner, J.P., J. Connolly, J.P., H. Constable, Mrs F.E.M. Davidson, J.P., W. Douglas, A.W. Grant, M. Kelly, O.B.E., J.P., Mrs H.A. Livingstone, W.R. McAdam, P. McCafferty, I.B. Macfarlane, C. McKeown, T. McMeel,

R. Millar, Mrs L.E. Montgomery, J.P., R.G.D. Montgomery, A.M. Murray, J. O'Hara, J.P., J. Pollock, F.W. Saunders, J.P., Mrs R.M. Scott, T.G. Simpson, J.P., D. Wynn. Chief Executive: E. Geddes; Director of Administration and Legal Services: P. Buchanan; Director of Architectural Services: G.M. Crossan; Regional Assessor: A.R. MacCorquodale; Director of Education: I. Collie; Director of Finance: J. Broadfoot; Industrial Development Director: B.M. Nicholson; Personnel Director: G.M. Paterson; Director of Planning: F. Bracewell; Director of Roads: G.I. McCrindle; Director of Social Work: H. Garland; Director of Water and Drainage: J.R. Robertson; Reporter to Children's Panel: J. Harris. Regional Council. Population of Region: 273,000.

Central Scotland Chamber of Commerce (1954), Suite A, Haypark, Marchmont Avenue, Polmont, Falkirk, FK2 ONZ. T.-Polmont 716868. President: A. Wilson. Secretary: H.B. Johnson.

Chamber Orchestra, Scottish, 12/18 Howden Street, Edinburgh, EH8 9HL. T.-031-667 7354. Chairman: J. Martin Haldane. General Manager: Ian Ritchie. The Orchestra gives concert series in major Scottish towns; plays in smaller towns where the facilities are not large enough to support a full symphony orchestra; tours extensively abroad.

Chartered Accountants of Scotland, Institute of (1854), 27 Queen Street, Edinburgh, EH2 1LA. T.-031-225 5673. President of Council: Professor W.C.C. Morrison; Vice Presidents: James McKinnon, G.A. Anderson; Members: E.J. Baden, E.W. Bannerman, A.R. Cole-Hamilton, J.B. Cowan, Carol C. Ferguson, M.G. Ferrier, T.B. Fleming, F.A. Harding, C.N. Hastings, R.A. Johnson, F.F. Kidd, L.L. McAllister, R.P. McEwan, I.D. Mackenzie, S. McLennan, D. Matheson, H.F. Somerville, J.K. Sommerville, J.A.C. Stothers, G.L. Tasker, I.N. Tegner, I.D. Watson, J.I. Wyper. Secretary: Eric Tait, M.B.E.
Oldest accountancy body in the world, with a membership of 11,230. The Institute is unique among accountancy bodies in educating its students as well as examining them. In 1984, it had 1,700 registered students. The professional designatory letters C.A. are exclusive in the British Isles to members of the Institute. Most C.A.s (52%) work in industry and commerce, with 30% in practising firms of accountants. It publishes a monthly journal, *The Accountant's Magazine*.

Chartered Foresters, Institute of, (1926), 22 Walker Street, Edinburgh, EH3 7HR. T.-031-225 2705. President of Council: D.A. Mithen, C.B.; Vice-President: R.T. Gray. Secretary and Treasurer: Mrs M.W. Dick. To maintain and improve the standards of practice and understanding of forestry, and to promote the professional status of foresters.

Chartered Surveyors, Royal Institution of, Scottish Branch (1897), 7 Manor Place, Edinburgh, EH3 7DN. T.-031-225 7078. Chairman, Scottish Branch: G.F. Robertson; Senior Vice Chairman: A.S. Chalmers; Vice Chairmen: A.R.M. Stewart, D.J. Hughes Hallett, I.C. Stanners; Hon. Secretary: S.M. Smith. Scottish Secretary: J.M. Ritchie.
Members of the R.I.C.S. are involved in the valuation, measurement, management, and development of land and buildings. They work in private practice, business and commerce, local authorities, Government service, and statutory bodies. The Institution has a worldwide membership of 72,000, including 6,000 in Scotland. Entry to the profession is either through the Institution's own examination system, or increasingly through degree and diploma courses supplemented by a period of practical training.

Chess Association, Scottish (1884), 44 Stewart Clark Avenue, South Queensferry, EH30 9QH. T.-031-331 1751. President: Walter Munn; Secretary: John M. Glendinning; General Administrator: Mrs L. Morrison.

Child and Family Alliance, Scottish (1983), 56 Albany Street, Edinburgh, EH1 3QR. T.-031-557 2780. Chairman: Morag Faulds; Vice Chairman: John Rea. Director: Rachel Jenkins; Administrative Secretary: Jeannie Graham; Training Officer: Stephanie Tristam; Information Officer: Joyce Wilson. S.C.A.F.A. organises conferences, produces a regular newsletter, provides information and training services for members, acts as a consultative body on questions relating to children and families, and aims to promote a more effective partnership between voluntary and statutory agencies.

Children's Panels, Scottish Association of (1977). Hon. Secretary: J.C. Harris, Blythbank Farm, West Linton, EH46 7DF. T.-0721 52208. Chairman: Dr J. Dalrymple; Vice Chairman: D. Shaw. Acts as a corporate voice for the views of members of children's panels throughout Scotland, and provides a means of communication between the Panels and other bodies.

Christian Salvesen Ltd., 50 East Fettes Avenue, Edinburgh, EH4 1EQ. T.-031-552 7101. Chairman: G.H. Elliot; Managing Director: B.E. Sealey. Food processing, cold storage and distribution, house building, ship management and ownership, fish processing and selling, oil related services, portable power generation. Turnover: £210m.

Churches Architectural Heritage Trust, Scottish (1978), 15 North Bank Street, The Mound, Edinburgh, EH1 2LP. T.-031-225 8644. Chairman: Dr Magnus Magnusson; Trustees: Rt. Hon. Lord Wheatley of Shettleston, P.C., W.A. McPhail, Sir Fitzroy Maclean of Dunconnell, Bt., C.B.E., Professor Andrew MacMillan, Sir Jamie Stormonth Darling, C.B.E., M.C., T.D., Rt. Hon. The Countess of Mar and Kellie, O.B.E., Sir Robin MacLellan, C.B.E., Very Rev. Professor Robin Barbour, M.C. Secretary: Mrs G.E. Donaldson; Fund Raising Director: R.M. Leask. Raises and disburses money to help pay for the repair and restoration of churches of artistic, historic, or cultural interest. The Trust also assists congregations in obtaining technical advice. It has raised £100,000 and has made grants of £80,000 to churches of all denominations in Scotland.

Churches Council, Scottish (1964), Scottish Churches House, Kirk Street, Dunblane, FK15 OAJ. T.-0786 823588. Chairman: Very Rev. Professor Robin Barbour. General Secretary: Rev. Canon Kenyon E. Wright; Administrative Secretary: Christine Hoskings. Scottish Churches Council consists of directly elected representatives of nine Protestant churches and five inter-denominational Christian organisations in Scotland. The Roman Catholic Church is represented as a participant observer. The aim of the Council is to promote greater unity, renewal, and mission among the Scottish churches. Two main committees, Mission and Unity, and Community, Justice, and Peace, try to co-ordinate church activities in these fields. Scottish Churches House is a 50-bed centre for conferences, consultations, and retreats.

Church History Society, Scottish (1922), Grange Manse, 51 Portland Road, Kilmarnock, KA1 2EQ. T.-0563 25311. President: Dr John Durkan; Vice President: Rev. Professor Alex. C. Cheyne; Hon. Secretary and Treasurer: Rev. Colin G.F. Brockie. Promotes the study of every aspect of Scottish ecclesiastical history.

Church of Scotland, 121 George Street, Edinburgh, EH2 4YN. T.-031-225 5722. Moderator of the General Assembly (1984): Rt. Rev. J.M.K. Paterson (Milngavie St. Paul's). Principal Clerk: Rev. D.F.M. Macdonald, C.B.E. Secretary, Assembly Council: Gordon M. Hector, C.M.G., C.B.E.; General Treasurer: W.G.P. Colledge; Solicitor of the Church: R.A. Paterson; Secretary and Clerk, General Trustees: Alan W. Cowe; Joint Secretaries, Dept. of Ministry and Mission: Rev. George L. Lugton, Rev. Dr Ian B. Doyle; General Secretary, Board of World Mission and Unity: Rev. D.H.S. Lyon; Secretary, Department of Communication: T.B. Honeyman; Director, Church of Scotland Publicity: D. Bruce Cannon; Editor, *Life and Work*: R.D. Kernohan; Director of Social Work: Rev. F.S. Gibson; Organising Secretary, Woman's Guild: Mrs K.M. Beveridge; General Secretary, Department of Education: Rev. Alasdair J. Morton; Secretary, Diaconate Board: Joyce Nicol.

Scotland's national church with a communicant membership of 918,000. There are more than 2,000 parishes or charges of the Church of Scotland, grouped under 46 Presbyteries and 12 Synods. The General Assembly meets annually in May, and conducts its business throughout the year by means of Standing Committees.

Citizens Advice Bureaux, Scottish Association of (1975), 82 Nicolson Street, Edinburgh, EH8 9EW. T.-031-667 0156. Chairman: Eric Gillett; Vice Chairman: Mary Sherrard; Hon. Treasurer: John Fergusson. Chief Executive Officer: John Wright. A network of 59 Citizens Advice Bureaux throughout Scotland. The Association provides resources of information, training, field staff, and legal consultancy through a staff of 14 professionals. There are offices in Glasgow and Inverness, as well as Edinburgh. The organisation provides free, confidential, and impartial advice, information and assistance to all enquirers.

Citizens' Theatre (1943), 119 Gorbals Street, Glasgow, G5 9DS. T.-041-429 5560. Hon. President: Mrs Rona Mavor; Hon. Vice Presidents: The Lord Provost of Glasgow; Dame Jean Roberts, J.P.; Sir William Gray, J.P.; George Singleton, C.B.E., J.P. Chairman, Board of Directors: W.L. Taylor, C.B.E., J.P.; Vice Chairman: Ronald V. Singleton; Members: Jean Adams, Mrs M. Adler-Bell, A. Edward Argent, Richard Buchanan, J.P., Professor David S. Butler, Councillor John Gray, Councillor Robert Gray, J.P., Councillor Charles Hebenton, J.P., James Hood, J.P., Councillor John T. Kernaghan, J.P., Councillor Robert N.S. Logan, Professor Janet B.I. McDonald, Councillor Jean A. McFadden, J.P., Councillor Laurence A. McGarry, Councillor Jeanette M. Mason, Stephen Mulrine, C.A. Oakley, J.P., J. Michael L. Smyth, Professor Ian N. Sneddon, O.B.E., Margaret Tomlinson. Artistic Director: Giles Havergal; General Manager: Paul Bassett.

The Citizens' Theatre Company, founded by James Bridie, is now directed by Giles Havergal, Philip Prowse, and Robert David MacDonald. It receives subsidy from the Scottish Arts Council, Strathclyde Regional Council, and Glasgow District Council. The theatre operates a uniquely low price structure (all seats for 1984-85 season cost £2). O.A.P.s and the unemployed are admitted free at the door. The season usually runs from September to May, incorporating eight classical productions and a Christmas show by the Citizens' Company, and a short series of visiting companies. The theatre seats 830.

Civic Trust, Scottish (1967), 24 George Square, Glasgow, G2 1EF. T.-041-221 1466. Chairman of Trustees: Rt. Hon. Viscount Muirshiel, K.T., C.H.,

C.M.G.; Chairman of Management Committee: J.W. Wilson, O.B.E.; Trustees: Sir Samuel Curran, Professor James Dunbar-Nasmith, C.B.E., George L. Edwards, Charles A. Fraser, M.V.O., Lady Herries, Professor F.G.T. Holliday, C.B.E., Dr Michael Kelly, O.B.E., J.P., D.M. McCallum, C.B.E., J.C.T. MacRobert, J.P. Rettie, C.J. Risk, C.B.E., W.F. Robertson, D. Cameron Smail, Harry S. Smith, M.B.E., J.R.D. Swan, William Taylor, C.B.E., J.P., David Walton; Hon. Treasurer: G.B. Thomson; Hon. Solicitor: Douglas M. McLeman; Consultant: Maurice Lindsay, C.B.E., T.D. Administrative Director: Sadie Douglas; Technical Director: John Gerrard.
The Scottish Civic Trust aims to encourage public interest in the good appearance of towns and countryside and to inspire generally a sense of civic pride and desire for high quality in Scottish architecture and planning. It is particularly concerned with the conservation of buildings of architectural distinction or historic interest, the elmination and prevention of ugliness, whether from bad design or neglect, and the encouragement of informed and constructive participation in planning matters. It operates locally through civic or amenity societies registered with the Trust, and is able to give advice on, and help with, environmental problems.

Civil Engineers, Institution of, Glasgow and West of Scotland Association (1884), 11 Campbell Drive, Bearsden, Glasgow, G61 4NF. T.-041-332 9811, Ext. 3591. Chairman: Dr G. Fleming; Hon. Secretary: D. Hill-Smith. Learned society.

Civil Liberties, Scottish Council for (1969), 146 Holland Street, Glasgow, G2 4NG. T.-041-332 5960. Chairman: Richard Kennedy; Vice Chairman: Roger Colkett; Members of Executive Committee: Susan Watson, Robert Carr, Ian Davidson, Dilip Deb, Ruth Forbes, Pat Hughes, Richard Kinsey, Norman MacEwan, Sarah Nelson, Jim Sillars, Robert Thomson. General Secretary: David Godwin. Protection and promotion of civil rights and liberties and fundamental freedoms by means of research, monitoring, campaigning, public information, and public education.

Clackmannan College of Further Education (1968), Branshill Road, Alloa, FK10 3BT. T.-0259 215121. Chairman, College Council: Councillor J. Pollock. Principal: W. Scott. College of further education offering courses in the following subject areas: accounting; business studies; secretarial studies; catering; computer studies; engineering; construction; motor vehicle engineering; hairdressing; health studies; hotel reception.

Clackmannan District Council (1974), The Whins, Alloa, Clackmannanshire. T.-Alloa 722160. Convener: James Millar; Vice Convener: Graham Watt; Councillors: D. Clark, T. Downs, R. Elder, A. Hutton, S. Markham, B. Masterson, J. McDonald, J. Paterson, W. Wallace, J. Watson. Chief Executive: Alex. E. O'Neill; Director of Finance: R. Dunbar; Director of Technical Services: S. Fowler; Director of Housing: R. Clark; Director of Environmental Health: W.S. Cunningham. District Council. Population of District: 48,000.

Clearing Bankers, Committee of Scottish, 19 Rutland Square, Edinburgh, EH1 2DD. T.-031-229 1326. Secretary: J.C. Sutherland; Assistant Secretary: R. Heathwood. Central point of contact in matters affecting members' banks collectively, but not matters affecting banks individually or competitively. The Committee is also responsible for formulating and expressing a Scottish Clearing Bank view on relevant subjects, either on its own initative or in response to a request or invitation.

Clinterty Agricultural College (1968), Kinellar, Aberdeen, AB5 OTH. T.-Kinellar 393. Principal: John Telfer; Depute Principal: Peter W. Thompson. Residential college providing for the needs of agriculture and agricultural engineering at craft level for North and North East Scotland. The college also adminsters a day release presence at eight outcentres in the North East of Scotland.

Clydebank College (1965), Kilbowie Road, Clydebank, G81 2AA. T.-041-952 7771. Principal: W. Greenock; Depute Principal: R.C. Langlands; Registrar: J.U. MacKay. College of further education providing courses in a wide range of subjects up to sub-degree level. There are about 5,000 students, including full-time, day release, block release, and evening.

Clydebank District Council (1974), District Council Offices, Clydebank, G81 1TG. T.-041-941 1331. Provost: H. Duffy; Councillors: Mary Campbell, Elizabeth Brown, Margaret McGarry, A. Veitch, K. Sweeney, A. Macdonald, J. McAllister, S. Divers, D. Grainger, J. McKendrick, G. Casey. Chief Executive: J.M. Brown; Director of Finance: J. Gallagher; Director of Technical Services: R.K. Bruce; Director of Environmental Services: J.O. Sayers. District Council. Population of District: 51,000.

Clyde Pilotage Authority, 16 Robertson Street, Glasgow, G2 8DU. T.-041-221 4046. Pilot Master: Captain Lewis W. Black.

Clyde Port Authority (1966), 16 Robertson Street, Glasgow, G2 8DS. T.-041-221 8733. Chairman: R.W.S. Easton, C.B.E.; Members: J.J. Blanche, W.M. Cuthbert, C.I. Gray, J. Mather, J.T. McEwen, J. Moore, T. O'Connor, J.N.D. Ramsay. Managing Director: J. Mather; Harbour Master: Captain D.B. McMurray; Director, Finance and Administration: J.T. McEwen; Secretary and Solicitor: J.B. Maxwell. Dock and Harbour Authority operating ports of Glasgow, Greenock, Hunterston, and Ardrossan. Responsible for conservancy of the river and Clyde Estuary.

Clyde River Purification Board, Rivers House, Murray Road, East Kilbride, G75 OLA. T.-035 52 38181. Director and River Inspector: Desmond Hammerton.

Clydesdale Bank PLC (1838), 30 St. Vincent Place, Glasgow, G1 2HL. T.-041-248 7070. Chairman: Sir Robert Fairbairn, J.P.; Joint Deputy Chairmen: Alexander Logan McClure, Sir Eric Yarrow, M.B.E.; Directors: W.R. Alexander, W.D. Coats, R.J.C. Fleming, O.B.E., T.D., W. Fraser, C.B.E., S.T. Graham, C.B.E., D.F.C., J.D. Greenwell, D.F. Hardie, C.B.E., J.P., Sir Norman Macfarlane, A.R. Macmillan, Sir David McNee, D.W. Nickson, C.B.E., I. Tennant. Chief General Manager: A.R. Cole-Hamilton; Deputy Chief General Manager: R.A. Laurenson; General Managers: H. Aitken, R.C. Legge, D.R. Robertson; Deputy General Manager: W.C. Harvey.
The Clydesdale Bank provides a complete banking service through its branches in Scotland, England, and its worldwide network of correspondents.

Clydesdale District Council (1974), District Offices, South Vennel, Lanark, ML11 7TJ. T.-0555 61331; 61511. Convener: Miss M.T. Hodgson; Members: S. Allan, J.P., Mrs A.P. Allison, J.P., T. Craig, Mrs E. Forrest, O.B.E., R. French, Mrs E. Hamilton, J.P., J. Hood, Mrs E. Logan, R. McMillan, J.P., W. Nisbet, T. Prentice, J.P., D.W. Smart, J.P., M. Wardlaw, Mrs N. Wilson, J.P., E. Wright, J.P. Chief Executive: P.W. Daniels; Director of Administration and Legal Services: D.P. Hepburn; Director of Finance and Management Services: D.S.H. Anderson; Director of Housing: R.A.

Morrison; Director of Planning and Technical Services: W.G. U'Ren; Director of Environmental Health: J. Hamilton, J.P.; Director of Recreational Services: R.I.D. Mair. District Council. Population of District: 57,000.

Clydesdale Horse Society of Great Britain and Ireland (1877), 26 Argyle Terrace, Dunblane, FK15 9DN. T.-0786 822470. President: John McMillan; Secretary: John Fraser. Breed society.

Clyde Valley Tourist Board (1982), South Vennel, Lanark, ML11 7JT. T.-0555 2544. Chairman: Councillor J. Swinburne. Tourism Manager: Andrew M.G. Campbell. Promotion of tourism within the Districts of Clydesdale, Hamilton, and Motherwell.

Clyde Yacht Clubs Association (1898), Anchor House, Blackhall Lane, Paisley, PA1 1TA. T.-041-887 8296. Chairman: N.A. Kennedy; Hon. Secretary: J.W.R. Watson. Organisation of yacht clubs on the Clyde and West coast of Scotland. Co-ordinates racing and cruising matters.

Coal Board, National, Scottish Area, Green Park, Greenend, Edinburgh, EH17 7PZ. T.-031-664 1461. Area Director: Albert Wheeler; Deputy Directors: George Gillespie (Mining), John Loudon (Administration). Management and organisation of coal production from 12 collieries and several opencast coal sites, and the marketing of the production.

Coarse Angling, Scottish Federation for. Hon.Secretary: Stuart McKenzie, 22 Roseburn Place, Edinburgh, EH12 5NL. T.-031-337 4566.

Coatbridge College, Kildonan Street, Coatbridge, ML5 3LS. T.-0236 22316. Principal: Edward J. Dowdalls. College of further education.

Coats Patons PLC (1960), 155 St. Vincent Street, Glasgow, G2 5PA. T.-041-221 8711. Chairman: W.D. Coats. Manufacturers and merchants of threads, yarns, knitting wools and garments. Turnover (1984): £888m.

Cockburn Association (Edinburgh Civic Trust) (1875), 15 North Bank Street, Edinburgh, EH1 2LP. T.-031-225 2085. Chairman: W.D. Cullen, Q.C.; Vice Chairman: P.W. Simpson; Hon. Treasurer: R.M. Martin. Secretary: Oliver Barratt. Charitable association whose objects are to promote and encourage (a) the maintenance and improvement of the amenity of the city of Edinburgh and its neighbourhood; and (b) the protection and preservation of the city's landscape and historic and architectural heritage.

Collins PLC, William (1819), Westerhill Road, Bishopbriggs, Glasgow. T.-041-772 3200. Chairman and Chief Executive: F.I. Chapman; Vice Chairmen: R.C. Smith, C.B.E., Sir Charles Troughton, C.B.E.; Group Managing Directors: C.E. Allen, G. Craig.
Holding company for the Collins group of companies engaged in book publishing and related activities. Publishes educational and reference books, paperbacks (imprints include Fontana, Pan, Granada, and Armada), Bibles, fiction, natural history, children's books, atlases, and diaries.

Colportage Society, Scottish (1793), 11 Newton Place, Glasgow, G3 7PR. T.-041-333 0546. Hon. President: Rev. George B. Duncan; President: Rev. Robert McGhee; Vice Presidents: Dr Ian R. Clark, Rev. Kingsley J. Rendell. Colporteurs: Mary McBain, Gerard Hutchison. 'A Bible in every home in Scotland' is the aim of the Society. Full-time and voluntary colporteurs are engaged in door-to-door work.

Comhairle Nan Eilean (Western Isles Islands Council) (1974), Sandwick Road, Stornoway, PA87 2BW. T.-0851 3773. Convener: A. Matheson; Members: D. Murray, W. MacLeod, D. MacLeod, A.A. Macdonald, Rev. D.

Macaulay, O.B.E., A. Graham, D. Maclean, A.A. Macleod, J.M. Macmillan, O.B.E., A.M. Mackenzie, M. Afrin, Marie Macmillan, D.W. Kennedy, J. Crichton, D. Mackay, D.R. Macaulay, I. Maclennan, D.M. Mackay, D.M. Mackinnon, D. Macdonald, W. Leonard, N. Johnson, J. Robertson, J.L. McArthur, Mary Bremner, J. Macintyre, R. Allan, H.N.M. Morrison, M.B.E. Chief Executive: R. MacIver; Director of Administration and Legal Services: D. Sinclair; Director of Finance: D. Macleod; Director of Architectural Services: J. Paterson; Director of Consumer Protection and Environmental Health: H. Fraser; Director of Education: N.R. Galbraith; Director of Engineering Services: G. Macleod; Director of Planning and Development: R. Haworth; Director of Social Work: Mrs N.E. MacLeod. Islands Council. Population of Islands: 30,000.

Commonwealth Institute, Scotland, 8 Rutland Square, Edinburgh, EH1 2AS. T.-031-229 6668. Chairman: Professor George Shepperson. Director: Charles Carrol; Education Officer: W. Norman Henderson. Educational body which provides information about the Commonwealth, its member nations, and the world issues which affect us all. It is sponsored by the Foreign and Commonwealth Office.

Commonwealth Games Council for Scotland (1931). Hon. Secretary: George A. Hunter, O.B.E., 139 Old Dalkeith Road, Edinburgh, EH16 4SZ. T.-031-664 1070.

Communist Party, Scottish Committee, 44 Carlton Place, Glasgow, G5. T.-041-429 2558. Chairwoman: Pat Milligan; Secretary: Jack Ashton.

Community and Voluntary Organisations, Scottish Council for (1943), 18/19 Claremont Crescent, Edinburgh, EH7 4QD. T.-031-556 3882. Policy Committee: James Anderson, Heather Birrell, Kay Carmichael, The Hon. Mrs Mary Corsar, David Dunsmuir, James Fraser, Nicholas Hinton, Alex. Howie, Sydney Hudson, Irvine Inglis, George Lightheart, Jean Malcolm, Malcolm May, Rev. Alan Moses, Donald MacKinnon, Jack F. McGregor, Barry Parker, Rae Paul, Wing Commander J.E. Pollington, Alan Rees, James Ross, Rev. Tom Scott, Councillor Keith Simpson, Lorna Bridges, Rev. K. Thomson, Jean Thow, Margaret Wilson, May Wilson, Alan Barr, C.J. Harley, James Gallacher, Graham Wilson. Director: Ross Flockhart. An independent voluntary organisation which works at national and local level to promote and support voluntary action and service in Scotland. The S.C.V.O. is an organisation of member bodies and some individuals representing a wide range of interest. Current objectives are to enable voluntary organisations to be effective, to extend the range of voluntary action and service, to advocate particular issues, to promote and safeguard the values of voluntary endeavour, and to provide services for these ends.

Community Drama Association, Scottish (1926), Saltire House, 13 Atholl Crescent, Edinburgh, EH3 8HA. T.-031-332 3980. Chairman: John Stoddart. Administrator: Alan Nicol. The development of amateur drama in Scotland, particularly on a community basis. The Association binds together amateur dramatic societies throughout the country, and offers them advice, encouragement, and practical help in the furtherance of their aims.

Community Education Council, Scottish (1982), Atholl House, 2 Canning Street, Edinburgh, EH3 8EG. T.-031-229 2433. Chairman: Baroness Carnegy of Lour; Members: G.S.H. Bain, A.F. Blacklaws, O.B.E., Professor L. Bown, O.B.E., Councillor J.P. Boyle, Ms. L. Bridges, W.S. Charles, B. Cooklin, P. D'Arcy, G.V. Drought, R. Findlay, Very Rev. G. Forbes, A. Forsyth, Dr E.M. Gray, C.B.E., J. Henry, G. Lorimer, Mrs M.

Miller, D. O'Rourke, Councillor R. Turpie, Councillor A.W. Worthington. Director: Ralph S. Wilson; Assistant Directors: Pablo Foster, Marcus Liddle, Allen Mercer.
Advises the Secretary of State for Scotland on all matters relating to community education, and promotes the development of community education. The Council engages in research, collation, and dissemination of information, and develops innovative work in the field. It publishes a monthly newspaper, *Scan*.

Company and Commercial Accountants, Scottish Association of (1979), 190 St. Vincent Street, Glasgow, G2. T.-041-221 9005. Chairman: John Mather; Secretary: David I. Strachan. For members and students of the Society of Company and Commercial Accountants resident in Scotland.

Congregational Union of Scotland (1896), 340 Cathedral Street, Glasgow. T.-041-332 7667. President: Rev. D. Morgan Phillips; Chairman: F. Jeffrey Fowkes. General Secretary: Rev. Robert Waters; World Mission Secretary: Rev. John R. Smith. Congregational churches are by definition independent fellowships, but their interdependence is expressed in belonging to this Union, which is thus able to act denominationally.

Conservation Projects Trust, Scottish (1984), 70 Main Street, Doune, Perthshire, FK16 6BW. T.-0786 841479. President: Sir James Stormonth-Darling, C.B.E., M.C., T.D. Chairman: Alistair Campbell, O.B.E.; Vice Chairman: Colin Taylor; Hon. Treasurer: Dr Alan Mowle. Director: Nicholas Cooke; Administrator: Catherine Smith; Area Officer (South West): Gavin Stewart; National Training Officer: Philip Webb. Established as the Scottish sister body to the British Trust for Conservation Volunteers, S.C.P. is the only Scottish voluntary body formed solely to promote and support practical conservation work in both the rural and urban environment. Volunteers help manage nature reserves and other wildlife areas, and maintain essential access or other amenities for visitors to Scotland's countryside. In 1984, S.C.P. volunteers completed more than 20,000 days of conservation work, much of this in urban areas of Central Scotland.

Conservative and Unionist Association, Scottish, 3 Chester Street, Edinburgh, EH3 7RF. T.-031-226 4426. President: Donald O.G. Maclean; Vice Presidents: Iain A. McCrone, Mrs J.M. Dalgleish, J.P.; Hon. Treasurer: Matthew D. Goodwin, C.B.E. Secretary: Ann C. Hay.

Conservative Party, Scottish, 3 Chester Street, Edinburgh, EH3 7RF. T.-031-226 4426. Chairman: Sir James Goold; Deputy Chairman: Dr Alistair Smith, C.B.E.; Vice Chairman: Ian Lang, M.P. Director: William R. Henderson; Deputy Directors: Robert M. Balfour, Peter D. Smith. Central organisational offices of the Conservative Party in Scotland.

Constabulary, H.M. Inspectorate of, St. Andrew's House, Edinburgh, EH1 3DE. T.-031-556 8501. H.M. Chief Inspector of Constabulary for Scotland: A. Morrison, C.V.O.

Consumer Council, Scottish (1975), 314 St. Vincent Street, Glasgow, G3 8XW. T.-041-226 5261. Chairman: Esme Walker; Vice-Chairman: Mary McKelvie; Members: Colin Hope, Esme Grieve, Barbara Kelly, Ronald Laing, William McBryde, Archie McCallum, Father Matthew McManus, Helen Millar, Maeve Robertson, Sylvia Sandeman, Jim Short, Douglas Williamson. Director: Peter Gibson.
The Scottish Consumer Council is a committee of the National Consumer

Council. It identifies and represents the interests of Scottish consumers, particularly the disadvantaged. The S.C.C. keeps a watching brief on the goods and services provided by central and local government and other public bodies, as well as by commercial firms and the professions. Research is carried out into areas of consumer concern and the S.C.C. presses for whatever changes are required in the law and in the provision of services to meet the needs of the consumers.

Co-operative Education Association, Scottish, 95 Morrison Street, Glasgow, G5. T.-041-429 2556. Chairman: R. Stewart. Secretary and Education Officer: Iain Macdonald. Promotion of adult education for Co-operative employees and members; promotion of new Co-operatives; courses in establishing new Co-operatives.

Co-operatives Development Committee, Scottish (1976), Templeton Business Centre, Templeton Street, Bridgeton, Glasgow, G40 1DA. T.-041-554 3797. Chairman: John Lewis; Vice Chairman: Nick Fleming; Treasurer: Alex. Dunlop. Director: Cairns Campbell. Formed to provide advice and assistance to worker-owned businesses in Scotland. It has undertaken pioneering work in helping co-operative growth, particularly among industrial and producer co-operatives. Partial rescues of failed businesses, or workforce buy-outs, have featured largely in the Committee's work, although not to the exclusion of other types of co-operative. In 1977, there was only one co-operative in Scotland; today, there are more than 50 providing 500 jobs.

Co-operative Union Ltd., Scottish Section, 95 Morrison Street, Glasgow, G5 8LP. T.-041-429 2556. Chairman: W.R. Smith; Secretary: R. Bluer. Employers' association for retail co-operative societies and the Co-operative Wholesale Society in Scotland.

Co-operative Women's Guild, Scottish (1892), 95 Morrison Street, Glasgow, G5 8LP. T.-041-429 1457. General Secretary: Mrs M. Lonsdale, J.P. Study and practice of the best means of strengthening and extending the Co-operative movement; to stimulate thought on all questions of social and political reform.

Corn Trade Association Ltd., Scottish (1957). Secretaries: Touche Ross & Co., 15 Melville Street, Edinburgh, EH3 7PQ. T.-031-225 6834. President: T. Duncan; Vice President: A.C. Brown. Trade Association for the grain trade.

Counselling, Scottish Association for (1977), 26 Frederick Street, Edinburgh, EH2 2JR. T.-031-225 5006. Hon. President: Rt. Rev. Michael Hare Duke; Hon. Vice-Presidents: Sheriff Nigel Thomson, Rev. Professor James Whyte. Executive Secretary: Margaret E. Clement. To promote and provide education and training for counsellors, to provide support and supervision, to promote the use of counselling as a valuable aid to the well-being of the community.

Country Dance Society, Royal Scottish (1923), 12 Coates Crescent, Edinburgh, EH3 7AF. T.-031-225 3854. Chairman: Mrs M.G. Parker, M.B.E., J.P.; Vice Chairman: Dr A. MacFadyen; Secretary: Muriel Gibson. To preserve and further the practice of traditional Scottish country dances.

Country Life Museums Trust, Scottish (1970), National Museum of Antiquities of Scotland, Queen Street, Edinburgh, EH2 1JD. T.-031-557 3550. Hon. President: Rt. Hon. The Earl of Haddington, K.T., M.C., T.D. Co-Chairmen: Professor Noel Farnie Robertson, C.B.E., John M. Urquhart, C.B.E.; Vice Chairman: Brian Lambie; Members of Council: Ronald Cant,

James D.G. Davidson, O.B.E., M.V.O., Captain William F.E. Forbes, William J. Ferguson, Donald S. Erskine, William D. Alexander, Robert F. Gregor, Marie Mackie, Sir Ilay Campbell, Bt., A.T. Clark, Graham H. Speirs, Kenneth Paterson, Alistair J. Robertson, A. Hamilton, John B. Tuckwell. Secretary: Alexander Fenton; Assistant Secretary: Gavin C. Sprott. Set up for charitable purposes to foster research into all aspects of rural life and to explore its educational potential through museum displays, principally in the Scottish Agricultural Museum, Ingliston (open May-September), through the development of open-air museums of country life, and through associated publications.

Countryside Activities Council, Scottish (1968). Hon. Secretary: Dr K.M. Watson, M.B.E., 39 Clepington Road, Dundee, DD4 7EL. T.-0382 41095. Hon. President: W.H. Murray, O.B.E. Chairman: Dr R. Aitken. Umbrella group of 23 outdoor organisations concerned with leisure-time activities in the countryside, such as walking, riding, cycling, mountaineering, camping, and hostelling.

Countryside Commission for Scotland (1967), Battleby, Redgorton, Perth, PH1 3EW. T.-0738 27921. Chairman: D.W. Nickson, C.B.E.; Vice Chairman: J. Roger Carr, J.P.; Members: J.M.S. Arnott, Felicity Ballantyne, Dr D.J. Bennet, A.W. Driver, Professor C. Gimingham, G.R. Marwick, D. Ross, R.R. Steedman, G.G. Stewart, I.R. Thomson. Director: John Foster; Deputy Director: Thomas Huxley; Secretary: William B. Prior.
The Commission is a government agency with responsibilities for helping to provide for better enjoyment of the Scottish countryside and the conservation of its natural beauty and amenity. It provides grants and advice, and publishes a wide range of material relating to its work. Catalogue on request.

Countryside Rangers Association, Scottish (1974), Lochore Meadows Country Park, Crosshill, Lochgelly, Fife, KY5 8BA. T.-Ballingry 860086. Chairman: Keith Graham; Vice Chairman: N.K. Bullivant; Secretary: Susan Manson. Professional association for countryside rangers.

Courier & Advertiser (1926), 7 Bank Street, Dundee, DD1 9HU. T.-0382 23131. Morning newspaper serving Dundee and surrounding area.

Court of Session, Parliament House, 11 Parliament Square, Edinburgh. T.-031-225 2595. Supreme civil court in Scotland. Principal Clerk of Session and Justiciary: A.M. Campbell.

Court of Session Rules Council, Parliament House, Edinburgh. T.-031-225 2595. Members: The Lord President, The Lord Justice Clerk, The Hon. Lord McDonald, D.B. Weir, Q.C., I.C. Kirkwood, Q.C., R.N.M. Maclean, Q.C., D.J.D. Macfadyen, Q.C., J.L. Mitchell, Advocate, W. Bryden, D.I.K. McLeod, M. Sischy, Professor P.N. Love, Alasdair McArthur. Appointed in terms of the Administration of Justice (Scotland) Act 1933.

Courts Administration, Scottish, 26/27 Royal Terrace, Edinburgh, EH7 5AN. T.-031-556 0755. Director: W.A.P. Weatherston. Responsible for the organisation and staffing of the courts, and other matters connected with the administration of justice.

Craft Centre, Scottish, 140 Canongate, Edinburgh, EH8 8DD. T.-031-556 8136. Chairman of Council: Barbara Davidson; Administrator and Secretary: Freda Spencer. To encourage the highest standards of craft work . by providing a showcase of members' products.

Craigie College of Education (1964), Ayr, KA8 OSR. T.-0292 260321. Chairman, Board of Governors: Professor J. Butt. Principal: Peter C. McNaught; Vice Principal: Richard L. Peddie; Clerk to the Governing Body and College Secretary: Raymond E.B. Thomson. The College provides pre- and in-service courses for teachers in the South West of Scotland. In association with the University of Strathclyde, it offers the degree of Bachelor of Education and the one-year postgraduate certificate for students already possessing a degree. A number of special qualifications are also offered including a one-year course leading to a special qualification for the teaching of infants and nursery children; one-term course leading to a special qualification as a teacher in a nursery school; upper-primary associateships; remedial qualifications. The College also contributes in the fields of community education, social work, and related professions.

Cricket Union, Scottish, 18 Ainslie Place, Edinburgh, EH3 6AU. T.-031-226 4401. Hon. Secretary: R.W. Barclay; Administrator: Robin Prentice; National Coach: D. Wilson.

Crofters Commission (1955), 4-6 Castle Wynd, Inverness, IV2 3EQ. T.-0463 237231. Chairman: J.F.M. Macleod; Vice Chairman: N.A. MacAskill; Members: I.G. Munro, Brian Hunter, Donald A. Morrison, Rev. A.I. Macarthur, Peter Morrison. Secretary: I.A. Macpherson.
Established by the Crofters (Scotland) Act with the principal duties of re-organising, developing and regulating crofting in the seven crofting counties of Scotland and keeping under general review all matters relating to crofters and crofting conditions.

Crop Research Institute, Scottish (1981), Invergowrie, Dundee, DD2 5DA. T.-Invergowrie 731. Director: C.E. Taylor; Secretary: N.D. Anderson; Head of Research Divisions: R.A. Fox (Crop Protection), Dr P.D. Waister (Crop Sciences), Dr N.L. Innes (Plant Breeding), Dr B.D. Harrison (Virology). Set up by the Department of Agriculture and Fisheries for Scotland. The work of the Institute is to improve the productivity and quality of crops by studying their breeding, culture, and protection from diseases and pests; fundamental research is also carried out which contributes to the establishment of scientific principles. Potato, barley (especially for malting), forage brassica (especially swede, rape, and kale), raspberry, and black currant are the major crops in the research programme.

Croquet Association, Scottish. Secretary: I.H. Wright, 17 Greygoran, New Sauchie, Clackmannan. T.-Alloa 213515.

Cross-Country Union, Scottish (1887). Hon. General Secretary: John E. Clifton, 38 Silverknowes Drive, Edinburgh, EH4 5HH. T.-031-336 3452. To foster and control cross-country running in Scotland.

Crown Office, 5-7 Regent Road, Edinburgh, EH7 5BL. T.-031-557 3800. Lord Advocate: Rt. Hon. Lord Cameron of Lochbroom, Q.C.; Solicitor-General for Scotland: Peter Lovat Fraser, Q.C., M.P.; Crown Agent (Deputy Secretary): I Dean; Deputy Crown Agent: J.D. Lowe; Establishment Officer (Principal): J. Paterson. The Crown Office is responsible for the public prosecution of crime in Scotland. All prosecutions in the High Court of Justiciary are conducted by Crown counsel instructed by the Crown Office. In the Sheriff and District Courts, prosecutions are conducted by the Procurator Fiscal Service, which is administered by the Crown Office.

Cumbernauld and Kilsyth District Council (1974), Council Offices, Bron Way, Cumbernauld, Glasgow, G67 1DZ. T.-02367 22131. Provost: J. Pollock; Members: T. Johnston, Mrs E. Irvine, C. Combe, D. Gilchrist, I.

MacDowall, J. Cullen, G.S. Murray, Mrs R. McKenna, Mrs C. Craigie, Mrs I. Hanlon, G. McElroy. Chief Executive: James Hutton; Director of Administration and Legal Services: James Gildea; Director of Technical Services: John Stark; Director of Recreation and Leisure: Daniel McGowan. District Council. Population of District: 63,000.

Cumbernauld College, Town Centre, Cumbernauld, G67 1HU. T.-02367 31811. Principal: John Ogden. College of further education.

Cumbernauld Development Corporation, Cumbernauld House, Cumbernauld. T.-02367 21155. Chief Executive: Brig. C.H. Cowan. Development of new town.

Cumnock and Doon Enterprise Trust (CADET) (1984), 46 Townhead Street, Cumnock, Ayrshire. T.-0290 21159. Chairman: Alex. Macdonald. Director: Alex. Neil. Enterprise trust established to create employment and new industry in the Cumnock and Doon Valley area.

Cumnock and Doon Valley District Council (1974), Council Offices, Lugar, Cumnock, KA18 3JQ. T.-0290 22111. Convener: D. Shankland; Members: R. Stevenson, E. Ross, D. Snellor, J. Allan, T. Gormanley, J. Hodge, J. Cannon, J. Paterson, T. Hainey. Chief Executive and Director of Administration: D. Hemmings; Director of Finance: K.W. Inch; Director of Technical Services: A.C. Morris; Director of Environmental Health and Cleansing: A.J. Paton. District Council. Population of District: 44,000.

Cunninghame District Council (1974), Cunninghame House, Irvine, KA12 8EE. T.-0294 74166. Convener: Teresa Beattie; Members: D. O'Neill, A. Rubie, J. Carson, J. Farrell, T. Dewar, T. McMillan, R. Cochrane, S. Dewar, J. Donn, Jane Gorman, J. Clements, G. Ritchie, D. Duncan, S. Gooding, D. Dickie, T. Morris, J. Kelso, T. Dickie, G. Steven, M. McGuire, Hannah Pollock, G.H. Barnett, Diane Davis, D. Munn, Edith Clarkson, D. Doris, W. Donald, J. Riddell, Evelyn Sillars. Chief Executive and Director of Administration: J.M. Miller; Director of Finance: I.L. Herd; Director of Technical Services: L. Dickens; Director of Planning: A. Reid; Director of Housing: R. Lindsay; Director of Leisure and Recreation: D.P. Webster; Director of Environmental Health: W. Tulloch; Director of Cleansing: W. Cowan. District Council. Population of District: 137,000.

Curriculum, Consultative Committee on the (1965), New St. Andrew's House, Edinburgh, EH1 3SX. T.-031-556 8400. Chairman: Dr James Munn, O.B.E.; Members: J. Bell, D.M. Brodie, Professor R.R. Burnside, Professor J. Butt, D. Campbell, R. Cummings, I.S. Flett, I.R. Fraser, D.L. Fulton, Sister M. Gallagher, Ms M. Graham, G. Kirk, Miss M. Livingstone, R.C. Louden, W. Michael, Dr A.D. Milne, A. Money, Professor A. Morrison, Maurine C. Murchison, O.B.E., Mrs H. Murray, Ms E. Quinn, R.B. Reid, D.G. Robertson, J. Stevenson, D. Taylor, Miss M. Taylor, R.S. Thomson. Secretary: David R. McNicoll.
The C.C.C. (with its structure of subject committees) is the major source of advice to the Secretary of State for Scotland on matters affecting the curriculum in schools; and the Scottish Curriculum Development Service which it controls is the central agency for curriculum development in Scotland.

Cyclists' Union, Scottish. General Secretary: Len M. Rankin, 13 Broom Terrace, Johnstone, Renfrewshire. T.-0505 21251.

D

Daily Record (1885), 40 Anderston Quay, Glasgow, G3 8DA. T.-041-248 7000. Editor: Bernard Vickers. National morning newspaper.

Dairy Council, Scottish (1957), 266 Clyde Street, Glasgow, G1 4JH. T.-041-221 4838. Chairman: W. Weir. Secretary: J. Russell. To promote and extend the sale of milk and milk products in the U.K. and elsewhere; to promote and undertake investigation, research, and education in matters affecting the processing, manufacture, or sale of milk and milk products.

Dairy Trade Federation, Scottish (1980), 24 Blythswood Square, Glasgow, G2 4QS. T.-041-226 3766. Secretaries and Treasurers: Thomson McLintock and Company. To promote the interests of the Scottish dairy industry in all its branches, particularly the processing and distribution of liquid milk and in the manufacture of milk products.

Darts Association, Scottish. Secretary: T.R. Frost, 3 St. Fillans Grove, Aberdour, Burntisland, Fife. T.-0383 860546.

Dawson International PLC (1972), Kinross, KY13 7DH. T.-Kinross 63521. Executive Directors: R.A.B. Miller (Chairman and Chief Executive), D.L.D. Blackburn, J.D. Embrey, G.A. Smith, J.B. Waterton. Non-Executive Directors: Sir Alan Smith, C.B.E., D.F.C. (President), W.R. Alexander, C.B.E., J.E. Bolton, C.B.E., D.S.C. Secretary: H. Somerville. Specialist textile manufacturers, operating in world markets. The Group is best known for its luxury knitwear and brand names which include Pringle of Scotland, Braemar, and Ballantyne. Turnover (1984): £179m.

Deaf, Scottish Association for the (1927), Moray House, Holyrood Road, Edinburgh, EH8 8AQ. T.-031-556 8137. Chairman: Dr Arnold M. Grier. Director: Tom McLaren, M.B.E. National voluntary organisation which co-ordinates the work of all voluntary groups working with and for hearing-impaired people of all ages and degrees of hearing loss in Scotland.

Deaf Sports Council, Scottish, 14 Grosvenor Crescent, Edinburgh, EH12 5EL. Organisation of various sports for deaf people only.

Decorators Federation, Scottish, 249 West George Street, Glasgow, G2 4RB. T.-041-221 7090. President: A.L. Colvin. Secretary: J.C. Henderson. Employers' organisation which negotiates wages and conditions for industry.

Design Council, Scotland (1945), Scottish Design Centre, 72 St. Vincent Street, Glasgow, G2 5TN. T.-041-221 6121. Chief Executive: W.M. Deeprose. The promotion by all practicable means of the standard of design in the products of British industry.

Development Agency, Scottish (1975), 120 Bothwell Street, Glasgow, G2 7JP. T.-041-248 2700. Chairman: Robin Duthie, C.B.E.; Deputy Chairman:

Douglas Hardie, C.B.E.; Chief Executive: George Mathewson; Members: William Aitken, M.B.E., Sir Kenneth Alexander, Andrew Barr, Robert Cowan, James Gordon, C.B.E., Charles Gray, John McCracken, Sir Norman Macfarlane, Sir Alan Smith, C.B.E., Ian Wood, C.B.E. Director (Finance): Robert McEwan; Director (Small Business and Electronics): Peter Carmichael, C.B.E.; Director (Planning and Projects): Edward Cunningham; Director (Area Development): Richard Colwell; Director (Property Development and Environment): Alan Dale; Director (Investment): Donald Patience; Director (North East Scotland): John Condliffe; Director (Locate in Scotland): Iain Robertson; Head of Marketing: Lloyd Fraser; Secretary: David A. Lyle.

The S.D.A. was formed with the objectives of furthering economic development, promoting industrial efficiency and international competitiveness, and improving the environment. Current priorities identified in the Agency's corporate plan are: small business development; support for technology; encouragement of investment and area development. The Agency aims to act as a catalyst to encourage commitment to and investment in Scotland's future growth. Emphasis is on partnership, working alongside the public and private sector.

Development Department, Scottish, New St. Andrew's House, Edinburgh, EH1 3TD. Secretary: T.R.H. Godden, C.B. Private Secretary: Andrew Dickson. Department of the Secretary of State for Scotland. Responsibilities cover policy and functions affecting the physical development of Scotland, including town and country planning, housing, urban renewal, roads and transport, water supplies and sewerage, control of air and river pollution, building control and conversion, historic buildings and ancient monuments. The Department is also responsible in Scotland for general policy on local government administration.

Dictionary Association, Scottish National (1929), 27 George Square, Edinburgh, EH8 9LD. T.-031-667 1011, Ext. 6681. Executive Council: Mrs K.A. Aikman Smith, Professor A.J. Aitken, Sir Kenneth Alexander, Professor R. Black, Dr Kenneth Buthlay, G.D. Cheyne, Professor D. Daiches, Dr Alexander Fenton, Professor A.D.S. Fowler, James Gilchrist, Professor William Gillies, Miss M.D.W. Keaney, R.L.C. Lorimer, Professor John MacQueen, J. Derrick McClure, M.P. McDiarmid, Mrs F.J. Riddy, Trevor Royle, Mrs L. Smith. Secretary: J.W. Mort; Editor-in-Chief: Mrs H.M.J. Robinson. Compilation of the Scottish National Dictionary.

Directors of Education in Scotland, Association of (1920), Education Department, Lothian Regional Council, 40 Torphichen Street, Edinburgh, EH3 8JJ. T.-031-229 9292. General Secretary: W.D. Semple. Professional body representing officers of grade of Assistant Director and above employed in the administration of the education service at local level.

Disability, Scottish Council on (1982), Princes House, 5 Shandwick Place, Edinburgh, EH2 4RG. T.-031-229 8632. Chairman: Marjorie M. McInnes, O.B.E.; Members, Executive Committee: Professor Cairns Aitken, Philip Dolan, Mrs Ivory Emm, Dr D.C. Falconer, Elizabeth Gibson, Lt. Cmdr. D. Richard M. Gregory, Nancy Harper, Mary Marshall, James A. McIntosh, Margaret Moodie, Rev. T. Watson Moyes, Elliott R. Paterson, Alan T. Rees, James Ritchie, Robert W.K.C. Rogerson, The Hon. Mrs Sandeman, Stanley A. Sklaroff, Audrey D. Smith, David Somerville, Hugh W.L. Stewart, Tom Taylor, Professor Chris Turner, Professor Henry J. Walton, Jock Young. Director: David Dunsmuir; Assistant Directors: J. Baillie (Projects and Services), R.B. Law (Administration and Finance).

Exists to provide a means of consultation and joint action for organisations working for the well-being of disabled people; to promote and provide means for effective communication and co-operation between statutory and voluntary agencies, industrial and other organisations, and individuals working in the field of disability; to increase the social awareness of the problems of disability; to increase the understanding of the problems of disability and encourage the provision and improvements of facilities and services; to promote the education of disabled people; to promote the integration of disabled people into the community.

Distillers Company plc, The (1877), 33 Ellersly Road, Edinburgh, EH12 6JW. T.-031-337 7373. Management Committee: J.M. Connell (Chairman), W.M. Forrest (Group Strategic Planning), D.C. Kerr (Scotch Whisky Exports), R.S. Temple (Finance), P.N. Whitley (Sales of Scotch Whisky, U.K./ E.E.C.), D.A. Connell, W.H. Elgood (Company Secretary), J.R.C. Holbech, Lord Maclean (non-executive), R.K. Martin, Sir William Pile (non-executive), D.W. Small, T. Tiplady, C.N. Younghusband.
Parent company of a group of subsidiaries whose fundamental business is the production and sale of potable distilled products. The Group's principal products include: Scotch whiskies, London gins, vodkas, cognacs, bourbons, Pimm's, carbon dioxide, yeast and food products for the catering trade. Turnover (1984): £1,134m.

Duke of Edinburgh's Award, The. Secretary for Scotland: G.H.K. Corsar, T.D., J.P., 69 Dublin Street, Edinburgh, EH3 6NS. T.-031-556 9097.

Dumbarton District Council (1974), Crosslet House, Argyll Avenue, Dumbarton. T.-Dumbarton 65100. Provost: Rodney McNamara; Members: Peter McCann, Bernard Morgan, Ian Leitch, Alexander Tuach, Ellen Roberton, Doreen Phillips, Norman Glen, Mary J. Dutch, William Petrie, Murdo MacGregor, George Hood, Ann McIntyre, William Neeson, Henry Crawley, Leslie Robertson. Chief Executive Officer: Lachlan MacKinnon; Director of Administration and Legal Services: Ian M.H. Lyon; Director of Finance: J.G. Ritchie; Director of Planning and Development: J. Webster; Director of Architectural Services: J. Oliver; Director of Environmental Health Services: A.B. Miller; Director of Housing Services: J. Pollock; Director of Civic Amenities: J. McErlane. District Council. Population of District: 79,000.

Dumfries and Galloway College of Technology (1959), Heathhall, Dumfries, DG1 3QZ. T.-0387 61261. Chairman, Board of Management: Mrs E.J. Smith; Vice Chairman, T. Kelly. Principal: J.W.M. Neil; Depute Principal: I.D. Penn; Assistant Principal: P.A. Hay. Serves the vocational education needs of the Dumfries and Galloway Region. The main building is situated in Dumfries, but smaller centres are located in various parts of the Region. Courses range from elementary courses for school leavers to higher diplomas.

Dumfries and Galloway Health Board (1974), Nithbank, Dumfries. T.-0387 53181. Chairman: J.M. Miller; Vice Chairman: J.A. McIntyre; Members: W.D. Beck, Mrs M.H. Bonn, W.H.J. Campbell, R.R. Goudie, A.U.G. Harper, J.D. Jack, Dr J. Miller Mair, H.S. McFadzean, Miss C.G.C. Paterson, W. Seright, W. Service, Mrs J.M.H. Steele, M. Webb, G. Willacy, Dr J.B. Wilson, W.I. Wilson. Secretary: R.B.K. MacGregor; Treasurer: M.D. Cook; Chief Administrative Medical Officer: Dr J.F. Kirk; Chief Area Nursing Officer: Miss E.A. Edwards; Chief Administrative Dental Officer: A.R. Wales; Chief Administrative Pharmaceutical Officer: D. Macfarlane. Provision of health service in Dumfries and Galloway Region.

Dumfries and Galloway Regional Council (1974), Council Offices, Dumfries. T.-0387 53141. Convener: John V.M. Jameson; Members: William Service, John McColm, D.R. Robinson, John Bell, David McHarg, James Brown, Roberta M. Tuckfield, Rev. Robert Hamill, Mary D. Dick-Smith, Elizabeth J. Smith, Mrs Ian Douglas, William Clemie, D. McCormick, Adam Turnbull, P. Fox, D.S.O., Donald F. Sutherland, Charles W. Grieve, James Cotts, Kenneth A. Kelly, Michael Webb, Alfred Turley, William Little, Thomas A. McAughtrie, Tom McCallum, Thomas M. Kelly, W.D. Beck, C. Dorothy Dalgliesh, Francis Park, Richard G. Greenhow, Edward C. Armstrong, M.B.E., C. Gordon Grieve, T.D., Patrick A.W. Hope Johnstone, Sir William E. Jardine of Applegirth, Bt., O.B.E., T.D., Walter Carlyle. Chief Executive: Leslie T. Carnegie; Director of Administration and Law: George M. Sinclair; Director of Consumer Protection: Gordon M. Smith; Director of Architecture: John Henderson; Chief Constable: John M. Boyd; Director of Education: J. Kenneth Purves; Electoral Registration Officer: Robert Frame; Director of Finance: John C. Stewart; Firemaster: Raymond F. Holland-Thomas; Industrial Development Officer: Alan J. Anderson; Director of Physical Planning: Alex. H. Dobbie; Director of Roads and Transportation: H. Duncan B. Murray; Director of Social Work: John W. Barbour; Director of Water and Sewerage: James McLean Cameron; Reporter to Children's Panel: Lewis R. Green.
Dumfries and Galloway Region covers an area of 2,460 square miles. It is relatively sparsely populated with a total population of 145,000, and it is essentially a rural area. The Regional Council took over responsibility for a wide range of local authority functions covering the areas of the former counties of Wigtownshire, Stewartry of Kirkcudbright, and Dumfriesshire. The Council employs 4,100 full-time and 2000 part-time staff.

Dumfries and Galloway Tourist Board (1983), Douglas House, Newton Stewart, Wigtownshire. T.-0671 3401/2549. Chairman: Tom Gillespie. Director: Iain Slinn. Marketing and development of tourism in Dumfries and Galloway.

Duncan of Jordanstone College of Art (1892), Perth Road, Dundee, DD1 4HT. T.-0382 23261. Chairman, Board of Governors: Richard H. Dewar; Vice Chairman: Hamish Ramsay. Principal: Myer Lacome; Vice Principal: Dr Christopher Carter; College Secretary: Garnet Reid; Head of School of Design: Atholl Hill; Head of Fine Art: Alan Robb; Head of Painting: David McClure; Head of Sculpture: Jake Kempsell; Head of School of Architecture: Professor James Paul; Head of School of Town and Regional Planning: Dr Hugh Begg; Head of School of Food and Accommodation: Dr G.W.I. Hodgson. One of the four Scottish art colleges. Disciplines include Town and Regional Planning, architecture, painting and sculpture, printmaking, printing, the various aspects of visual communications, printed and woven textiles, ceramics, jewellery, and silversmithing.

Duncraig Castle College (1946), Plockton, Ross-shire. T.-0599 84 229. Principal: Fergus D.S. McGhie; Depute Principal: Dorothy J. Whan. Duncraig Castle and its estate were bequeathed to the Education Authority in 1945, and since then it has functioned as a residential educational establishment for girls, giving training in domestic science, homecraft, and catering. Since 1960, Duncraig has been recognised as a college of further education.

Dundee Association for Social Service (1953), Castlehill House, 1 High Street, Dundee, DD1 1TE. T.-0382 21545. Chairman: Ralph Henderson; Vice Chairman: Mary Neville. Director and Secretary: Malcolm May. Aims to promote and sustain the development of voluntary action in Dundee and District through servicing voluntary and community organisations; linking and co-ordinating developments and activities; co-operating with local and public authorities; encouraging self-help activity in the community; and sponsoring projects.

Dundee College of Commerce (1956), 30 Constitution Road, Dundee, DD3 6TB. T.-0382 29151. Chairman, College Council: G.R. Linton. Principal: C.M. Brown; Assistant Principals: N.M.B. Black, C. Mackenzie, D.A. White, J.C. Gibb, G.S. Laird. One of the three Colleges of Commerce in Scotland. It offers a fully comprehensive range of courses in business studies and commerce from the certificate in office skills to postgraduate training in secretarial studies, personnel management and other subjects.

Dundee College of Education (1906), Gardyne Road, Broughty Ferry, Dundee, DD5 1NY. T.-0382 453433. Chairman, Board of Governors: Professor J.M. Howie. Principal: W.A. Illsley; Vice Principal: D.R.A. Keatch; Assistant Principal: W. Shearer; College Secretary: M. McCarry. The College offers a wide range of full-time and part-time courses for teachers, community educators, and social workers, both at initial training and in-service training levels, and provides residential and other conference facilities. Its theatre, exhibition hall, and sports complex are extensively used.

Dundee College of Technology, (1901), Bell Street, Dundee, DD1 1HG. T.-0382 27225. Chairman of Governors: J.J. Donnelly; Vice Chairman: D.T. Stewart. Principal: H.G. Cuming; Vice Principal: D.A. Kennedy; College Secretary: J.R. Smith; Heads of Departments: S. Sarkar (Civil Engineering), P.L. Bainbridge (Electrical and Electronic Engineering), A. McConkey (Mechanical and Industrial Engineering), D.H. Jex (Surveying and Building), K. Srinivasan (Accountancy and Economics), W.S. Howe (Business Studies), W.J. Emond (Mathematics and Computer Studies), B. King (Molecular and Life Sciences), R.R. Gardner (Physics); Director of Centre for Educational Development: A.M. Stewart; Director of Computer Services: D.E. Ord. Scottish Central Institution. The College has three faculties: Engineering and Construction; Management and Social Studies; and Science. It offers full-time and part-time courses of vocational higher education at postgraduate, first degree, diploma, and certificate level in a wide range of engineering, science, business, and other professional disciplines.

Dundee District Council, City of (1974), City Chambers, Dundee. T.-Dundee 23141. Chairman: Lord Provost Thomas Mitchell; Deputy Chairman: Ken Fagan; Members: Thomas McLaughlin, Stuart Ramsay, James M. Walker, Charles L. Sinclair, Janet W. Allen, Neil MacAlindin, David A. Carus, Charles Barton, Frederick W. Welsh, Robert Grubb, Frank Christie, Andrew Hanley, Norman A. McGowan, Stephen F. Blackwood, James M. Martin, John M. Barnett, Catherine O. Murray, Mary M. Ward, David M. Coutts, Iain M. Luke, John S. Leitch, James Cameron, Neil I.C. Powrie, Henry W.C. Vaughan, Grant Wilson, Charles Bowman, William P. Roberts, Francis D. Boag, Thomas M. McDonald, Charles D.P. Farquhar, William Inches, Helen Wright, John H. Henderson, Peter A. Court, William Richardson, James P. Gowans, Andrew Lynch, Michael Duff, Dorothy F.L. Pattullo, J. Derry Fleming, Andrew F.D. Lyall, Alan G. Grewar. Chief Executive: James F. Hoey; Director of Administration: Michael Brown; Director of Finance: Alexander Longair; Director of Housing: George A. Smith; Director of Technical Services: Ronald G. Carlisle; General Manager, Parks: Allan Booth; Chief Librarian: J.B. Ramage; Curator, Art Galleries and Museums: Adam B. Ritchie; Leisure and Recreation Manager: Alex. Stuart; Chief Personnel and Management Services Officer: Terence

Copping; General Manager, Public Works: R.P. Jackson; Chief
Environmental Health Officer: James Bryce Luke; General Manager,
Cleansing: William A. Lewis; Chief Planning Officer: Alistair T.
Barrie; Chief Architect/Quantity Surveyor: Ian M. Dunsire; Chief Engineer: James
W.F. Hutcheon; Chief Solicitor: Thomas Renfrew. District Council.
Population of District: 183,000.

Dundee Industrial Association, Meadow Workshops, Blackness Trading
Precinct, West Henderson Wynd, Dundee, DD1 5BY. T.- 0382 26001.
Development Manager: Ron Bear. Enterprise agency.

Dundee Repertory Theatre (1939), Tay Square, Dundee, DD1 1PB. T.-0382
27684 (Administration); 0382 23530 (Box Office). Chairman, Board of
Directors: Professor S.G.G. MacDonald. Theatre Director: Robert
Robertson; General Manager: Tom Gardner. Repertory company providing
dramatic entertainment of all kinds and acting as the venue for a variety of
other arts activities, including music, dance, and art exhibitions.

Dundee Tourist Board, City of, City Chambers, Dundee, DD1 3BY. T.-0382
23141. Promotion of tourism.

Dundee, University of (1967), Nethergate, Dundee, DD1 4HN. T.-0382 23181.
Chancellor: Rt. Hon. The Earl of Dalhousie, K.T., G.C.V.O., G.B.E.,
M.C.; Principal and Vice Chancellor: Adam Neville, M.C., T.D.; Vice
Principal: Professor Peter D. Griffiths; Rector: Gordon Wilson, M.P.;
Secretary: Robert Seaton; Finance Officer: Alexander E. McCallum.
University Court: (ex officio) The Chancellor, Principal and Vice Chancellor,
Vice Principal, Rector, Chairman (or Assessor), Tayside Regional Council,
Chairman (or Assessor) Dundee District Council, Chairman (or Assessor),
Angus District Council, Chairman (or Assessor), Perth and Kinross District
Council; (Chancellor's Assessor) Col. A.B. Houstoun; (Rector's Assessor)
P.J. Farquhar; (appointed by Tayside Regional Council) Mrs B. Vaughan;
(Assessor of Graduates' Council) Col. D.M. Naulty; (elected by Senatus
Academicus) Professors A.P. Cracknell, D.A.T. Dick, A.B. Wilkinson, J.B.
Caird, B. Makin, and R.G. Mitchell, Dr C.J.R. Braithwaite, Dr I.T.A.C.
Adamson; (elected by the Readers, Senior Lecturers and Lecturers) C.J.
Davey, J.S. Berridge; (co-opted) D. Carnegy-Arbuthnott, J.S. Fair, J.P.
McPherson, Mrs M.N. Nicholls.
Senatus Academicus (Professorial Members): I.A.D. Bouchier, J.D.
Lambert, J.R. Grinyer, A.D. Barr, C. Blake, H.M. Begg, C.J. Bartlett, J.S.
Beck, R.W. Bentham, J.S. Brimacombe, J.B. Caird, D.M. Chisholm, P.
Cohen, N.L. Cooper, P.S. Corbet, A.P. Cracknell, A. Cuschieri, D.A.T.
Dick, Heather M. Dick, G.W. Fenton, C. du V. Florey, R. Foster, A.R.
Grieve, R.M. Harden, P.W. Howie, D.S. Jones, R.A. Kennedy, J.D.E.
Knox, R.W. Last, D.G. McDevitt, S.G.G. MacDonald, J.D. McEwen, B.
Makin, Elisabeth L.G. Mapstone, A.R. Mitchell, R.G. Mitchell, G.
Murdoch, A.F. Newell, K. Newton, J. Norton-Smith, D.M. Ramsay, J.A.
Raven, M.J. Rennie, C.H. Rochester, B.D. Sleeman, W.E. Spear, P.
Sprent, K.J. Standley, I.H. Stevenson, W.D.P. Stewart, H.D. Tunstall
Pedoe, A.E. Vardy, A.B. Wilkinson, I.D. Willock.
University with six Faculties: Medicine and Dentistry; Science; Law;
Engineering and Applied Science; Arts and Social Sciences; and
Environmental Studies. There are 57 academic departments, offering a wide
and flexible range of undergraduate studies. Many of of the courses are
strongly vocational and provide the academic training for particular
professions. At postgraduate level, specialist degree and diploma courses are
available in branches of medicine, dentistry, pure science, law, engineering,

education, and social sciences. Research work is undertaken throughout the University.

Dundee, University of, Department of Extra-Mural Education, The University, Dundee, DD1 4HN. T.-0382 23181. Director: Alexander G. Robertson. Provides a link between the academic community of the University and the wider public. Organises a varied programme of evening and day-time classes, held in the University and other centres in the area, courses, conferences, public lectures, residential schools, and study tours at home and abroad.

Dunfermline and West Fife Chamber of Commerce (1900), 10 Viewfield Terrace, Dunfermline, KY12 7JH. T.-0383 721156. President: J.R. Richards. Secretary and Treasurer: Alan M. Stewart.

Dunfermline College of Physical Education (1905), Cramond Road North, Edinburgh, EH4 6JD. T.-031-336 6001. Principal: Miss J.A. Carroll; Vice Principal: B.S. Duffield; Assistant Principal: R.R. Bone; Secretary: A.S. Adam. The only college in Scotland for the training of women students of physical education. Offers a variety of degree, diploma, and certificate courses, and short in-service courses for teachers, coaches, etc.

Dunfermline District Council (1974), City Chambers, Dunfermline. T.-0383 722711. Provost: Robert Mill, J.P.; Members: James Johnston, David S. Campbell, J.P., Robert Dow, John Reid, Effie Ritchie, J.P., Michael Judge, J.P., John Bell, J.P., James Cameron, J.P., Arthur Martin, Alexander Corbett, J.P., David Black, Joseph Paterson, Robert P. Wilson, Rev. Douglas Aitken, Thomas McMullin, William McGilvary, David Melville, Margaret A. Millar, John Connelly, J.P., William Hamilton, James I. Burns, Dr John B. Yates, Edward Collins, Alexander Sawers, Avril A. Hughes, Elizabeth Grant, Jean Lockhart, Gerard J. Murray, J.P., William J. Rosiejak, Elizabeth Harris, William Stuart, Patrick Callaghan, Frank A. Moyes. Chief Executive: G. Brown; Director of Administration: F.M. Coutts; Director of Finance: A.R. Maxwell; Director of Technical Services: L.J. Walker; Director of Planning: T.W. Shepherd; Director of Housing: A. Davidson; Director of Environmental Health: K.N. Fraser; Director of Leisure, Recreation, and Amenities: T.W. Robson; Director of Libraries, Museums, and Art Galleries: J.K. Sharp. District Council. Population of District: 126,000.

Dunoon and Cowal Tourist Board (1969), Information Centre, Dunoon, PA23 7HL. T.-0369 3785. Chairman: Ian R. Taylor. Tourism Manager: Iain F. Clason. Promotion of tourism.

E

East Kilbride Development Corporation (1947), Atholl House, East Kilbride, G74 1LU. T.-05352 41111. Chairman: J. Allan Denholm; Deputy Chairman: Charles Gray; Members: Jean Chalmers, Maurice Crichton, Peter McGregor, Donald McLean, Michael D. McMillan, Colin Robb, David Sanderson. Managing Director: G.B. Young; Director of Finance: H. Stevenson; Director of Development: G. Grassie; Director of Technical Services: T. Gibson; Controller of Works: I.A. Macpherson; Housing Manager: D. Dickson. East Kilbride has been planned and built in 37 years by a Development Corporation appointed by the Secretary of State for Scotland to create a complete and new community nine miles south of Glasgow. Started on 10,000 acres round a village of 2,400 inhabitants, it now has a population of 72,000.

East Kilbride District Council (1974), Civic Centre, East Kilbride, G74 1AB. T.-East Kilbride 28777. Chairman: Provost George McKillop. Members: James Cameron, Alan Dick, Colin Robb, Helen Biggins, Stewart Crawford, Adam Ingram, Edward McKenna, John McP. Sutherland, Edith Findlay, John Reilly, Ewan Ross, Peter McGregor, Ronald Cameron, Alaster Chalmers, John Buchanan. Chief Executive: W. Gordon McNay; Director of Finance and Management Services: K. Love; Director of Administration and Legal Services: J.M. Gallagher; Director of Planning and Technical Services: D. McNidder; Director of Recreation and Leisure Services: T. Cruttenden; Director of Environmental Health and Housing: H.D. Henry. District Council. Population of District: 83,000.

East Lothian Antiquarian and Field Naturalists' Society (1924), Haddington House, Haddington, East Lothian, EH41 4BZ. President: Sir David Ogilvy, Bt.; Hon. Secretary: S.A. Bunyan. The study of the antiquities, archaeology, local history, and natural history of East Lothian.

East Lothian District Council (1974), Council Buildings, Court Street, Haddington, EH41 3HA. T.-062 082 4161. Chairman: Thomas Wilson; Vice Chairman: George M. Wanless; Members: D.J.I. Allan, G.P. Campbell, J. Caven, J.P. Crichton, Mrs P. Fawcett, T. Ferguson, J.B. Macnair, Mrs M. McKay, P. O'Brien, D. Paton, A. Purves, L. Reid, J.W. Stephenson, A.P. Watson, Rev. Dr D.H. Whiteford. Chief Executive: David B. Miller; Director of Administration: Malcolm Duncan; Director of Finance: John Lindsay; Director of Architectural Services: Ian G. Campbell; Director of Physical Planning: David G.B. Duncan; Director of Environmental Health: J.B. Cunningham; Director of Housing: T.C. Bathgate; Director of Leisure, Recreation, and Tourism: R.A.P. Mellor. District Council. Population of District: 81,000.

East Lothian Tourist Board, Brunton Hall, Musselburgh, EH21 6AF. T.-031-665 3711. Tourism Officer: L. Abbie.

East of Scotland College of Agriculture (1901), Edinburgh School of Agriculture, West Mains Road, Edinburgh, EH9 3JG. T.-031-667 1041. President: A.W. Barbour; Vice President: Dr Jean Balfour, C.B.E.; Members, Board of Governors: W.D. Alexander, T.R.B. Dykes, Professor G.S. Ferguson, T.D., R.J. Forrest, J. Goodfellow, D. Hinton, J.A. Inverarity, Professor C. Kemball, A.R.J.D. Miller, F. Morrison, Major N.P. Thomson. Principal: Professor P.N. Wilson; Assistant to Principal: J.L. Beveridge; Secretary and Treasurer: D.S. Land; Head of Extension Services: K.V. Runcie; Head of Animal Division: Professor C.T. Whittemore; Head of Crop Division: Professor J.C. Holmes; Head of Microbiology Division: Professor J.F. Wilkinson; Head of Veterinary Division: A.O. Mathieson; Farms Director: Dr W.J.M. Black. The College provides agricultural education at diploma and higher diploma levels as part of a teaching programme undertaken jointly with the University of Edinburgh. It also operates an advisory service, and undertakes an extensive programme of agricultural research.

Eastwood District Council (1974), Council Offices, Eastwood Park, Rouken Glen Road, Giffnock, Glasgow, G46 6UG. T.-041-638 1101. Convener: Provost Mrs J.M. Edmondson; Members: Mrs J.Y. Macfie, B.J. Baird, Mrs A. Coldwell, Mrs M.W. Dundas, I.S. Hutchison, J.W.S. Jamieson, H. Livingstone, I.B. MacPhail, M.S. Miller, I. Robertson, L.M. Rosin. Chief Executive Officer: M.D. Henry; Director of Finance: W.R. Crosbie; Director of Planning and Technical Services: R.C. Bowman. District Council. Population of District: 54,000.

Economic Society, Scottish, Department of Political Economy, University of Aberdeen. T.-0224 40241, Ext. 5320. President: Professor I. Stewart; Secretary: R.F. Elliott; Treasurer: P.W. Wood. To advance the study of economic and social problems in accordance with the Scottish tradition of political economy inspired by Adam Smith; to provide a forum for the discussion of Scottish economic and social problems. Publishes the *Scottish Journal of Political Economy*.

Edinburgh Architectural Association (1858), 15 Rutland Square, Edinburgh, EH1 2BE. Professional association.

Edinburgh Bibliographical Society (1890), c/o National Library of Scotland, George IV Bridge, Edinburgh, EH1 1EW. T.-031-226 4531. President: J.V. Howard; Secretary: I.C. Cunningham. Promotion and encouragement of bibliographical studies.

Edinburgh Chamber of Commerce, 3 Randolph Crescent, Edinburgh. T.-031-225 5851. Chief Executive: D.M. Mowat, J.P.

Edinburgh College of Art (1909), Lauriston Place, Edinburgh, EH3 9DF. T.-031-229 9311. Chairman, Governing Body: Ian M. Robertson, C.B., M.V.O., J.P.; Governors: Councillor Valerie Woodward, Professor R.W. Hepburn, Professor V.B. Torrance, Michael N. Laing, Eric W. Hall, John Richards, C.B.E., Martin Huggins, Charles Swan, Councillor D.C.E. Gorrie, O.B.E., Denis F.M. Peploe, Ian McKenzie Smith, Fred A. Bushe, Robert R. Steedman, Jan Magnus Fladmark, Betty L.C. Moira, David G. Antonio, John A. Craig, Anthony Franks, Kirkland Main, James A. Gray, John Ward, Robert L. Smith, Keith Grant. Principal: John L. Paterson; Vice Principal: W. Ferrie Wood; Secretary and Treasurer: John Nice; Members of Academic Council (ex officio): Professor James D. Dunbar-Nasmith,

Department of Architecture; John A. Craig, Department of Town and Country Planning; Douglas C.J. Brown, School of Design and Crafts; David A.R. Michie, School of Drawing and Painting; Anthony Hatwell, School of Sculpture; Dr Colin J. Bailey, Department of Humanities and Complementary Studies; Glenn Craig, Librarian. One of the four Central Art Institutions in Scotland.

Edinburgh Council of Social Service (1868), 11 St. Colme Street, Edinburgh, EH3 6AG. T.-031-225 4606. Chairman: Professor Duncan B. Forrester; Vice Chairman: Trevor Davies. Director: Edward Matthews; Assistant Director: Alan Rees. Co-ordination of voluntary social services; community work; community transport; volunteer recruitment.

Edinburgh District Council, City of (1974), City Chambers, High Street, Edinburgh. T.-031-225 2424. Convener: Rt. Hon. John H. McKay; Members: William Hardie, J.P., Eric J. Drummond, Jane Ball, J.P., Elizabeth Robertson, James S. Tait, Robert C. Aldridge, Alexander Wood, Eleanor T. McLaughlin, William Fizpatrick, J.P., Cornelis Waugh, J.P., Margaret H. McAlpine, J.P., Robert G.D. Dalgleish, J.P., John G.R. Crombie, Norman Irons, Lesley Hinds, Moira B.M. Knox, J.P., Frances R. Wood, J.P., Roderick A.S. Sivewright, James Burnett, James Hastie, J.P., Donald C.E. Gorrie, J.P., Veronica J. Crerar, Ralph Brereton, J.P., Ian T. Campbell, C.B.E., V.R.D., Hon. David W.G. Guest, Kenneth Smith, Christopher McKinnon, Russell Imrie, Rev. Elizabeth Wardlaw, Paul C. Martin, Mark J. Lazarowicz, Nigel Griffiths J.P., Henry Kinloch, John C. Wilson, J.P., James J.F. Henderson, J.P., Edna M. Bryce, Paolo Vestri, Val Woodward, Norma Jones, Robert Cairns, Richard Kerley, William P.M. Dundas, Thomas Burke, George Kerevan, J.P., Dickie Alexander, J.P., William K. Macfarlane, Kenneth G. Ferguson, Eric M. Kean, J.P., A. Trevor Clark, C.B.E., M.V.O., Marjorie Bain, Ruby Paterson, J.P., Derrick Maclennan, J.P., Gertrude Barton, James L. Walls, Daphne Sleigh, Anthony P. Metcalfe, Bjorg Mackenzie, J.P., John C. Campbell, J.P., Sadie K. Rooney, Garry J. Coutts, David H. Brown. Chief Executive: M.M. Duncan; Director of Administration: W. Blyth; Director of Finance: Dr C. Stout; Director of Cleansing: A. McCreath; Director of Public Relations and Tourism: A. Fyall; Director of Economic Development and Estates: W. Ross; Director of Planning: N. Fort; Director of Housing: M. Wilson; Director of Recreation: B.M. Connolly; Director of Technical Services: R. Cooper; Director of Environmental Health: A. Turner; Director of Personnel and Management Services: D.B. Hughes. District Council. Population of District: 444,000.

Edinburgh Festival Fringe Society (1969), 170 High Street, Edinburgh, EH1 1QS. T.-031-226 5257. Chairman: Dr Jonathan Miller. Administrator: Michael Dale. Organisation of the Festival Fringe. The Society helps performers to appear (at their own risk) and publishes a programme, as well as organising the sale of tickets.

Edinburgh Festival Society (1947), 21 Market Street, Edinburgh, EH1 1BW. T.-031-226 4001. Chairman, Festival Council: The Lord Provost; Depute Chairman: J. Dunbar Nasmith; Members: W. Berry, Dr H.C.W. Bunney, Dr A.A. Donaldson, The Hon. Mrs E. Fairbairn, H. Hunter Gordon, K. Lawson, K. Newis, P.H. Scott, Councillors Mrs G. Barton, J.C. Campbell, A.T. Clark, N. Irons, G. Kerevan, M. Lazarowicz, Mrs M.H. McAlpine, P.C. Martin, Mrs R. Paterson, P. Vestri. Director: Frank Dunlop; General Administrator: Christopher Barron; Publicity Manager: Chris Grady; Planning Manager: Sheila Colvin.

Annual international festival of music and drama now firmly established as a major cultural event and incorporating music, opera, theatre, dance, and exhibitions.

Edinburgh Mathematical Society (1883), Department of Mathematics, University of Edinburgh, King's Buildings, Mayfield Road, Edinburgh, EH9 3JZ. T.-031-667 1081. President: Professor W.D. Munn; Vice President: Professor J.R. Hubbuck; Secretaries: Dr J. Martin, C.J. Shaddock. For the mutual improvement of its members in the mathematical sciences, pure and applied. Meetings, publication of proceedings, Colloquium.

Edinburgh New Town Conservation Committee (1970), 13a Dundas Street, Edinburgh, EH3 6QG. T.-031-556 7054. Chairman: Sir Alan Hume. Director: Desmond Hodges; Assistant Director: James Clark. The Committee recommends grants for the repair of the historic buildings in the Georgian New Town. Advice on repairs is available at the Conservation Centre, where there is a reference library and permanent exhibition.

Edinburgh, University of (1583), Old College, South Bridge, Edinburgh, EH8 9YL. T.-031-667 1011. Chancellor: H.R.H. The Prince Philip, Duke of Edinburgh, K.G., K.T., P.C., O.M., G.B.E.; Principal and Vice Chancellor: Dr J.H. Burnett; Rector: Rt. Hon. David Steel, P.C., M.P.; Vice-Principals: Professor W. Cochran, Professor C.P. Brand. University Court: The Rector, The Principal, The Rector's Assessor, Hon. Lord Cameron, K.T., D.S.C., Professor K.A. Fowler, D.O. Edge, D.F. Wright, Farquhar Macintosh, C.B.E., G.H. Elliot, D.G. MacDonald, John Mannix, Hilary O'Neill, Graeme Carter, Councillor J. Gilchrist, Lord Provost John H. McKay, J. McLelland, Rt. Hon. Lord Murray, P.C., I.G.S. MacGregor, Professor (Emeritus) D.C. Simpson, M.B.E., Professor D.N. MacCormick, Professor S. Michaelson, Professor Malcolm Anderson.

Senatus Academicus (Professorial Members): Professors J. McIntyre, A. Iggo, J.M. Mitchison, L.G. Whitby, J. MacQueen, G.A. Shepperson, D. Ward, A.W. Hendry, A.C. Cheyne, R.W. Hepburn, W. Cochran, P.E.A. Johnson-Marshall, J.T. Coppock, H. Anderson, C.P. Brand, J.R. Greening, E.A.V. Ebsworth, S. Michaelson, P. Vandome, A.G. Mackie, D.M. Vowles, W.E. Watson, C.B. Wilson, A.W. Bradley, J. Erickson, R.A. Cowley, N.A. Furness, E.C. Riley, J.F. Wilkinson, K. Leighton, H.J. Walton, J.T. Baxter, A.P.M. Forrest, M. Tilmouth, W. Duncan, W.A. Wilson, C.I. Phillips, Sir Alastair Currie, W.W. Robson, D.N. MacCormick, G.S. Ferguson, S. Coke, K.M. Creer, A.W.G. Manning, I.W. Noble, J.K. Mason, R.E. Kendell, R.C.B. Aitken, F.H. McClintock, J.G. Collee, K.A. Fowler, G. Poggi, P.G. Jarvis, T.A. Lee, K. Murray, M.J.M. Larkin, J. Williamson, B.L. Ginsborg, D.W. Harding, D.T. Baird, G.D. Chisholm, J.S. Robson, R.E. Asher, I. Oswald, R.M. Burstall, J.C. Southam, P. Sutcliffe, G. Charlton, M.M. Yeoman, D.C. Flenley, D.B. Forrester, J.R. Campbell, N.J. Entwistle, D.W. Brocklesby, J.W. Farquhar, E.G. Forbes, M.F. Oliver, G.W.S. Barrow, T.L.S. Sprigge, W. Gillies, E.G. Rees, G. Nuki, J.F. Smyth, Malcolm Anderson, J.J.K. Best, R.A. Sinfield, J.P. Thorne, D.J. Wallace, J.P. Mackey, J.R. Hurford, Michael Anderson, R.J. Donovan, P.H. Davis, D.L. Shaw, H.T. Dickinson, S.P.F. Hughes, M.S. Longair, P. France, J.P. Renwick, J.G.R. Howie, J. Mavor, J.A.A. Hunter, E.K. Borthwick, P.W. Higgs, J.D. Miller, R. Black, C.R.W. Edwards, Rosalind M. Mitchison, A.E. Owen, R.A. Stockwell, P.B.H. Birks, J.D. Latham, B.G.J. Upton, N.S. Willetts, S.H. Palsson, P.F. Williams, I. McConnell, P.F. Bradley, Penny P. Prophit, W.G. Hill, A.J. Holden, D.M. Weir, P.N. Wilson, W.M. Garraway, J.A. McGeough, A. Miller, R.

The Scottish Companion 59

Ramage, A.A. Spence, M.R. Lee, T.G.R. Bower, A.G. Brown, P.H. Jones, A.J.R.G. Milner, J.G. Scaite, C.B. Trevarthen, C.T. Whittemore. Secretary: A.M. Currie, O.B.E.; Deputy Secretary: J. MacPherson, M.B.E.; Director of Finance: D. Brown; Buildings Officer: N.B. Anderson, J.P.
The University of Edinburgh was originally the College of Edinburgh or The Tounis College, founded in 1583 by the Town Council of Edinburgh, under general powers granted by the Charter of King James VI. From the first, the College possessed the privilege of conferring degrees. Gradually, in succeeding Acts, the College came to be styled the University; but it remained under the control and patronage of the Town Council until 1858 when, by the Universities Act, all the Universities of Scotland received new and autonomous constitutions. Today, the University confers degrees in eight Faculties: Arts, Divinity, Law, Medicine (including Dentistry), Music, Science, Social Sciences, Veterinary Medicine. It is one of the largest unitary, non-collegiate universities in Britain, offering not only every principal subject taught in any British university, but also an unmatched range of undergraduate and postgraduate courses. There are 8,600 full-time undergraduate and 1,300 postgraduate students, including students from some 90 countries around the world.

Edinburgh, University of, Department of Extra-Mural Studies, 11 Buccleuch Place, Edinburgh, EH8 9FT. T.-031-667 1011, Ext. 6246. Director: B.C. Skinner. Exists to provide weekly courses, conferences, weekend schools, summer schools, and study tours for Scottish people.

Edinburgh Venture Enterprise Trust (EVENT) (1983), Hanover Buildings, Rose Street, Edinburgh, EH2 2YQ. T.-031-226 5783. Chairman: J.M.B. Macmillan; Vice Chairman: C.A. Fraser. Director: P.J. Duke; Assistant Director: J.F. Jacobs. Enterprise trust offering specialist financial and business advice to companies requiring assistance or individuals setting up in business. Free service sponsored by local companies.

Edinburgh Volunteer Exchange, 48 Dalry Road, Edinburgh, EH11 2BA. T.-031-346 0540. Joint Organisers: Maggie Macleod, Nan McKenna, Mary Weir. Operated by Edinburgh Council of Social Service, provides a recruiting service for organisations in the city and an information and advisory service to people who wish to do voluntary work in Edinburgh.

Educational Institute of Scotland (1847), 46 Moray Place, Edinburgh, EH3 6BH. T.-031-225 6244. President: Kenneth McLachlan. General Secretary: John D. Pollock; Depute General Secretary: Robert Beattie; Organising Secretary: Frederick L. Forrester; Further Education Officer: Arthur H. Houston; Assistant Secretary: James B. Martin. The E.I.S. was founded for the purposes of 'increasing the efficiency of teachers, improving their conditions and raising the standard of education in general.' In 1851, it was granted a charter by Queen Victoria empowering it to examine and certificate 'persons engaged, or desiring to be engaged, in the education of young people in Scotland'. The Institute no longer has such a role, but is generally concerned with the interests and welfare of teachers, and is recognised as a trade union. It has 46,000 teachers in membership.

Educational Technology, Scottish Council for (1934), Dowanhill, 74 Victoria Crescent Road, Glasgow, G12 9JN. T.-041-334 9314. Chairman: Dr T.R. Bone. Director: R.B. MacLuskie. Promotion of educational technology.

Educational Visits and Exchanges, Central Bureau for, 3 Bruntsfield Crescent, Edinburgh, EH10 4HD. T.-031-447 8024. Secretary, Scotland: J.R. Wake.

Education and Action for Development, Scottish (1978), 29 Nicolson Square, Edinburgh, EH8 9BX. T.-031-667 0120. Organisers: Stephen Maxwell, Paul Baker, Susan Moffat, Mark Lazarowicz; Administrator: Anne Chisholm. S.E.A.D. exists to develop Scottish awareness of the challenge and problems of world development. It produces publicity material, organises meetings and conferences, handles media enquiries, and liaises with other world development groups. It is the only body of its kind in Scotland.

Education Department, Scottish, New St. Andrew's House, Edinburgh, EH1 3DU. T.-031-556 8400. Secretary: J.A. Scott, M.V.O. Private Secretary: T.W. Lodge.
Department of the Secretary of State for Scotland, which supervises the public education system in co-operation with the regional and island education authorities. It allocates finance for educational buildings, prescribes standards, and offers advice on designs for these buildings. It gives guidance on the content of education and, with the co-operation of the General Teaching Council, seeks to match the supply of teachers to the demand. The Department directly finances the central institutions and colleges of education, and administers students' allowances. It exercises general supervision of the provision for community education, and is responsible for grants to certain voluntary organisations. It looks after the Secretary of State's responsibilities for the arts, sport, and recreation. **Social Work Services Group.** Responsible for the discharge of the Secretary of State's functions under the Social Work (Scotland) Act 1968. These include the administration of grants to the List D schools, advice and guidance to social work authorities and voluntary organisations, and responsibilities in relation to the children's hearing system. The group is also responsible for child care, including adoption and fostering.

Electrical Contractors' Association of Scotland (1900), 23 Heriot Row, Edinburgh, EH3 6EW. T.-031-225 7221. Director and Secretary: D.D.W. Montgomery. The Association represents almost 600 electrical contracting firms employing 14,000 people. Wage negotiations; industrial relations; apprenticeship, supervisory, and management training; technical and contractual matters; marketing and management services.

Electricity Board, South of Scotland (1955), Cathcart House, Spean Street, Glasgow, G44 4BE. T.-041-637 7177. Chairman: Donald J. Miller; Deputy Chairman: Ian M.H. Preston; Members: Andrew Barr, Michael Joughin, Nicholas C. Kuenssberg; Professor Donald I. MacKay; Donald McLean; Mrs J.A. Thomson; George B. Whyte. Director of Engineering: Dr A.F. Pexton; Director of Finance and Commercial Development: G.H. Reid; Board Secretary: D.A.S. MacLaren; Chief Financial Officer: W.J. Sutherland; Chief Commercial Officer: D. Simmons; Chief Personnel Officer: T.J. Mercer; Chief Contracts and Purchasing Officer: A.M. Blair; Chief Engineers: J.W. Currie (Generation Design and Construction), D. Green (Generation Operation), R.M. Gove (Transmission/Distribution), A.E. Souch (Planning of Services); Management Services Controller: W.W. Wilson; Public Relations Officer: J. McGuire.
The S.S.E.B. is responsible for the generation, transmission, and distribution of electricity in an area covering the Solway to the Clyde on the West and from Holy Island to the Tay on the East coast. Generated almost 20 billion units of electricity in 1983/84.

Electricity Consultative Council for the North of Scotland District (1948), 2 York Place, Perth, PH2 8EP. T.-0738 36669. Chairman: Mrs C.A.M. Davis; Deputy Chairman: J. Kelly; Members: E.W. Cameron, O.B.E. (Central

Region); D. Bodger, Mrs N.A. Duthie, Councillor R.H. Graham, Councillor R.G. Milne, J.P., Councillor Mrs P.J. Ramsey, W.C. Strachan, R.R. Webster, J.P. (Grampian Region); R.H. Farrow, Mrs M.E. Fraser, J.P., D.J. Mackay, Provost H. McLean, M.B.E., Councillor J.S. Munro, R.H. Preston (Highland Region); R.G. Bain (Orkney Islands); Councillor W.A. Smith, B.E.M. (Shetland Islands); Mrs A.M. Kahane, Councillor D.V. Webster (Strathclyde Region); Councillor J. Cameron, J.P., Councillor Mrs S.D.R. Kydd, Provost J.M. Mathieson, J.P., T. Mooney, J.R. Munro, Miss L. Parker (Tayside Region); Mrs M.A. Macmillan (Western Isles). Secretary: D.D. McDonald. Independent body appointed by the Secretary of State for Scotland and entirely separate from the Hydro-Electric Board. Exists to protect the interests of consumers of electricity, and to give any guidance and support needed in dealing with the Hydro Board.

Electricity Consultative Council for the South of Scotland District (1947), 249 West George Street, Glasgow, G2 4QE. T.-041-248 5588. Chairman: G.B. Whyte. Secretary: W. Porter; Assistant Secretary: Miss M. Martin. The Council is required to consider any matter affecting the distribution of electricity, including the variation of tariffs and the provision of new or improved services and facilities within the district, which is brought to its notice by consumers.

Elmwood Agricultural and Technical College (1953), Carslogie Road, Cupar, Fife, KY15 4JB. T.-0334 52781. Chairman, College Council: Councillor J.G. Souter. Principal: W.A. Wilson; Depute Principal: W.S.F. Fyfe; Registrar: K.M. Ovenstone. Responsible for a wide range of full-time, day release, and evening classes. Only such college in Scotland to offer certain courses, e.g. that leading to the award of the Scottish National Diploma for Agricultural Secretaries.

Employment, Department of, Pentland House, 47 Robb's Loan, Edinburgh, EH14 1UE. T.-031-443 8731. Benefit Manager, Scotland: M. Rowe. Responsibility in Scotland for administration of the unemployment benefit service, the Redundancy Payment Act, and unemployment temporary alleviation measures.

Engineering Employers' Association, Scottish (1865), 105 West George Street, Glasgow, G2 1QL. T.-041-221 3181. President: D.L. Borthwick. Director: Lt. Col. H.A.J. Jordan, M.B.E.; Deputy Director: A.M. Littlejohn. To promote sound employment policies and industrial relations; assist members at meetings with trade union officials and help resolve disputes; interpret employment legislation and provide expert representation at industrial tribunals and employment appeal tribunals; give specialist advice on health and safety and help set safety standards; exercise influence to ensure that the needs of industry are met.

Engineering Laboratory, National (1947), East Kilbride, Glasgow, G75 OQU. T.-03552 20222. Director: Dr D.A. Bell; Deputy Director: H.L. Wunsch; Business Co-ordinator: Dr D.J. Myles; Research Co-ordinator: Dr K.J. Marsh; Marketing Co-ordinator: J.T. McKinlay. N.E.L., one of the Department of Trade and Industry's research establishments, is a centre for mechanical engineering research and development. It is the largest organisation of its kind in Britain, with a staff of 600, and advanced facilities for engineering design, consultancy, development, and testing.

Engineering Training Scheme, Scottish (1957), 127 St. Vincent Street, Glasgow. T.-041-221 6420. Chairman: R.M. Gove. Chief Executive: John K. McIntyre; Secretary: Mrs I.K. Liddell; Senior Administrative Officer: Miss

R. Dempsey. Industrial training of graduate and undergraduate engineers within a framework established with the relevant professional institutions and Engineering Industry Training Board.

English-Speaking Union (Scotland) (1954), 22 Atholl Crescent, Edinburgh, EH3 8HQ. T.-031-229 1528. Chairman, Scottish National Committee: Robert C. Cumming; Vice Chairmen: James Miller, Martin Sinclair. Director: Brian Gorman; Assistant Director: Judith Fleming. Voluntary, non-political organisation concerned with promoting greater friendship and understanding between the peoples of the Commonwealth and the U.S.A. It operates a programme of exchanges, scholarships, and awards, and organises fund-raising events by membership.

Environmental Health Institute of Scotland, Royal (1983), Virginia House, 62 Virginia Street, Glasgow, G1 1TX. T.-041-552 1533. President: Dr T.S. Wilson; Senior Vice President: Charles Gibson. Secretary: Anne B. McKenzie. Professional body promoting the advancement of all aspects of health and hygiene.

Environmental and Offshore Medicine, Institute of (1976), Ashgrove Road West, Aberdeen. T.-Aberdeen 681818. Director: Professor A.S. Douglas. Established by the University of Aberdeen. Research and teaching in offshore medicine/hyperbaric medicine, climatic medicine. Provides occupational health services to offshore and onshore industries.

Environment, Department of the, Property Services Agency (1972), Directorate of Scottish Services, Argyle House, 3 Lady Lawson Street, Edinburgh, EH3 9SD. T.-031-229 9191. Director: A.S. Gosling; Assistant Director: D.R. Smith. Provides and maintains buildings and other installations for the Government and armed services.

Epilepsy Association of Scotland (1954), 48 Govan Road, Glasgow, G51 1JL. T.-041-427 4911. Chairman: Stephen P. Newall; Vice Chairman: Dr W.S. Watson; Chairman, Development and Education Committee: Dr J.R. Minto, O.B.E.; Chairman, Medical and Social Research Committee: Dr I.D. Melville Chief Executive Officer: James M. Caddie; Development Officer: Vivien Cairnie; Appeals and Publicity Officer: Ann Furst. Committed to improving the lives of Scotland's 25,000 men, women, and children with epilepsy. The Association informs and educates the community, supports medical and social research, and provides help for people with epilepsy and their families.

Episcopal Church, Scottish, 21 Grosvenor Crescent, Edinburgh, EH12 5EE. T.-031-225 6357. President: The Most Rev. Alastair Iain Macdonald Haggart, Primus, Bishop of Edinburgh; Trustees: Rt. Hon. Lord Home of the Hirsel, K.T., P.C., Ronald Scott-Dempster, Rt. Hon. Lord Kilbrandon, P.C., James John Lamb, O.B.E., T.D., Ivor Reginald Guild, The Most Rev. Alastair Iain Macdonald Haggart. Secretary General and Treasurer: Ian D. Stuart; Deputy Treasurer: D. Logan Smith; Deputy Secretary General: Martin D. Patterson. Bishops: (Aberdeen and Orkney) Rt. Rev. Frederick Charles Darwent; (Argyll and the Isles) Rt. Rev. George Kennedy Buchanan Henderson, M.B.E.; (Brechin) Rt. Rev. Lawrence Edward Luscombe; (Edinburgh) Most Rev. Alastair Iain Macdonald Haggart; (Glasgow and Galloway) Rt. Rev. Derek Alec Rawcliffe, O.B.E.; (Moray, Ross and Caithness) Rt. Rev. George Minshull Sessford; (St. Andrews, Dunkeld and Dunblane): Rt. Rev. Michael Geoffrey Hare Duke. Convener, Standing Committee: A.A.R. Carleton; Members: Brian Dale, Rev. Canon A.I. Watt, The Most Rev. Primus, Rt. Rev. The Bishop of St Andrews, Rt. Rev.

The **Bishop of Brechin**. The Scottish Episcopal Church has a membership of 68,000 with churches situated throughout Scotland. It is governed by a General Synod with 163 members divided between lay and clerical. The Church has Boards and Committees which deal with Education, Social Responsibility, Overseas and Home Mission affairs, as well as a full range of the usual pastoral, financial, and administrative concerns.

Equal Opportunities Commission (1975), Scottish Office, 249 West George Street, Glasgow, G2 4QE. T.-041-226 4591. Scottish Officer: Ron Miller; Assistant Scottish Officer: Ms Leslie Brown. The Commission provides a confidential advice service on all matters relating to sex discrimination and equal pay. This service is available to individuals, employers, and trade unions. It is provided free.

Esk Valley College (1952), Newbattle Road, Dalkeith, Midlothian, EH19 3BQ. T.-031-663 1951. Chairman, College Council: P. McCullagh. Principal: J.B. Moss; Depute Principal: Dr N. Leitch; Assistant Principal: G. Burnie. Wide range of full-time programmes for those preparing for a career, and day-release courses for those already in employment. Provides vocational training for school leavers and retrains adults.

Esperanto Federation, Scottish (1905), 92 Liberton Brae, Edinburgh, EH16 6LB. T.-031-664 1060. Chairman of Council: Professor Stanley Nisbet; Secretary: R.D.M. Calder; Treasurer: Mrs K. Brent. Propagation, use, and teaching of the international language, Esperanto.

Ettrick and Lauderdale District Council (1974), Council Chambers, Paton Street, Galashiels. T.-Galashiels 4751. Provost: A.L. Tulley; Vice Chairman: W. Hardie; Members: C.I. Jones, Mary Bryson, A.T. Turnbull, A. Scott, Isabella Phaup, A.N. Merry, J.A. Grant, T.R. Dumble, J.M. Barron, J.W.R. Mather, L.G.W. Thomson, J. Elspeth Shelley, T.W. Henderson, A. Brodie. Chief Executive: John D. Bell; Depute Chief Executive: Thomas K. Griffin; Director of Finance: Duncan M. Brown; Director of Environmental Services: Michael Halls; Director of Housing: James H. Blacklaws. District Council. Population of District: 33,000.

European Communities, Commission of the, Office for Scotland, 7 Alva Street, Edinburgh, EH2 4PH. T.-031-225 2058. Representative for Scotland: Stanley Budd; Documentalist/Librarian: Vanessa Henderson. To supply information about the European Communities to enquirers from Press, television and radio, local authorities, businessmen and investors, schools and universities, etc. To maintain links with those bodies in Scotland particularly concerned with Community affairs, and to ensure that Scotland's particular problems and potential are known in Brussels.

Evangelistic Council, Scottish (1929), 11 Newton Place, Glasgow, G3 7PR. T.-041-333 0546. Hon. President: Rev. George B. Duncan; President: Rev. Robert McGhee; Vice Presidents: Dr Ian R. Clark, Rev. Kingsley J. Rendell; Hon. Secretary: John Dodds. Associate Secretary: Lucy McGuinness. The Council's work is to spread the Christian message throughout Scotland by Bible Witness rallies, village children's work by caravan missioners, and in summer missions in the country or at the seaside.

Evening Express (1879), P.O. Box 43, Lang Stracht, Mastrick, Aberdeen, AB9 8AF. T.-0224 690222. Editor: H. Roulston. Evening newspaper serving Aberdeen and surrounding area.

Evening News (1873), 20 North Bridge, Edinburgh, EH1 1YT. T.-031-225 2468. Editor: Ian Nimmo. Evening newspaper serving Edinburgh and the East of Scotland.

Evening Telegraph & Post (1905), 9 Bank Street, Dundee, DD1 9HU. T.-0382 23131. Evening newspaper circulating in Central Scotland.

Evening Times (1876), 195 Albion Street, Glasgow, G1 1QP. T.-041-552 6255. Editor: G. McKechnie. Evening newspaper serving Glasgow and Strathclyde Region.

Examination Board, Scottish (1964), Ironmills Road, Dalkeith, Midlothian, EH22 1LE. T.-031-663 6601. Chairman: F. Macintosh, C.B.E.; Members: D.A. Adams, N.L. Anderson, Professor C.J. Bartlett, Councillor R.D. Birch, J.L. Brodie, Miss M.R.W. Caden, W.S. Charles, Miss S.M.M. Cooper, H.G. Cuming, Councillor T. Dair, Councillor Mrs C.D. Dalgleish, Mrs C.A.M. Davis, K.W. Dron, Professor E.A.V. Ebsworth, A.L. Fowler, I.L. Fraser, Mrs R.A. Galt, Professor J.R. Gray, Councillor M.R. Green, G.J. Higgins, Professor A.D. Hook, Councillor Mrs A.I. Huggins, T.J. McCool, H.G. Millar, C.W. Miller, J.B. Moss, R. Nimmo, Professor A.K.G. Paterson, D.M. Paterson, R. Paul, H.L. Philip, Professor W. Ritchie, J. McD. Roy, D. Sharkie, Professor D.J. Tedford, Councillor Mrs B. Vaughan, Professor D.A.G. Waddell. Director: J.H. Walker; Depute Director: M.R.M. Hendry; Assistant Director: J.N. Gillam.

Formerly known as the Scottish Certificate of Education Examination Board (1964-81). Its functions are: to make arrangements for, and to conduct, examinations each year for the award of certificates relating to secondary education; to award such certificates on such conditions approved by the Secretary of State as the Board may impose; to advise the Secretary of State on such matters relating to examinations for pupils receiving secondary education as the Secretary of State refers to it, or as the Board considers necessary; to give effect to such direction as the Secretary of State may give to the Board under these regulations as to the discharge of its functions.

F

Falkirk College of Technology (1962), Grangemouth Road, Falkirk, FK2 9AD. T.-0324 24981. Chairman, College Council: Michael Kelly, O.B.E., J.P. Principal: W.L.E. Henderson; Depute Principal: Robert McF. Wales; Assistant Principal: David E. Kelso; Registrar: John Douglas. Falkirk College is the major establishment of further and higher education in Central Scotland with more than 8,000 enrolments in 1983/84 on courses ranging from non-vocational evening classes to higher diploma, final professional, and degree programmes.

Falkirk District Council (1974), Municipal Buildings, Falkirk, FK1 5RS. T.-Falkirk 24911. Provost: J. Docherty; Members: J.H. Jenkinson, W.S. McKell, D. Mailer, J.P. Marshall, J. Johnston, J. Davidson, D. Goldie, R.A.D. Thomson, G. Goldie, A.S. Gallacher, M. Nicol, J. Ferguson, F.B. McKeever, A. Thom, M. Bissett, J. Constable, H. Constable, Elizabeth Eaglesham, S. Martin, J. Wilson, T.P. Martin, P. Bryans, G. Laing, D. Bryson, L.W. Bryson, A. Donaghy, J.D. Docherty, W.A. Feighan, J. Valentine, W.W. Milne, Lorna E. Montgomery, Margaret Sutherland, A.H. Fowler, C. Mackay; J. Kennedy. Chief Executive Officer: J.P.H. Paton; Senior Depute Director: R.M. Porter; Junior Depute Director: W.B. Kilgour; Director of Finance: W. Weir; Director of Planning: W.F. Frame; Director of Architectural Services: D.B. Russell; Director of Housing: P. Craig; Director of Environmental Health: M. MacDonald; Director of Amenity and Recreation: D.J.G. Mould; Director of Libraries and Museums: A.H. Howson; Director of Direct Works: P.B. Young. District Council. Population of District: 144,000.

Falkirk Enterprise Action Trust (1983), Suite A, Haypark, Marchmont Avenue, Polmont, FK2 0NZ. T.-0324 716868. Chairman, Board of Trustees: W.R. Alexander, C.B.E. Secretary: H.B. Johnson; Director: John M. Jackson. Set up as private sector initiative to provide advice and practical assistance to small, local firms, including start-ups.

Family Conciliation Service (Lothian), Scottish (1984), 127 Rose Street South Lane, Edinburgh, EH2 5BB. T.-031-226 4507. Chairman: Alan Finlayson; Secretary: Catherine Bryson. Co-ordinator: Julia Ross. Confidential service to help separating and divorcing couples to settle disputes, especially over children. Provides an informal means of clarifying confused situations and reduces conflict by mediating between partners, preferably before formal divorce proceedings are started.

Farmers' Union of Scotland, National (1913), 17 Grosvenor Crescent, Edinburgh, EH12 5EN. T.-031-337 4333. President: I.D. Grant; Vice Presidents: G.A.B. Anderson, J.W. Hay. Director and General Secretary:

D.S. Johnston; Deputy General Secretary: R.I. Sandilands. To watch over, protect, and promote the interests of agriculture, horticulture, and aquaculture in all its branches, and to encourage the development of the industry by such means as may seem necessary.

Fencing Union, Scottish Amateur. Secretary: Dr D.R.B. Mends, 11 Eyre Crescent, Edinburgh, EH3 5ET. T.-031-557 0335. National Coach: Professor H.T. Bracewell, Breastmill House, Kirkliston, EH29 9EA. T.-031-333 3016.

Field Studies Association, Scottish (1958), Kindrogan Field Centre, Enochdhu, Blairgowrie, Perthshire, PH10 7PG. T.-Strathardle 286. Chairperson: Professor Joy Tiuy; Executive Secretary: Alex. McLeod. Warden: B.S. Brookes, M.B.E. To promote the development of field studies in Scotland, and to create among both adult and younger members of the general public a greater awareness and understanding of the Scottish countryside. Courses are run covering a wide variety of specialist and general subjects, from archaeology and botany to painting and photography.

Fife Health Board (1974), Glenrothes House, North Street, Glenrothes, Fife. T.-Glenrothes 754355. Chairman: J.C. Balfour, O.B.E., M.C.; Members: Dr P. Aitken, Mrs J.H.P. Buchanan, J. Edmiston, H.C. Forwell, Mrs A. Ferguson, D.L. Fulton, Dr J.B. Gallacher, Dr M.L. Graeme, Mrs C. Haddow, K.R. Hayward, J.H. Henderson, J. Ivers, Dr A.H. Lawson, I.A. McCrone, Miss A. McFadden, J. Murray, G. Reid, Mrs C.C. Sharp, D. Stoddart, C. Whitlock. Secretary: I.G. Dorward; Treasurer: N.R. Lammie; Chief Administrative Medical Officer: Dr R. Gardiner; Chief Area Nursing Officer: Mrs S. McDade. Fife Health Board is responsible for the provision of health services in Fife Region.

Fife Regional Council (1974), Fife House, Glenrothes, Fife. T.-Glenrothes 754411. Convener: R. Gough; Members: K.G. Aitken, W.G. Anderson, W.T. Barclay, J. Braid, W. Brand, W. Clarke, W. Coull, M. Coyne, T.M. Dair, Dr P.S. Davison, R. Gardiner, I.G. Gardner, P.J. Gemmell, Vera Gemmell, C.J. Groom, K.R. Hayward, Elizabeth B. Henderson, A.G. Highland, M.C., P. Hutchison, A.A. Jackson, C. Laing, Teresa M. Little, C. Logan, J.W. MacDougall, Edith J. McFee, I.M. McGeachie, H.B. McLeish, J. McMurdo, Jean H. Mackie, Constance I. Mitchell, Dr L. Moonie, A.W. Patey, J. Ramage, W. Rowley, A.M. Sharp, Agnes J. Smith, I. Smith, J.G. Souter, G. Stanfield, D.C. Stewart, R.N. Turpie, A.H. Walker, A.K. Walker, A. Wishart. Chief Executive: J.M. Dunlop, C.B.E.; Director of Administration: W. Breslin; Director of Finance: D.M. Mitchell; Director of Architectural Services: J.D.T. Cowling; Regional Assessor and Electoral Registration Officer: J. Thomson; Chief Constable: W. McD. Moodie; Director of Education: M. More; Director of Engineering: W. Rowson; Firemaster: J. Thomson; Director of Personnel and Management Services: W. Muir; Director of Physical Planning: W.G. Taylor; Regional Reporter to Children's Panel: A.F. Kelly; Director of Socal Work: M.A. Gillespie; Director of Supplies: J.J. McHugh; Director of Trading Standards and Consumer Protection: E. Abrahams. Regional Council. Population of Region: 341,000.

Film Council, Scottish (1934), 74 Victoria Crescent Road, Glasgow, G12 9JN. T.-041-334 9314. Chairman: John Donachy. Director: R.B. MacLuskie. Promotion of film culture in Scotland.

Fine Art Commission for Scotland, Royal (1927), 9 Atholl Crescent, Edinburgh, EH3 8HA. T.-031-229 1109. Chairman: Professor A.J. Youngson; Members: Louise G. Annand, M.B.E., John P. Boys, Bernat Klein, C.B.E., William

K. Mackay, Professor I. Metzstein, Professor F.N. Morcos-Asaad, Albert Morrocco, John D. Richards, C.B.E., Robert R. Steedman, Fiona M.E. Walker, H. Anthony Wheeler, O.B.E. Secretary: Charles Prosser. The Commission advises on the quality of the built environment in so far as this affects the public interest (including considerations of urban environmental planning design, architecture, and conservation). It also advises on works of art in relation to building exteriors and interiors. Reports by the Commission, made at intervals of several years, are published by H.M.S.O.

Finlay, James PLC (1909), Finlay House, 10/14 West Nile Street, Glasgow, G1 2PP. T.-041-204 1321. Chairman and Chief Executive: Sir Colin Campbell, Bt., M.C. International traders and financiers. Turnover (1984): £175m.

Fire Services Examination Board (Scotland) (1950), Room 274, St. Andrew's House, Edinburgh, EH1 3DE. T.-031-556 8501, Ext. 2861. Chairman: D. Dick, O.B.E. Secretary: R.L. Knowles. Formed under the authority of the Fire Services (Appointments and Promotion) (Scotland) Regulations to conduct the examinations qualifying for promotion to the ranks of leading fireman, sub-officer, and station officer.

Fishermen's Federation, Scottish (1973), 35 Albert Street, Aberdeen, AB1 1XU. T.-0224 641981. President: William F. Hay, M.B.E. Chief Executive and Secretary: Robert Allan. Political arm of the catching sector of the fishing industry in Scotland, consisting of several fishermen's associations. The Federation maintains close contact with Government Departments, political parties, and the E.E.C. institutions to ensure that they are constantly aware of its views on proposed legislation affecting the industry.

Fishermen's Organisation, Scottish (1973), 601 Queensferry Road, Edinburgh, EH4 6EA. T.-031-339 7972. Chairman: William F. Anderson; Vice Chairman: John Mitchell. Chief Executive and Secretary: Iain M. MacSween. Producers' organisation as defined by relevant E.E.C. legislation. 600 member vessels with turnover of £80m.

Fishing Co-operatives (1973), Unit 2, Primrose Industrial Estate, Primrose Lane, Rosyth, Dunfermline, Fife, KY11 2SS. T.-0383 413265/6. President: W. Hughes; Vice President: R. Fraser; Secretary: P. Donald. Secretary/Manager: J.A.H. Wallace. Comprises the Scottish Federation of Fishermen's Co-operatives Ltd. and the Fishing Co-operatives Trading (Scotland) Ltd. The main objectives of S.F.F.C. are to protect and promote the interests of fishermen's co-operatives in Scotland and elsewhere and to represent their interests, while F.C.T.S. Ltd. acts as buying agent on behalf of member societies. In addition, it operates a warehouse at Rosyth which services many of the requirements of the societies.

Football Association, Scottish, 6 Park Gardens, Glasgow, G3 7YF. T.-041-332 6372. Secretary: E. Walker.

Football Association, Scottish Amateur. Secretary: I. McTweed, 8 Gertrude Place, Barrhead, Glasgow, G78 1JY. T.-041-881 4025.

Football League, Scottish (1890), 188 West Regent Street, Glasgow, G2 4RY. T.-041-248 3844. President, Management Committee: David Letham; Vice President: I.R.G. Gellatly; Treasurer: J.S. Steedman; Members: J.Y. Craig, J.P., A.W. Mercer, R.H. Simpson, R.H. Davidson, J. Baxter, Dr J. Crorie, E. Mitchell, J. Jenkins, P.I. McKay. Secretary: James Farry. To promote the game of Association Football, and organise League Championship and League Cup competitions.

Scotland's Premier Division football clubs are as follows:

Aberdeen, Pittodrie Stadium, Pittodrie Street, Aberdeen, AB2 1QH. T.-0224 632328 and 633497. Chairman: Richard M. Donald; Vice Chairman: Christopher Anderson, O.B.E. Manager: Alex. Ferguson.

Celtic, Celtic Park, 95 Kerrydale Street, Glasgow, G40 3RE. T.-041-554 2710. Chairman: Desmond White; Vice Chairman: Thomas L. Devlin. Manager: David Hay.

Dumbarton, Boghead Park, Miller Street, Dumbarton, G82 2JA. T.-Dumbarton 62569/67864. Chairman: R.A. Robertson; Vice Chairman: A.M. Jackson. Manager: David Wilson.

Dundee, Dens Park, Dundee, DD3 7JY. T.-Dundee 826104. Chairman: Ian R.G. Gellatly. Manager: Archie Knox.

Dundee United, Tannadice Park, Tannadice Street, Dundee, DD3 7JW. T.-Dundee 826289. Chairman: J.J. Grant; Vice Chairman: G.F. Fox. Manager: James Y. McLean.

Heart of Midlothian, Tynecastle Park, Gorgie Road, Edinburgh, EH11 2NL. T.-031-337 6132. Chairman: A. Wallace Mercer. Manager: Alex. Macdonald.

Hibernian, Easter Road Stadium, Edinburgh, EH7 5QG. T.-031-661 2159. Chairman and Managing Director: Kenneth Waugh.

Morton, Cappielow Park, Sinclair Street, Greenock, PA15 2TY. T.-23571/25594. Chairman: Hugh M. Currie. Manager: William McLean.

Rangers, Ibrox Stadium, Glasgow, G51 2XD. T.-041-427 5232. Chairman: John Paton; Vice Chairman: Thomas Dawson. Manager: John Wallace.

St Mirren, St. Mirren Park, Love Street, Paisley, PA3 2EJ. Chairman: J.Y. Craig, J.P. Manager: Alex. Miller

Forestry Commission (1919), 231 Corstorphine Road, Edinburgh, EH12 7AT. T.-031-334 0303. Chairman: Sir David Montgomery; Deputy Chairman and Director General: G.D. Holmes, C.B.; Members: J. Forbes, Captain W.F.E. Forbes, Lord Gibson-Watt, P.C., M.C., G.O. Hutchison, J.N. Kennedy, G.J. Francis, D.T.J. Rutherford, J.D. Pollock, I.D. Coutts, C.B.E. Secretary: P.J. Clarke; Director, Research and Development: A.J. Grayson; Director, Private Forestry and Land Use Planning: A. Morrison; Director, Estate Management: J.M. Gwynn; Director, Harvesting and Marketing: G.J. Francis; Controller of Finance: C.F. Turquand; Deputy Establishment Officer: C.W. Simmonds.
National forest authority for Great Britain. The Commissioners give advice on forestry matters, and are responsible to the Minister of Agriculture, Fisheries and Food, and the Secretaries of State for Scotland and Wales. The Commission has a dual role. As forestry authority, its responsibilities include research, safety and training, felling controls, plant health, and the provision of advice and grant aid to private forestry. As forestry enterprise, its major objective is the production of timber and the encouragement of new industries by guaranteeing long term supplies of timber. In pursuing timber production, the Commission pays regard to amenity and the provision of rural employment, as well as wildlife conservation, landscape design, and the provision of facilities for recreation.

Forestry Society, Royal Scottish (1854), 1 Rothesay Terrace, Edinburgh, EH3 7UP. T.-031-226 3157. President: J.A.S. Watson; Vice Presidents: J. Henderson, W.J. Christie. Hon. Secretary: N.J. Findlay. Secretary: W.B.C. Walker. The advancement of forestry.

Forth Ports Authority, (1968), Tower Place, Leith, Edinburgh, EH6 7DB. T.-031-554 4343. Chairman: G.A. Hepburn; Vice Chairman: W.A.C. Thomson; Members: F.M. Cook, R. Gough, A. Barr, H.M. Thompson, W.J. Leaman, J.B. Houston. Managing Director: H.M. Thompson; Director (Engineering and Marine): W.J. Leaman, O.B.E.; Finance Director: J.B. Houston; Secretary: G. Renwick; Personnel Manager: A.C. Morrison; Chief Harbourmaster, Firth of Forth: Captain A.R.C. Childs. Port Manager, Grangemouth: J.W. Simpson; Port Manager, Leith and Granton: J.R. Grant; Port Manager, Fife Ports: Captain R.M. Taylor. Statutory port authority responsible for the operation and management of the ports of Burntisland, Grangemouth, Granton, Kirkcaldy, Leith, Methil, and the River and Firth of Forth. Activities also include stevedoring, warehousing, estate management, ship-towage, and shipping agency. The Authority is the largest multi-purpose port authority in Scotland, with a cargo throughput in 1983 of 28.8 million tonnes. Turnover for 1983 was £22.3m. The Authority and its wholly-owned subsidiaries employ about 1,000 people.

Forth River Purification Board, (1975), Colinton Dell House, West Mill Road, Colinton, Edinburgh. T.-031-441 4691. Director: W.F. Collett. Promoting the cleanliness of the River Forth and tributaries, and the Forth estuary, under Part II of the Control of Pollution Act 1974.

Forth Valley Health Board, (1974), 33 Spittal Street, Stirling, FK8 1DX. T.-Stirling 63031. Chairman: G.J.V. Horsman, O.B.E.; Vice Chairman: L.J.M. Hynd, O.B.E.; Members: J.F.C. Armstrong, Dr F.O. Brown, J. Cross, A.B. Cruickshank, Mrs F. Davidson, Dr L. Dunbar, Mrs M.R. Ferguson, Dr J.R.G. Furnell, J.M. Hendry, Mrs M.C. Lambie, J.G.G. Lees, W.D.M. Leithead, Miss M.K. Ritchie, Mrs R.M. Scott, Dr W.J. Thomson, Mrs J.S. Young. Secretary: J.M. Eckford; Treasurer: D.F. Hird; Chief Administrative Medical Officer: Dr J.L. Graham; Chief Area Nursing Officer: J.G. Sutherland. Provision of health service for population of 272,000.

Forth Valley Tourist Board, (1983), Burgh Halls, The Cross, Linlithgow, West Lothian, EH49 7AH. T.-0506 843306. Tourist Officer: Jane Rodger; Assistant Tourist Officer: Dorothy Lumsden. Covers the Districts of Dunfermline, Falkirk, and West Lothian.

Fort William and Lochaber Tourist Board, (1969), Travel Centre, Fort William, Inverness-shire. T.-0397 3781. Chairman: I. Milton. Area Tourist Officer and Secretary: B.L. Simpson; Assistant Tourist Officer: Mrs E.W.B. Howie. Promotion of tourism.

Fraser of Allander Institute, (1975), University of Strathclyde, Curran Building, 100 Cathedral Street, Glasgow, G4 ORQ. T.-041-552 4400. Director: Professor James McGilvray; Research Professor: Professor David Simpson; Director of Research: Dr Iain McNicoll. Research on the Scottish economy. Publishes quarterly economic commentary, research reports, and articles. Also carries out research consultancy work in Scotland and overseas. Research capability includes economic forecasting, industrial economics, regional economics, development economics, economics of oil, and labour economics. The Institute is controlled by the University of Strathclyde.

Free Church of Scotland (1843), The Mound, Edinburgh, EH1 2LS. T.-031-226 5286. Principal Clerk of Assembly: Rev. Clement Graham; General Treasurer: Iain D. Gill. A Christian Church professing the doctrines of the Westminster Confession of Faith. It is organised in some 170 local churches throughout Scotland for pastoral care and evangelical outreach, operates two eventide homes, supports Christian missions overseas in India, South Africa, and Peru, and co-operates with the Christian Witness to Israel in the evangelisation of Jewish people.

Free Presbyterian Church of Scotland (1893), 13 Kingsborough Gardens, Glasgow, G12 9NH. T.-041-339 0553. Moderator of Synod: Rev. A.F. MacKay; Clerk of Synod: Rev. D. MacLean; Assistant Clerk: Rev. A.E.W. MacDonald; General Treasurer: William D. Fraser. Reformed in doctrine, worship, and practice. The Church's strength lies in the Highlands and Islands, but there is a Presbyterial presence as far afield as Australia, New Zealand, and Zimbabwe.

Freshwater Fisheries, Consultative Committee on, Department of Agriculture and Fisheries for Scotland, Chesser House, 500 Gorgie Road, Edinburgh. Chairman: I.A. Duncan Millar; Members: W. Brown, K. Burns, A.E. Campbell, A.D. Jamieson, T.E. Mathie, H. Park, J. Reid, A.V. Tokely. Appointed to advise the Secretary of State on proposals for the making of Protection Orders for freshwater fishings.

Friends of the Earth (Scotland) (1979), 53 George IV Bridge, Edinburgh, EH1 1EJ. T.-031-225 6906. Joint Co-ordinators: Donald McPhillimy, Andrew Kerr. Campaigns for the rational use of the earth's resources.

Further Education Association, Scottish (1964), Gordon Chambers, 90 Mitchell Street, Glasgow, G1 3NQ. T.-041-221 0118. President: A. Abdy. General Secretary: Graham Alison; Assistant General Secretary: Maureen Mitchell. Professional association and trade union representing lecturers in colleges of further education throughout Scotland.

G

Galleries of Scotland, National, 125 George Street, Edinburgh, EH2 4JN. Trustees: Robert Begg (Chairman); Hamish Miles, The Marquess of Bute, Jack Notman, Martin Kemp, John Risk, Jack Knox. Director: Timothy Clifford; Secretary and Accountant to the Board of Trustees: James Gordon. The National Galleries consist of:

National Gallery of Scotland, The Mound, Edinburgh. Keeper: Hugh Macandrew. This also houses the Department of Prints and Drawings (Keeper: Keith Andrews).

Scottish National Portrait Gallery, Queen Street, Edinburgh. Keeper: Duncan Thomson.

Scottish National Gallery of Modern Art, Belford Road, Edinburgh. Keeper: Douglas Hall.

Galloway Cattle Society of Great Britain and Ireland (1877), 131 King Street, Castle Douglas, DG7 1LZ. T.-Castle Douglas 2753. Secretary: Chris Graves. Administration of Society Herd Book; promotion of breed; support of members.

Games Association, Scottish. Secretary: A. Rettie, Craigview, 19 Abbot Street, Perth. T.-0738 29759. Highland and Border games.

Gardens Scheme, Scotland's (1931), 31 Castle Terrace, Edinburgh, EH1 2EL. T.-031-229 1870. Chairman, Executive Committee: The Hon. Mrs Macnab of Macnab. General Organiser: R.S. St Clair-Ford; Secretary: Mrs I.R. Rodger. Scotland's Gardens Scheme is an independent charity. More than 200 gardens throughout Scotland open each year to the public on specific days for the benefit of two main beneficiaries: the Queen's Nursing Institute (Scotland) and the Gardens Fund of the National Trust for Scotland. Each garden owner may also select his own charity to which 40% of his gross takings are allocated. Two six-day and some day tours are organised each year.

Garnock Valley Development Executive (1984), 44 Main Street, Kilbirnie, KA25 7BY. T.-0505 685455. Chairman: Tom Dickie. Managing Director: Bill Dunn; Project Co-ordinator: Robin Jackson. To support existing businesses in the area; continue to attract new business; encourage local initiatives and any other measures to improve the performance of the local economy.

Gas Consumers Council, Scottish (1972), 86 George Street, Edinburgh, EH2 3BU. T.-031-226 6523. Chairman: Col. W.A. Dalziel, C.B.E., T.D., J.P.; Members: W.G. Beaton, Councillor W. Donald, Mrs E. Fraser, Mrs E.E. Gunstone, Councillor J. Hendry, Mrs J.R. Lamond, Councillor N. Lindsay, C.A. MacArthur, Councillor J. McGinley, Mrs A.M. Mackenzie; Councillor Mrs J.M. Mason, M. Morrison, Councillor A.M. Sharp, J.P., Councillor

T.G. Simpson. Secretary: Miss Y. Wilson. Statutory body representing the interests of gas consumers (and potential consumers) in Scotland. It is funded by the Government and completely independent of the gas industry. The work includes helping individual consumers with their problems and seeking improvements in overall policies through consultation with Scottish Gas.

Gas, Scottish (1973), Granton House, 4 Marine Drive, Edinburgh, EH5 1YB. T.-031-559 5000. Chairman, British Gas Corporation, Scottish Region: R.W. Hill; Deputy Chairman: F.F. Robb. Regional Secretary: A.J. Hynes; Public Relations Manager: H.C. Lipscomb; Director of Engineering: L. Potts; Director of Marketing: R.M. Currie; Director of Finance: D.M. Dewar; Director of Personnel: J.J. Walmsley; Controller of Supplies: R.W. Rae; Controller of Planning and Management Services: A.C. Beaton. To develop and maintain an efficient, co-ordinated and economical system of gas supply. Income from gas sales in Scotland totals £379m. per year.

Genealogy Society, Scottish (1953), 21 Howard Place, Edinburgh, EH3 5JY. T.-031-556 3844. Hon. Secretary: Joan P.S. Ferguson. To promote research into Scottish family history and undertake the collection, exchange, and publication of material relating to genealogy. Academic and consultative body only.

General Accident Fire & Life Assurance Corporation plc (1885), Pitheavlis, Perth, PH2 0NH. T.-0738 21202. Chairman: G.R. Simpson, D.S.O., M.V.O., T.D.; Deputy Chairmen: Earl of Airlie, D.A. Blaikie; Members, Board of Directors: R.W. Adam, Sir Denis Barnes, K.C.B., L. Bolton, J.C. Corcoran, J.C. Frangoulis, C.B. Heath, Sir Duncan McDonald, Sir Norman Macfarlane, B.C. Marshall, D.W. Nickson, C.B.E., R.S. Rauch, T. Roberts, W.N. Robertson, H.D. Waldron. Chief General Manager: B.C. Marshall; General Managers: J.C. Frangoulis, T. Roberts, W.N. Robertson. One of Britain's largest insurance organisations. Formed in Perth, it is now represented in 50 countries and employs more than 17,000 people worldwide. The Corporation is involved in all forms of life and non-life insurance, including marine and aviation. It is one of the largest writers of non-life business in the U.K. and is also the country's leading insurer of motor vehicles. General Accident is Scotland's third largest company.

General Practitioners, Royal College of (Scottish Council) (1952) 2 Hill Square, Edinburgh, EH8 9DR. T.-031-667 3115. Chairman: Dr D.W. MacLean; Hon. Secretary and Treasurer: Dr H.D.R. Munro. To encourage, foster, and maintain the highest possible standards in general medical practice.

General Register Office for Scotland (1855), New Register House, Edinburgh, EH1 3YY. T.-031-556 3952. Registrar General for Scotland: Dr C.M. Glennie; Deputy Registrar General for Scotland: J.S. Wheeler; Principals: G.F. Baird (Census), I.G. Bowie (Computer Services), I.G. Dewar (Registration); Statisticians: D.A. Orr (Population), D. Salmond (Vital Events).
The G.R.O. (S.) supervises the local registration of births, marriages, and deaths, and publishes statistics of vital events and of population estimates. It is also responsible for carrying out the Census in Scotland and for maintaining the National Health Service Central Register for Scotland.

General Teaching Council for Scotland (1966), 5 Royal Terrace, Edinburgh, EH7 5AF. T.-031-556 0072. Elected Members: (Principals of Colleges of Education) Thomas R. Bone, Gordon Kirk, Peter C. McNaught, Sister Margaret Sheridan; (Lecturers in Colleges of Education) Grant Thomson; (Further Education) David S. Black, Nicol MacNicol, William Richardson;

(Secondary) John Anderson, Neil Cooney, Jean S. Donaldson, Stanley M. Forrest, J.P., Alistair B. Fulton, Rose A. Galt, Susan McCormick, Ian W. Mackenzie, John McPherson, J. Stuart Patterson, Thomas Wallace; (Primary) Aileen A. Beck, Douglas Gilchrist, Lorna C.A. Goudie, J. Michael Hannah, Antonia M. Ireland, Patricia M. McCall, Wilma M. McEwan, Alasdair Maclean, Sheila B. Rennie, James C. Smith, Isabel M.B. Taylor. Appointed Members: (Convention of Scottish Local Authorities) Astrid I. Huggins, Michael Kelly, O.B.E., J.P., Joseph F. McLean, Barbara Vaughan; (Association of Directors of Education in Scotland) Ian S. Flett, C.B.E., Ian G. Halliday, James K. Purves; (The Universities of Scotland) Professors James B. Caird, John H. Duthie, Noel J. Entwistle, David W.A. Sharp; (Central Institutions) David A. Kennedy, Claudine L. Morgan; (Church of Scotland) Rev. Ian C.M. Fairweather; (Roman Catholic Church) John Vallely; (Members nominated by Secretary of State for Scotland) George Jackson, James C. McLintock, G. Malcolm Murray, Margaret Tait. Registrar: James Miller, J.P.
The functions of the Council are (a) to keep under review standards of education, training and fitness to teach appropriate to persons entering the teaching profession; (b) to consider and make recommendations to the Secretary of State on matters (other than remuneration and conditions of service) relating to the supply of teachers; (c) to establish and keep a register of teachers and to determine whether in any particular case under its disciplinary powers registration is to be withdrawn or refused.

Geographical Society, Royal Scottish (1884), 10 Randolph Crescent, Edinburgh, EH3 7TU. T.-031-225 3330. Secretary: Donald G. Moir; Hon. Treasurer: W.R. Ballantyne.

Girl Guides Association (Scotland) (1910), 16 Coates Crescent, Edinburgh, EH3 7AH. T.-031-226 4511. President, Council for Scotland: Baroness Carnegy of Lour; Scottish Chief Commissioner: Mrs G.D.M. Reid. General Secretary: Miss A.K. James; Deputy General Secretary: Miss S.M. McCulloch. Provides a programme embracing a wide range of leisure time activities and interests, which give opportunities for self-training in the development of character, responsible citizenship, and service to the community. There are 94,000 members in Scotland.

Girls' Brigade, The (1890), 1 Melrose Street, Glasgow, G4 9BJ. T.-041-332 1765. National President: Mrs J.T. Holmes; National Vice Presidents: Mrs J.H. Cameron, Miss S. Macfarlane; National Chaplain: Rev. R. Cook. Brigade Secretary: Miss H.R. McLeod; National Training Officer: Mrs S. Buchan. Christian organisation for girls between the ages of 5 and 18 years. It provides a wide range of activities which encourage the girls to become mature adults. Current membership for Scotland is 19,000. There is a world membership of about two million in 52 countries.

Glasgow Chamber of Commerce (1783), 30 George Square, Glasgow, G2 1EQ. T.-041-204 2121. President: Martin Smith; Deputy President: H.L.I. Runciman. Secretary: Ewan Marwick. Serves business interests throughout the West of Scotland, and has 2,400 firms in membership. Makes representations on matters of interest; provides an information service; deals with export documentation and trade inquiries; publishes a monthly journal and a Scottish trade directory; runs trade missions.

Glasgow College of Building and Printing (1972), 60 North Hanover Street, Glasgow, G1 2BP. T.-041-332 9969. Chairman, College Council: R. Clark. Principal: D. McEwan; Depute Principal: W. Duthie; Assistant Principal: J.

Rice; Academic Registrar: J.K. Graham; Registrar: Mrs J.C. Blackburn. Specialised courses to meet the educational needs of the construction and communication industries. Full-time diploma and certificate courses, day and block release, specialist short courses. There are 3,500 students each session.

Glasgow College of Food Technology (1973), 230 Cathedral Street, Glasgow, G1 2TG. T.-041-552 3751. Principal: Dr. W. Bannatyne; Depute Principal: J. McCabe. The College provides a comprehensive range of full-time and part-time courses in catering, hotel management, tourism, and food technology up to higher diploma. Courses in bakery and meat trades are also offered.

Glasgow College of Nautical Studies (1969), 21 Thistle Street, Glasgow, G5 9XB. T.-041-429 3201. Chairman, College Council: I.A. Lyall. Principal: T. Ireland; Depute Principal: A.C. Smith; Registrar: T.P. Braidwood. Maritime and further education college. Courses include Department of Transport senior and cadet courses for the Merchant Navy; SCOTEC and other courses; evening classes including courses for yachtsmen and radio amateurs.

Glasgow College of Technology (1971), Cowcaddens Road, Glasgow, G4 OBA. T.-041-332 7090. Chairman, College Council: C.C. Drury; Vice Chairman: J.M. Wotherspoon. Director: Dr N.G. Meadows; Depute Director: Dr N.K. Buxton; Senior Assistant Director: K.S. Reader; Assistant Directors: Dr P.W. Bush, Dr K.C. Clements-Jewery; Academic Registrar: L. Brodie; Chief Administrative Officer: A.C. Morton. Provides courses of higher education leading to the award of certificates, diplomas, and degrees by S.C.O.T.V.E.C. and C.N.A.A., and provides tuition for a variety of professional qualifications. Courses are offered in various branches of technology, in applied physical and biological sciences, in business and management studies, and in vocationally relevant aspects of the social sciences. Currently financed by Strathclyde Regional Council, the College will become a central institution from 1 September 1985.

Glasgow Council for Voluntary Service (1974), 11 Queens Crescent, Glasgow, G4 9AS. T.-041-332 2444. Chairperson: Helen Allison; Vice Chairperson: Vicky Jack; Treasurer: Gibb Mathie; Hon. Secretary: Graham Hoey. Director: Colin Williams; Assistant Director: John Anderson. Initiates and/or supports the development of new organisations and initiatives within the voluntary sector. Offers practical help to voluntary groups, represents them locally and nationally, and operates a sports and arts resource project.

Glasgow District Council (1974), City Chambers, George Square, Glasgow, G2 1DU. T.-041-221 9600. Lord Provost: Robert Gray; Committee Conveners: Robert McKenzie (Environmental Protection), Pat Lally (Finance), Daniel Crawford (General Purposes), James McLean (Housing), Philip O'Rourke (Arts and Culture), Dennis Murphy (Buildings and Property), Matthew Adam (Licensing), Hugh Macrae (Parks and Recreation), Maria Fyfe (Personnel), John Henderson (Planning), Jean McFadden (Policy and Resources).
Members: A. MacKenzie, J. McLean, A. Mosson, M. Caldwell, J. McVicar, N. McL. Stobo, D. Brown, J. Mullen, Maria Fyfe, E.A. Fitzgerald, J. McQueenie, R. McKenzie, J. McCarron, H. Macrae, P. Lally, J. Moynes, Margaret Sinclair, J. Henderson, C. McCafferty, C. Brown, J. Barr, Marjorie O'Neill, W. Milligan, R.E. Brown, D. Murphy, L. Flanagan, A. Simpson, J. Cornfield, J. Mutter, W. Aitken, R.N.S. Logan, R. Innes, F. White, J. Lavelle, P. Moore, C. Davison, D. Mason, A. McLean, R. Gray,

A. McGarrity, D.C. MacGregor, C.C. McNicol, J.H. Young, D. Crawford, Susan Baird, Patricia Chalmers, P. O'Rourke, E.J. Nolan, J. McNally, I.J.A. Dyer, C. Stevenson, J. Shields, A.S. Livingston, J. Chatham, J. Gaffney, Gretel Ross, Jean McFadden, S. Bates, M. Adam, Rose McCloy, R. Davey, D. Wiseman, T. Dingwall, B.G. Campbell, J.F. Ross. Town Clerk and Chief Executive: Steven F. Hamilton; Senior Town Clerk Depute: Charles P. Horsburgh; Town Clerk Deputes: James Campbell, Theodore Crombie, M.B.E., Ian G. Fraser, Roy C. Henderson; Director of Architecture and Related Services: William D. Worden; Director of Building and Works: Brian J. Gallagher; Director of Corporate Services: Robert S. Hoyle; Director of Operations: Frederick L. Harrison; Director of Building Control: Robert McGowan; Director of Cleansing: Andrew L. Anderson; Director of Computer Services: Derrick S. Norris; Director of Environmental Health: James Jackson; City Estates Surveyor: Remo Verrico; Director of Finance: William J. English; Director of Halls and Theatres: Thomas Malarkey; Director of Housing: Paul Mugnaioni; Director of Libraries: Andrew Miller; Director of Museums and Art Galleries: Alasdair A. Auld; Director of Parks and Recreation: Keith J. Fraser; Director of Personnel: James Weir; Director of Planning: James H. Rae. Glasgow is the largest city in Scotland and the third largest in the U.K. It covers an area of 49,753 acres and has a population of about 750,000. It is the second largest of Scotland's local authorities. State of parties (May 1984 District Elections): Labour, 59; Conservative, 5; Alliance, 2.

Glasgow Herald (1782), 195 Albion Street, Glasgow, G1 1QP. T.-041-552 6255. Editor: Arnold Kemp. National morning newspaper.

Glasgow Institute of the Fine Arts, Royal (1861), 12 Sandyford Place, Glasgow, G3 7NE. T.-041-248 7411. President: Sir Norman Macfarlane; Hon. Secretary: Danny Ferguson; Hon. Treasurer: Robert W. Begg. The Institute's main function is the promotion of an open annual exhibition of paintings, sculpture, etc., in the McLellan Galleries, Glasgow. It has 1,300 members.

Glasgow Marriage Guidance Council (1947), 27 Sandyford Place, Sauchiehall Street, Glasgow, G3 7NG. T.-041-248 5249. Chairman: Sheriff Brian Kearney; Vice Chairman: Dr Maud P. Menzies; Hon. Secretary: Myrtle McFadyen; Hon. Treasurer: J. McKee. Organising Secretary: Marion Hamilton. To foster the success and stability of marriage by providing confidential couselling for people with difficulties in their marriage or in other personal relationships, and an educational service in relationships for young people, engaged and married couples, and parents.

Glasgow Opportunities (1983), 7 West George Street, Glasgow, G2 1EQ. T.-041-221 0955. Chairman: J.H.F. Macpherson. Director: G. Paterson. GO is an enterprise agency providing free, confidential business advice to people wishing to set up in business in Glasgow. Advice is also given to existing businesses wishing to expand.

Glasgow School of Art (1840), 167 Renfrew Street, Glasgow, G3 6RQ. T.-041-332 9797. Director: Professor Anthony Jones; Head of Fine Art Studies: William Buchanan; Head of Design Studies: Dugald Cameron; Head of Department of Architecture: Professor Andrew MacMillan; Head of Department of Planning: B.K. Parnell. One of the oldest and largest colleges of art in Britain. Scottish Central Institution which offers degree courses to virtually all its full-time students.

Glasgow, University of (1451), Glasgow, G12 8QQ. T.-041-339 8855. Chancellor: Sir Alexander Cairncross, K.C.M.G.; Principal and Vice Chancellor: Sir Alwyn Williams; Vice Principals: Professor D. Flint, T.D., Professor L.C. Hunter, Professor J.S. Gillespie; Rector: M. Kelly, C.B.E., J.P.; Dean of Faculties: Emeritus Professor William Walker Chambers, M.B.E.; Secretary of the University Court: J. McCargow, J.P.; Registrar: F. Gillanders; Clerk of Senate: Professor A.S. Skinner; Librarian and Keeper of Hunterian Books and MSS: H.J. Heaney; Clerk of the General Council: W.E. Gibson.

University Court: The Rector (Chairman), The Principal, James Mullen, William J. Harley, J.P., Robert Courtney Smith, C.B.E., Rev. Johnston R. McKay, T.D., Donald Dickson, Colin D. Donald, D.H. Clark, D.C. Muirhead, Helen S. Dunsmore, Professor Dennis C. Gilles, Professor Mervyn Lewis, Professor Alfred L. Brown, Professor William M. Gordon, Professor Michael R. Bond, Robert G. Bruce; President and Assessor, Students' Representative Council; Ronald V. Emanuel; Maureen Gardner; Sir Norman Macfarlane; Ian R. Clark, C.B.E., Alexander R. Macmillan, James Gordon, C.B.E.

Senatus Academicus: (Professorial Members): Professors D.M. Walker, Q.C., I.N. Sneddon, O.B.E., M.L. Samuels, J. Lamb, A.A.McB. Duncan, D.S. Thomson, W. Mulligan, D. Flint, W.S. Foulds, J.A. Simpson, P.H. Butter, H.G. Morgan, H.B. Sutherland, D.C. Gilles, R.M.S. Smellie, I.A. Boyd, T.D.V. Lawrie, D.K. Mason, A.S.G. Curtis, D.W.A. Sharp, J.S. Gillespie, W.B. Jennett, E.K.C. Varty, J.H. Subak-Sharpe, W.F.H. Jarrett, J. Macdonald, R.G. Hemingway, W.M. Gordon, A.R. MacGregor, R.S. Downie, L.C. Hunter, M.C. Macnaughton, A.C. Wardlaw, G.A. Sim, R.B. Goudie, Sir Abraham Goldberg, M.B. Wilkins, O.F. Hutter, D.M. MacDowell, F.M. Martin, P.G. Walsh, M.M. Dryden, J.E.T. Eldridge, N.G. Round, R. Davidson, D.L. Hamblen, G.W. Kirby, R.J. Scothorne, A. MacMillan, W.D. Munn, D. Faulkner, R.P. Ferrier, L. Alcock, M.R. Bond, M.A. Ferguson-Smith, G.S. Cowie, R.G. Finch, W.A. Harland, B.E. Leake, D.D. Lawson, J.H. Barber, K.C. Calman, D.T.H. Weir, P. Henry, P. M. Brown, N.G. Wright, D. Campbell, J.K. Luffingham, C.R. Whitfield, I.B. Thompson, A. Coull, D.A. McGowan, F. Cockburn, F.H. Stone, R. B. Jack, N.D.C. Grant, Rona McL. MacKie, A.W.J. Thomson, A.L. Brown, A.C. Kennedy, J.L. Reid, T.D. Campbell, S.J. Gray, G. M. Urquhart, D.C. Carter, D. Wheatley, F.I. Caird, Janet B.I. McDonald, J.A.M. Inglis, A.D. Hook, K. Vickerman, D.V. Donnison, B.E. Richards, K.G. Robbins, D.J. Sherratt, H.J. Macdonald, B.F. Scott, C. Smethurst, R.C. Paterson, J. M. M. Cunningham, Delphine M.V. Parrott, M. Peaker, W.D. George, A.J. Sanford, J. Baillie, J. McKie, M.P. Arkinson, M.D. Houslay, A.J. Hedley, R.W. Ogden, J.C. Brown, R.N.M. MacSween, A.A.A.H. Tait.

The University was founded in 1451 by a Bull of Pope Nicholas V on the application of William Turnbull, Bishop of Glasgow. Its charter provided for studies in theology, canon and civil law, arts and any other lawful faculty. Today, the University has the following faculties: Arts; Divinity; Engineering; Law; Medicine; Science; Social Science; Veterinary Medicine. The 'old college' was situated in the High Street for more than four centuries; the University moved to its present site on Gilmorehill in 1870. There are 10,000 full-time and 1,800 part-time students attending.

Glasgow, University of, Department of Adult and Continuing Education (1961), 57-61 Oakfield Avenue, Glasgow, G12 8LW. T.-041-339 8855, Ext. 394. Director: Professor Lalage Bown; Titular Professor: Thomas Wilson; Deputy Director: Dr William Hutchison. Exists to provide opportunities for adults to share in the ideas and knowledge in which the University deals. In 1982/83, it mounted 360 extra-mural classes, 99 specialist and professional courses, and 126 conferences and lecture series, covering 34 subject areas, and with 12,330 enrolments.

Glass Merchants and Glaziers Association, Scottish (1940), 13 Woodside Crescent, Glasgow, G3 7UP. T.-041-332 7144. Acting Secretary: W.I. Barclay. Trade association.

Glenrothes and Buckhaven Technical College (1968), Stenton Road, Glenrothes, KY6 2PD. Principal: T.J. Burness; Depute: W. Thompson; Assistant: J.S.R. Johnston. College of further education. Special features: Centre for Industrial Studies (post-experience short courses); Accredited Centre, M.S.C. Training Unit; Industrial Institute (school link); Computer Assisted Training Services (open technology project). 1,700 students.

Glenrothes Development Corporation (1948), Balbirnie House, Glenrothes, KY7 6NR. T.-0592 754343. Chairman: Sir George Sharp, O.B.E., J.P.; Vice Chairman: Councillor R.L. Gough; Members: Councillor R. King, R.W. Adams, O.B.E., Mrs M. Wood, O.B.E., A.M. Sharp, A. Philp, I.A. McCrone, W.J. Turcan. Chief Executive: Martin Cracknell; Director of Administration and Legal Services: A.A. Dow; Director of Finance: A.F. Laird; Commercial Director: J.A.F. McCombie; Technical Director: A.H. Bannerman; Public Relations Officer: T. Johnston. New Town Development Corporation developing Glenrothes from original village population of 1,000, through present level of about 40,000, to eventual target of 55,000. Centre for high technology industry.

Glenrothes Enterprise Trust, North House, North Street, Glenrothes. T.-0592 757903. Director: Brian Turnbull.

Goethe-Institut Glasgow Scottish-German Centre (1957), 2-3 Park Circus, Glasgow, G3 6AX. T.-041-332 2555. Director: Dr Georg Heuser; Head of Language Dept.: Drs Ernst R. Rinke; Financial Administrator: James Sheffield. For promoting the study of the German language abroad, and for international cultural co-operation.

Golf Union, Scottish, 54 Shandwick Place, Edinburgh, EH2 4RT. T.-031-226 6711. Secretary: A. Jamieson.

Gordon District Council (1974), Gordon House, Blackhall Road, Inverurie, Aberdeenshire. T.-Inverurie 20981. Chairman: J. Presly; Vice Chairman: G. Lumsden; Members: R.G. Bisset, R.L.C. Chalmers, J. Cullen, V. Davidson, N. Donald, W.R. Fiddes, P.G.J. Miller, Mrs P.J. Ramsey, Mrs M.J. Wainman, I. Walker. Chief Executive: A.C. Kennedy; Director of Legal Services: J.A. Riddell; Director of Finance: A.J. Wilson; Director of Environmental Health: A. McKinnon; Director of Housing: P. Donaldson; Director of Planning: E. Geraldine Scott; Director of Recreation and Technical Services: J. Bruce. District Council. Population of District: 66,000.

Gordon District Tourist Board (1983), St. Nicholas House, Broad Street, Aberdeen, AB9 1DE. T.-0224 632727. Chairman: R. Graham. Director: Gordon E. Henry. Promotion of tourism.

Gordon Highlanders Regimental Headquarters, Viewfield Road, Aberdeen, AB1 7XH. T.-0224 38174. Regimental Secretary: Major I.D. Martineau.

Grampian Health Board (1974), 1 Albyn Place, Aberdeen. T.-0224 589901. Chairman: C.W. Ellis; Vice Chairman: Professor R.D. Weir; Members: Mrs E.A. Bailey, Professor A.G.M. Campbell, H.D. Cochran, D. Davidson, N. Donald, Mrs J.B.M. Ellis, O.B.E., Captain C.A. Farquharson, Dr J.G.

Henderson, Mrs C. Houldsworth, Mrs J.R. Lamond, Mrs M. Mackenzie, M.B.E., T.D., Dr M. McGregor, J. Murison, G.S. Peterkin, Dr N.C. Sharp, M.B.E., Miss E.A. Sheldon, M.B.E., Dr E.A. Smith, C.B.E., Professor E.A. Tait, Professor W. Walker. Secretary: Dr H.R.M. Wilson; Treasurer: A. Wingfield; Chief Administrative Medical Officer: Dr M. Murchison; Chief Administrative Nursing Officer: D. Macdonald; Chief Administrative Dental Officer: G.M. Howie; Chief Administrative Pharmaceutical Officer: A. Williams. Provision of health service.

Grampian Regional Council (1974), Woodhill House, Ashgrove Road West, Aberdeen, AB9 2LU. T.-0224 682222. Convener: J. Sorrie; Members: J.C. Russell, E.P. Harrison, J.A. White, Roma L. Hossack, N. Robertson, H.A.C. Munro, H. Watt, W. Kelty, W.A. Grant, J.A.S. McPherson, L.C. Gordon-Duff, H.J. Sim, Dr Margaret McGregor, S. Coull, J. Ingram, I.F. Watson, A.W. Wright, H.W. Auchinachie, D. Anderson, D.C.H. McLean, P.G.J. Miller, J.R. Robertson, R.W. Gordon, Morag C. Morrell, P.K. Johnston, Christina M. Wood, R. Middleton, W. Rose, D. Tumelty, E. Hendrie, June R. Lamond, G. Grant, J.A. Porter, J.A. Dempsey, B. Salter, L. Ironside, Margery Urquhart, A.F. Mutch, J.C. Campbell, N.R. Stephen, J.N. Keay, Margaret R. Clyne, Ellen Williamson, Dr Geoffrey Hadley, P.S. Tong, J. Young, J.M.M. Humphrey, A.M.P. Burn, R.M. Kinghorn, A.W. Henry, I.B. Robertson. Chief Executive: J.D. Macnaughton; Depute Chief Executive: J.C. Liddell; Director of Law and Administration: A.G. Campbell; Director of Finance: T.E. Carter; Director of Education: J.A.D. Michie; Director of Architectural Services: W.S. Scott; Director of Social Work: Miss M.C. Hartnoll; Chief Constable: A.G. Lynn; Reporter to Children's Panel: R.G. Pearson: Firemaster: T. Bond; Director of Manpower Services: A.C. McDougall; Assessor and Electoral Registration Officer: H.B. Sturgeon; Director of Consumer Protection: K. Beaumont; Director of Roads: George Kirkbride; Director of Physical Planning: T.F. Sprott; Director of Public Transportation: J.S. Westaby; Director of Water Services: I.D. Brown; Director of Estates: W.W. Murray; Director of Lighting: E. Wilkie. Regional Council. Population of Region: 490,000. Political Composition of Council: Conservative, 26; Labour, 14; S.N.P., 5; Alliance, 5; Independent, 2; 2 vacancies.

Grampian Television PLC (1961), Queen's Cross, Aberdeen, AB9 2XJ. T.-0224 646464. Chairman, Board of Directors: Iain M. Tennant, J.P.; Deputy Chairman: Calum A. Macleod; Chief Executive: Alex. Mair, M.B.E.; Directors: Robert L. Christie (Operations Manager), The Lord Forbes, K.B.E., J.P., Fiona J. Lyall, Angus Stewart Macdonald, Neil Paterson, Sir George Sharp, O.B.E., J.P., Donald H. Waters, Neil R. Welling (Head of Sales and Marketing). Head of News and Current Affairs: Edward Brocklebank. ITV company serving the North and East of Scotland. Grampian Television's transmission area is the largest of any in the ITV network.

Greater Glasgow Health Board (1974), 225 Bath Street, Glasgow, G2 4JT. T.-041-204 2755. Chairman: Donald F. Macquaker; Vice Chairman: Dr John MacKay, O.B.E.; Members: Miss E. Donachie, James F. Dunnachie, Andrew D. Garland, Lady Goold, Lady Gunn, O.B.E., J. Ross Harper, Paul W. Holst, John Jackson, Isabel D. Kerr, Professor I.M. Ledingham, Bashir A. Maan, J.P., Margaret McGarry, Professor E.M. McGirr, C.B.E., James A. Peel, Dorothy Rigg, Dr G.B.S. Roberts, Harry Sherriff, David S. Sinnott, Colin Williams. Secretary: R.D.R. Gardner; Treasurer: A.M.

Paterson; Chief Administrative Medical Officer: Dr G.D. Forwell; Chief Area Nursing Officer: Miss M.W. Aitken; Chief Administrative Dental Officer: R. McKechnie; Chief Administrative Pharmaceutical Officer: Miss E.A. Meikle. Provision of health service in the Greater Glasgow area.

Greater Glasgow Tourist Board, 35-39 St. Vincent Place, Glasgow, G1 2ER. T.-041-227 4885. Chief Executive: Edward Friel.

Greenock Chamber of Commerce (1813), 73 Union Street, Greenock. T.-0475 20175. President: J.G. Quigley. Secretaries and Treasurers: Henderson & Co. To promote the commercial and manufacturing interests of Greenock and district.

Greenock Telegraph (1857), 2 Crawfurd Street, Greenock, PA15 1LH. Editor: Kenneth Thomson. Evening newspaper for Greenock and district.

Grocers' Federation, Scottish (1918), 153 Constitution Street, Leith, Edinburgh, EH6 7AD. T.-031-554 1122. President: W.J. Wylie; Senior Vice President: D. Edgar. Chief Executive: L. Dewar; Depute Chief Executive: M.J. Kempton. Representative of retail grocers and provision merchants in Scotland; promotes the formation of local associations and the interests of the retail grocery and provision trade; confers with local and national authorities on matters affecting the trade; seeks to maintain the status of the trade.

Gymnastics Association, Scottish Amateur, 18 Ainslie Place, Edinburgh, EH3 6AU. T.-031-226 4401. Administrator: Ian Hall; National Coach: G. Forster.

H

Hamilton District Council (1974), Town House, 102 Cadzow Street, Hamilton. T.-Hamilton 282323. Provost: S. Casserly; Members: M. Tremble, T. Grieve, I. McKillop, G. Smith, Joyce Millward, Nancy Cochrane, D.Dorricot, T. Murphy, J. Swinburne, R. Newberry, J. Borland, J. Speirs, P. Grenfell, H. Dunsmuir, R. Gibb, Teresa Maxwell, Senga Dallas, Barbara McKinnon, J. Lowe. Chief Executive: F.T. Malcolm; Director of Finance: H.S. Gray; Director of Architecture: E.D.W. Duncan; Director of Housing: Andrew Martin; Director of Planning: G.F. Gilfillan; Director of Environmental Health: A. Baird; Director of Leisure and Recreation: A. Whitfield. District Council. Population of District: 109,000.

Hannah Research Institute (1928), Ayr, KA6 5HL. T.-0292 76013. Chairman of Council: Sir Alwyn Williams; Vice Chairman: J. Caldwell. Director: Professor M. Peaker; Principal Staff: Dr W. Banks (Dairy Foods/Milk Utilization), Dr W.W. Christie (Biological Chemistry), Dr D.G. Dalgleish (Physical Chemistry), Dr P.C. Thomas (Animal Nutrition and Production), Dr R.G. Vernon (Lactational Physiology and Biochemistry), N.A.D. McCance (Secretary). The Institute is one of 29 agricultural and food research service institutes in Great Britain, and is financed by grant from the Department of Agriculture and Fisheries for Scotland. The research areas are agreed with the Department on the scientific advice of the Agricultural and Food Research Council. There are 150 permanent staff, of whom 100 are on science grades. Two departments are concerned with animal science, and three with food science. The Institute farm is used entirely for research. Direct contact with the dairy industry is maintained through the Consultative Panels for Milk Production and Milk Utilization.

Harris Tweed Association Ltd., (1909), Ballantyne House, 84 Academy Street, Inverness, IV1 1LU. T.-0463 231270. Chairman: Calum MacLeod. Chief Executive: D.J. Mackay. Formed to monitor and protect the Orb Trade Mark of the Harris Tweed and for the marketing and promotion of Harris Tweed.

Headteachers' Association of Scotland (1936), Park Cottage, 21 Victoria Place, Airdrie. T.-02364 62780. Secretary: P.J. Quinn. To promote interest in education in Scotland and to facilitate exchange of information and ideas among headteachers and others.

Health and Social Security, Department of, Central Office for Scotland, Argyle House, 3 Lady Lawson Street, Edinburgh, EH3 9SH. T.-031-229 9191. Controller for Scotland: F.S. Clark.

Health Education Group, Scottish (1980), Woodburn House, Canaan Lane, Edinburgh. T.-031-447 8044. Director: S.C. Mitchell; Community Medical

Specialist: Dr M. Church; Nursing Adviser: Miss L. Coutts; Educational Adviser: I. Young; Media and Publicity Officer: J.W. Dennison. The Scottish Health Education Group applies a vigorous health education policy across Scotland. Its objective is to improve the lifestyle of the population in relation to health. The programme includes action on alcohol, smoking, immunisation, dental health, mental health, the elderly, etc. Aims to help each person to make the best possible choice for optimum health and well-being. The Group is part of the Scottish Health Service.

Health Service Planning Council, Scottish, St. Andrew's House, Edinburgh, EH1 3DE. T.-031-556 8501, Ext. 2196. Chairman: Dr W. Keith Davidson, C.B.E., J.P. Keeps under review the development of the Health Service in Scotland and advises the Secretary of State on the exercise of his functions under the Health Service Acts.

Health Service, Scottish, Common Services Agency (1974), Trinity Park House, South Trinity Road, Edinburgh. T.-031-552 6255. Chairman: Sir Simpson Stevenson. Secretary: J.R.Y. Mutch; Treasurer: J.W. Morrison. Provides the Scottish Home and Health Department and area Health Boards with a variety of executive and advisory services necessary to the Health Service throughout Scotland and which are better organised centrally than locally. These services include the Ambulance and Blood Transfusion Services, Health Education, and Information Services.

Heraldry Society of Scotland (1977), c/o National Museum of Antiquities of Scotland, Queen Street, Edinburgh, EH2 1JD. T.-031-557 3550. Chairman: C.J. Burnett; Secretary: W.R.M. Adams; Treasurer: Dr C.D. Green. To promote the study and encouragement of heraldry in Scotland within an international context. Publishes a yearly journal, organises public lectures, and arranges excursions to places of heraldic and historic interest.

Heriot-Watt University (1966), Chambers Street, Edinburgh, EH1 1HX. T.-031-225 8432. Riccarton Campus, Edinburgh, EH14 4AS. T.-031-449 5111. Chancellor: Lord Thomson of Monifieth, K.T., P.C.; Principal and Vice-Chancellor: Dr Tom Johnston; Vice Principal: Professor John Rorke, C.B.E.; Chairman of Court: Hon. Lord Ross; Director of Administration and Secretary of the University: Duncan I. Cameron; Registrar and Deputy Secretary: David Sturgeon; Finance Officer: Ronald T. Cutt.
Deans and Heads of Departments: Faculty of Science: Dean: Professor Robin J. Knops; Actuarial Mathematics and Statistics: Professor James R. Gray; Brewing and Biological Sciences: Professor David M. Manners; Chemistry: Professor Brian G. Gowenlock; Computer Science: Professor M. Howard Williams; Mathematics: Dr J. Christopher Eilbeck; Pharmacy: Dr Gordon C. Jefferson; Physics: Professor S. Desmond Smith. Faculty of Engineering: Dean: Dr Colin W. Davidson; Building: Professor Victor B. Torrance; Chemical and Process Engineering: Professor Cecil W. Nutt; Civil Engineering: Professor Arthur Bolton; Electrical and Electronic Engineering: Dr Colin W. Davidson; Mechanical Engineering: James L. Murray; Offshore Engineering: Dr D. Gareth Owen; Petroleum Engineering: Professor George Stewart. Faculty of Economic and Social Studies: Dean: Michael J. Mepham; Accountancy and Finance: Professor John R. Small; Business Organisation: Dr Anthony Keenan; Economics: Dr Philip J. Welham; Languages: Professor Anthony W. Stanforth. Faculty of Environmental Studies: Dean: John A. Craig; Architecture: Professor James D. Dunbar-Nasmith; Town and Country Planning: John A. Craig. Acting Librarian: Michael Wills; Director, Television Centre: Dr Kenneth D.

Stephen; Director, Computer Centre: Allen J. McTernan; Director, Institute of Offshore Engineering: Dr Clifford S. Johnston; Director, The Esmee Fairbairn Research Centre: Professor Keith G. Lumsden; Director, Computer Application Services and Director, Research Park Promotion: Ian G. Dalton; Director of Unilink: T. Kennedy Crichton. Technological university which has developed and maintains close links with Scottish industry and commerce. It has 3,100 full-time students in four faculties. The university is located partly in central Edinburgh and partly on a campus at Riccarton, on the western boundary of the city, which will eventually house most of the university's departments. At Riccarton, the Research Park includes a number of high technology research and development projects.

High Court of Justiciary, Parliament House, 2 Parliament Square, Edinburgh, EH1 1RF. T.-031-225 2595. Principal Clerk of Session and Justiciary: A.M. Campbell. Supreme criminal court in Scotland. It tries cases on indictment in Edinburgh and on circuit throughout the country.

Highland and Agricultural Society of Scotland, Royal (1784), P.O. Box 1, Ingliston, Newbridge, Edinburgh, EH28 8NF. T.-031-333 2444. Chairman, Board of Directors: F. Morrison; Chairman Designate: J.T. Wood; Hon. Secretary: J.M. Campbell, C.B.E.; Hon. Treasurer: John Forbes; Convener, Development and General Purposes Committee: J.H. Dewhurst; Convener, Public Relations and Education Committe: D. Goldie. Chief Executive: J.D.G. Davidson, M.V.O.; Secretary: J.R. Good; Accountant and Treasurer: J.M. Arthur.
Scotland's national agricultural society with a membership of more than 17,000. It is incorporated by Royal Charter with the principal object of promoting agriculture and agricultural education. The Society organises the annual Royal Highland Show.

Highland Cattle Society (1884), Blackchub, Keir, Thornhill, Dumfriesshire. T.-0848 30438. President: David L. Fellowes. Secretary: A.H.G. Wilson. Breed society.

Highland Health Board (1974), Reay House, 17 Old Edinburgh Road, Inverness, IV2 3HG. T.-0463 239851. Chairman: James McWilliam; Members: Miss J.F.M. Brims, Dr R.D. Guy, Miss M.T. Hadden, Mrs M. Hinds, W.G. Johnston, Dr W.M. Lancaster, Rt. Hon. Lord Macdonald of Sleat, J.P., Mrs M.A. MacDougall, Dr A.D. McIntosh, A.A. MacKenzie, Mrs L. MacKenzie, Mrs R.J. MacLennan, T.D. Martin, B.A. Merchant, W. Monaghan, Mrs I. Munro, Mrs R.M. Tulloch. Chief Administrative Medical Officer: Dr A.R. Morrison; Chief Area Nursing Officer: Miss E.M. Hood; Chief Administrative Dental Officer: J.I. Tullis; Chief Administrative Pharmaceutical Officer: M.M. Smith; Secretary: R.R.W. Stewart; Treasurer: J.C. Gray. Provision of health service.

Highland Regional Council (1974), Regional Buildings, Glenurquhart Road, Inverness, IV3 5NX. T.-0463 234121. Convener: I.S. Campbell; Vice Convener: J.C. Robertson; Members: William S. Smith, Anderson Murray, James W. Oag, Bill Mowat, Robert Gunn, John M. Young, Roy E. Godfrey, Allan M. Gilmour, David I. MacRae, Francis R.M. Keith, Ronald R. McDonald, Adam Macdonald, W.A. Fraser, George W.C. Ginn, T. David Martin, George M. Burness, Hamish Fraser, Duncan J. McPherson, Valerie MacIver, Roland Mardon, Isobel C. Rhind, Henry Miller, Duncan Grant, Rev. John M.M. Macarthur, John R. Campbell, Malcolm J. MacKay, James Henderson, Thomas Kirkwood, Thomas Peddie, Donald A. Corbett, James Cameron, Alistair Milne, William R. McPhee, Hamish H.M. Sutherland,

Allan G. Sellar, Peter Drummond, Thomas MacKenzie, Peter J. Peacock, Gary H. Johnston, Lachlan R.D. Mackintosh of Mackintosh, Patrick C. Paterson, Katrina H. Coutts, James S. Munro, Anthony Whitefoord, Alexander Lindsay, Alexander J. Russell, Robert H. Farrow, Nigel J.O. Graham, John H. Cattanach. Chief Executive: R.H. Stevenson; Director of Law and Administration and Depute Chief Executive: H. Farquhar; Director of Architectural Services: A.M. Fulton; Director of Consumer Protection: G.E. Turnbull; Director of Development: P. Mackintosh; Director of Education: C.E. Stewart; Director of Finance: J.W. Bremner; Director of Libraries and Leisure Services: H.W. Wilkinson; Director of Manpower Services: N.W.D. McIntosh; Director of Planning: R.W.G. Cameron; Director of Roads and Transport: G.K.M. Macfarlane; Director of Social Work: J.G. Bailey; Director of Water and Sewerage: J.D. Addly; Assessor and Electoral Registration Officer: A.W. Currie; Reporter to the Children's Panel: Miss B. Humphries; Chief Constable: D.B. Henderson; Firemaster: W. Shand.

Regional Council which covers an area of 2,500,000 hectares, the Districts of Badenoch and Strathspey, Caithness, Inverness, Lochaber, Nairn, Ross and Cromarty, Skye and Lochalsh, and Sutherland, and a population of 196,000. The Council employs 9,400 people (including police and fire) and has a revenue budget of £117m.

Highland River Purification Board (1975), Strathpeffer Road, Dingwall, IV15 9QY. T.-Dingwall 62021. Chairman: N.W. Graesser. Director and River Inspector: D. Buchanan; Clerk to the Board: D.W. Martin; Treasurer: A.G. Imlah. To control pollution of rivers and tidal waters and conserve water resources within the area.

Highlands and Islands Development Board (1965), Bridge House, Bank Street, Inverness, IV1 1QR. T.-0463 234171. Chairman: Robert Cowan; Deputy Chairman: R.D. Cramond; Full-time members: G.G. Drummond, R.A. Fasken; Part-time members: A.S. Macdonald, W.E. Bryan, C.A. Macleod. Secretary: J.A. Macaskill; Assistant Secretary: S. Edmond.

The H.I.D.B. was established by Act of Parliament to promote the economic and social development of the Highlands and Islands, and to enable the area to play a more effective part in the economic and social development of the nation. The area in which the Board operates comprises 47% of the land area of Scotland; the current population is 352,000. The Board, which is funded by the Treasury, has a budget of £35.6m., of which £16m. is spent on loans, grants, and equity, for a variety of development projects. In addition, the Board invests £12.6m. in factories and other buildings and special projects at its own hand. As well as assisting the development of small to medium scale manufacturing industry, the Board helps the farming and fishing industries, aids tourism, and advises the Secretary of State for Scotland on ways of improving the life of the area.

Hill Farming Advisory Committee for Scotland (1947), c/o Department of Agriculture and Fisheries for Scotland, Chesser House, 500 Gorgie Road, Edinburgh, EH11 3AW. T.-031-443 4020, Ext. 2531. Chairman: D.G. Mackay. Secretary: J.M. Stephen. To advise the Secretary of State for Scotland on the exercise of his powers under the Hill Farming Act 1946 and on any other matter relating to hill farming that may be referred to the Committee.

Hill Farming Research Organisation (1954), Bush Estate, Penicuik, Midlothian, EH26 0PY. T.-031-445 3401. Board of Management: J.A. Parry (Chairman), C.H. Armstrong, Professor D.G. Armstrong, R.E. Edwards,

Professor C.H. Gimingham, D.T.M. Lloyd, Professor G.A. Lodge, A.S. Macdonald, T.H. McLelland, J. Manuel, J.M. Sharp, G. Wilson, R.W. Weir. Director: J. Eadie; Secretary: W.W. Mather; Deputy Director and Head of Plants and Soils Dept.: Dr P. Newbould; Head of Animal Production Dept.: Dr T.J. Maxwell; Head of Grazing Ecology Dept.: Dr J. Hodgson; Head of Animal Nutrition Dept.: Dr J. Milne. Independent state-aided institute funded by the Department of Agriculture and Fisheries for Scotland. Its present remit is to improve the economic viability of meat production from the hills and uplands of the U.K.

Historic Buildings Council for Scotland (1953), 25 Drumsheugh Gardens, Edinburgh, EH3 7RN. T.-031-226 3611. Chairman: The Marquess of Bute; Members: C. McWilliam, K. Newis, C.B., C.V.O., The Hon. Lord Jauncey, Professor J. Dunbar-Nasmith, C.B.E., Dr M. Lindsay, C.B.E., T.D., H.F. Smith, M.B.E., J.P., I. Begg, Councillor Ian Hutchison, O.B.E., J.P., Marc Ellington, Mrs K. Dalyell, Dr R.G. Cant. Secretary: D.J. Christie; Assistant Secretary: Miss P.H.B. Smith.

The Council was set up to advise the Secretary of State for Scotland on grants and policy to preserve and use buildings of outstanding historic or architectural interest. Since 1972, the Council has also advised on grants and policy for conservation areas. Executive responsibility for grants, listing, and other statutory functions of the Secretary of State rests with the Scottish Development Department (Historic Buildings Branch), whose officials service the Council. The Council deals with recommendations on grants for repairs to individual buildings and churches in ecclesiastical use and schemes to preserve or enhance conservation areas. Over the years, many types of buildings and kinds of owners have been awarded grants, and owners ranging from the National Trust for Scotland to private individuals have been supported. Grant is selective and decided on the merits of individual buildings, the schemes of work proposed, and the financial resources of applicants, and subject to annual allocation of funds.

History of Medicine, Scottish Society of the (1948), c/o Anaesthetic Dept., Western General Hospital, Edinburgh. T.-031-332 2525. President: Dr A.M.B. Masson; Hon. Secretaries: Dr D.J. Wright, Dr D. Dow. Regular meetings around Scotland on the subject of the history of medicine, dentistry, and allied subjects.

History Society, Scottish (1886). Hon. Secretary: Dr David Stevenson, Dept. of History, University of Aberdeen, Old Aberdeen, AB9 2UB. Founded to publish historical source material illustrating the history of Scotland. More than 150 volumes have been issued.

Hockey Association, Scottish (1901), 18 Ainslie Place, Edinburgh, EH3 6AU. T.-031-226 4401. Chairman: Dr A.B. Tramschek. Director of Administration: J.M. Walker, J.P. Administration of men's hockey in Scotland. Selection of international teams and organisation of domestic competitions.

Home and Health Department, Scottish, St. Andrew's House, Edinburgh. T.-031-556 8501. Secretary: W.K. Reid, C.B. Private Secretary: John Gilmour.

Department of the Secretary of State for Scotland. Its responsibilities include the police service, the fire service, civil defence, and, where necessary, the co-ordination of action by the Scottish departments on civil emergencies. It has responsibilities for electoral procedures, including registration of electors, and also for a wide range of ceremonial and formal matters. The

Department is responsible for the legal aid system in Scotland, and for all questions of Scots civil law which are not the specific responsibility of another department, including matrimonial and family law, charity law, land and tenure, and general questions relating to the Departments of the Registers of Scotland and the Scottish Record Office. The Department deals with criminal justice policy and procedure in Scoland, including advice on the exercise of the Royal Prerogative, criminological research, and criminal injuries compensation. It is also responsible for the Scottish licensing law, betting and gaming legislation, and related matters. The management of the Scottish prison service is another of its functions. Within the department, the Scottish Office Superannuation Division deals with policy issues relating to the pensions of teachers, health service employees, police, fire service, and local government staff; it directly manages the teachers' and N.H.S. schemes. The Department's functions cover all aspects of health care for the people of Scotland, including food standards and food hygiene. In particular, it is responsible for the administration of the N.H.S. in Scotland, G.P. services – doctors, dentists, chemists, and opticians – and the provision of community health services. Management and local planning responsibility rests with the health boards, financed by the Exchequer through the Department and working under its general oversight. Certain services, such as supplies, ambulance, and blood transfusion, are administered on a national basis by a Common Services Agency. Broad policy advice is provided by the Scottish Health Service Planning Council and advice on research and development relevant to the health service by the Chief Scientist Organisation.

Homing Union, Scottish, Bank of Scotland Buildings, Hopetoun Street, Bathgate, West Lothian. T.-Bathgate 52943. President: G. Thomson. Secretary: Mrs J. Gauld. Organisation of sport of homing pigeons.

Homosexual Rights Group, Scottish (1969), 58A Broughton Street, Edinburgh, EH1 3SA. T.-031-556 4049. Convener: John Ramage; Depute Convener: Alison Dilly; Secretary: Tom Shearer; Treasurer: Jim Halcrow. One in 10 or 11 of the population is homosexual. S.H.R.G. exists to give a non-party political voice to Scotland's largest minority. It owns a lesbian and gay community centre, and coffee and snacks shop, in Edinburgh.

Horse Society, British, Scottish Committee. Development Officer: W.A. Bowes, Slates Farm, Kilmacolm, Renfrewshire. T.-050 587 2682.

Hospital Advisory Service, Scottish (1970), 21 Hill Street, Edinburgh, EH2 3JP. T.-031-225 3108. Director: Dr C. Cohen; Administrative Secretary: D. Duff. Established by the Secretary of State for Scotland to provide information and advice on hospitals and units for the mentally ill, mentally handicapped, geriatric medicine, and young physically disabled.

Hospital Endowments Research Trust, Scottish (1954), 16 Hope Street, Charlotte Square, Edinburgh, EH2 4DD. T.-031-226 2561. Chairman: Sir Andrew Watt Kay; Members: Gavin Boyd, C.B.E., Mrs J.B.M. Ellis, O.B.E., Robert W. Pringle, O.B.E., Sir James Goold, Professor M.J. Baker, Sir Ivor R.C. Batchelor, C.B.E. Secretariat: W. & J. Burness, W.S. The Trust has been supporting medical research in Scotland for 30 years, acting on a broad policy of promoting health through research into the causation, treatment, and prevention of common and disabling conditions. In the future, the Trust aims primarily to support the research of promising young doctors and scientists, and to provide them with the opportunity to gain a sound research training.

Hotel School, Scottish (1945), Curran Building, 94 Cathedral Street, Glasgow. T.-041-552 4400. Head: Professor David J. Jeffries, O.B.E. The School is a department of the University of Strathclyde and offers degree and diploma courses in hotel management.

House-Builders Association, Scottish (1965), 13 Woodside Crescent, Glasgow, G3 7UP. T.-041-332 7144. Secretary: W.I. Barclay. Private housebuilding section of the Scottish Building Employers' Federation.

House of Fraser PLC, 69 Buchanan Street, Glasgow, G1 3LE. T.-041-221 6401. Chairman: Professor R. Smith; Managing Director: W. Crossan. Department store group. Turnover (1984): £955m.

Housing Associations, Scottish Federation of, 42 York Place, Edinburgh, EH1 3HU. T.-031-556 1435/6. Director: Donald R. MacLennan; Research and Development Officer: Peter Lee. Representative body for housing associations in Scotland. It organises training courses and seminars for the members and provides model rules for registration of new societies.

Housing Corporation, The (1964), Scottish Office, Rosebery House, 9 Haymarket Terrace, Edinburgh, EH12 5YA. T.-031-337 0044. Chief Officer: Raymond K. Young; Operations Director: John V. Gardner; Regional Manager, Edinburgh: Alan M. Brown; Regional Manager, Glasgow: James M. Hastie. Government agency promoting, financing, and supervising registered housing associations. These associations are non-profit-making friendly societies, run by voluntary committees and providing acommodation for people in housing need.

Howden Group PLC (1854), 195 Scotland Street, Glasgow, G5 8PJ. T.-041-429 4747. Chairman: R.C. Meech (Canada); Managing Director: J.D.H. Hume, C.B.E. The Group specialises in the design, manufacture, and installation of air, gas, and fluid handling equipment. Its products include air preheaters, fans, gas circulators, blowers, heat exchangers, compressors, pumps, dust collectors, and fabric filters. Turnover, 1984: £159m.

I

Ice Figure Skating Association, Scottish. Hon. Secretary: Mrs L. Paterson, c/o Murrayfield Ice Rink, Riversdale Crescent, Edinburgh, EH12 5XN.

Ice Hockey Association, Scottish. Secretary: William Jamieson, 4 Millerfield Place, Edinburgh, EH9 1LW. T.-031-667 8699.

Independent Broadcasting Authority (1954), Fleming House, Renfrew Street, Glasgow, G3 6SU. T.-041-332 8241. Member for Scotland: Rev. Dr W.J. Morris, J.P. Officer for Scotland: G.B. Marjoribanks; Senior Assistant Officer for Scotland: W.A. Jamieson; Assistant Officer for Scotland: V.M. McDowall. The I.B.A. is the central body responsible for the provision of Independent Local Radio, Independent Television, Breakfast-Time Television, and Channel Four services in the U.K.

Industrial Heritage Society, Scottish (1984), c/o Royal Scottish Museum, Chambers Street, Edinburgh, EH1 1JF. T.-031-225 7534. Chairman: J.L. Wood; Vice Chairman: J.R. Hume; Hon. Secretary: Mrs C.L. Thompson. The Society was formed by the amalgamation of the Scottish Society for Industrial Archaeology with the Scottish Society for the Preservation of Historical Machinery. Its aims are to promote the study of, and interest in, the history of industry in Scotland, and to secure the recording and preservation of sites, buildings, machinery, artefacts, and records illustrating that history.

Industrial Pollution Inspectorate for Scotland, H.M., Pentland House, 47 Robbs Loan, Edinburgh, EH14 1TY. T.-031-443 8681. Chief Inspector: R.R.A. Pride. Pollution control services.

Industrial Tribunals (Scotland), Central Office of (1964), St. Andrew House, 141 West Nile Street, Glasgow. T.-041-331 1601. President: R.C. Hay; Secretary: A.J. Campbell. Independent judicial organisation with jurisdiction over various employment matters assigned by statute.

Industry Department for Scotland, New St. Andrew's House, Edinburgh, EH1 3TD. Secretary: Dr R.G.L. McCrone, C.B. Private Secretary: Joan Spence. Department of the Secretary of State for Scotland. Advises the Secretary of State on industrial and economic development in Scotland, including matters relating to the development of North Sea oil resources. It discharges his responsibility for selective financial assistance to industry, for the steering of industrial development within Scotland, and for the activities within Scotland of the Manpower Services Commission. The Department is also responsible for policy in relation to the Scottish Development Agency, Highlands and Islands development, electricity, tourism, new towns, and rural development.

Information Office, Scottish, New St. Andrew's House, Edinburgh, EH1 3TD. T.-031-557 0557. Director: C.F. Corbett. Information and publicity about the work of the Scottish Office departments.

Inland Revenue, Board of, Scottish Office, 80 Lauriston Place, Edinburgh, EH3 9SL. T.-031-229 9344. Controller: W.S. Linkie.

Inland Waterways Association, Scottish (1972), 11 Arden Street, Edinburgh, EH9 1BR. T.-031-229 7149. Chairman: D.D. Mackinnon; Secretary: Nancy M. Philp. Promotion of the use of the Scottish waterways for commercial and leisure purposes, and representation of the interests of canal users.

Inquiry Reporters, 16 Waterloo Place, Edinburgh, EH1 3DN. T.-031-556 9191. Chief Reporter: A.G. Bell. Conduct of public local inquiries under the Planning Acts and some other statutes.

In-Service Training of Teachers, National Committee for the (1976), 43 Jeffrey Street, Edinburgh. T.-031-556 9233. Chairman: Dr M. Green; Members: Councillor Mrs J.H. Mackie, F. Pignatelli, I.S. Flett, Dr W.A. Gatherer, J. Anderson, R. Robertson, J. Watson, Dr R.T.D. Glaister, Professor J.D. Nisbet, Professor D.W.G. Timms, G. Donald, Rose A. Galt, Miss J.C. Carroll, Sister D. Sweeney, P. Andrews, A. Armour, H.L. Philip; Ex-Officio Members: Dr W.A. Illsley, W. Shearer, J.K. Gardiner, H. Perfect, R. Stark, J. Brown, W.B. Marker, I.M. Watt, R.J. Staward, A. Davidson. Constituted by the Secretary of State for Scotland as an advisory body on all aspects of in-service training.

International Gathering Trust, Scottish (1975), 25 Dublin Street, Edinburgh. T.-031-557 4059. President: Brigadier John C. Balharrie, M.B.E., M.C.; Vice President: Alastair M. Dunnett; Chairman: Lt. Col. H.C. Paterson, T.D.; Vice Chairmen: James S. Adam, Dr Micheil MacDonald, Hugh MacPherson. Executive Director: R.A.B. McLaren. Encouragement of international friendship by strengthening and extending the strong ethnic links among Scots world wide. International Gatherings of the Clans and Scots are organised on a four-yearly cycle.

Inverclyde District Council (1974), Municipal Buildings, Greenock, PA15 1LX. T.-0475 24400. Provost: Sir Simpson Stevenson; Members: Dr Thomas Fyfe, Allan Robertson, Daniel Morrison, John H. Moody, Robert M. Hill, James McEwan (Gibshill), Francis A. McGlone, Catherine Allan, James M. Carter, James McEwan (Broomhill), James Boyd, M.B.E., Henry Mulholland, Joseph Sullivan, Rebecca McFadyen, David M. Roach, James Mitchell, J. Foss Finnie, Thomas Scott, Joseph Hendry. Chief Executive: I.C. Wilson, J.P.; Director of Administration: J.R. Thompson; Director of Finance: R.N. McPherson, J.P.; Director of Housing: A. Craig; Director of Planning and Technical Services: J.S. Mackie; Director of Recreational Services: J.A. Douglas; Director of Environmental Health: P. Tait; Industrial Development Officer: J.D. Walker; Chief Librarian and Cultural Services Officer: Miss I.J. Monteith. District Council. Population of District: 100,000.

Inverclyde Enterprise Trust (1984), 26 Clyde Square, Greenock, PA15 1NB. T.-0475 86240. Chairman: J.G. Quigley; Trust Director: P. Hingston. Enterprise agency.

Inverness and Highland Chamber of Commerce (1893), 13A Island Bank Road, Inverness. T.-0463 233570. President: G.H. Johnston. Secretary/Treasurer: Douglas W. Brookes, T.D.

Inverness District Council (1974), Town House, Inverness, IV1 1JJ. T.-0463 239111. Provost: J.A. Sellar; Members: Donald A. Corbett, Alexander D.

MacLean, Alexander Chisholm, James Cameron, William J. Smith, Alistair Milne, Hamish M. Bauchop, William R. McPhee, Mario Bernardi, M.B.E., David R. Munro, Allan G. Sellar, Thomas MacKenzie, O.B.E., William A.E. Fraser, Duncan F. Chisholm, William McAllister, Sheila S. MacKay, William Sinclair, James Cattell, Janet N. Home, Donald W.N. MacAskill, Ann Glynne-Percy, Murdo Campbell, Jervis M. Johnson, Rt. Hon. Lord Burton, Alex. Graham, William D. Aitken, Rev. Peter Fraser. Cheif Executive: B. Wilson; Director of Administration: T. McClenaghan; Director of Architectural and Technical Services: R.W. Fraser; Director of Housing: D.I. MacKenzie; Director of Finance: A.G. Imlah; Director of Environmental Health: G. Mellan; Director of Cleansing: W. Fraser. District Council. Population of District: 57,000.

Inverness, Loch Ness and Nairn Tourist Board (1971), 23 Church Street, Inverness IV1 1EZ. T.-0463 234353. Area Tourist Officer: Mrs J. Slesser. Promotion of tourism.

Inverness Technical College (1960), 3 Longman Road, Longman South, Inverness, IV1 1SA. T.-0463 236681. Principal: W.J. Hedley; Depute Principal: J.J. Jeffrey. Largest further education college in the Highlands. Caters from craft level studies to higher diploma work in six departments. Higher diplomas in business studies, accounting, secretarial studies, electrical and electronic engineering, and mechanical and production engineering.

Iona Community (1938), Pearce Institute, Govan, Glasgow, G51 3UT. T.-041-445 4561. Convener, Council of Community: Rev. Stanley Hood. Leader: Rev. Ron Ferguson; Wardens, Iona Abbey: Rev. Ian and Rev. Kathy Galloway; Youth Co-ordinators: Rev. John Bell, Graham Maule; Justice and Peace Worker: Helen Steven; Urban Worker: Rev. Walter Fyfe. Ecumenical community (Protestant and Roman Catholic) seeking new and radical ways of living the Gospel in today's world. The community, which rebuilt Iona Abbey, runs residential programmes on Iona and Mull, as well as mainland work concerned with unemployment, justice and peace, youth, and church renewal.

Irvine Development Corporation (1966), Perceton House, Irvine, KA11 2AL. T.-0294 214100. Chairman: Sir Charles O'Halloran; Vice Chairman: Douglas C. Muirhead; Members: A.C. Lambie, Theresa Beattie, W.C. McDowall, Mrs Rae Grant, T. Dickie, Jeanette Mason, M. Goodwin. Managing Director: Brigadier Tony Rickets; Director of Technical Services: I. Downs; Commercial Director: M. Thomson; Director of Finance and Administration: J. Murdoch; Chief Quantity Surveyor: P. Thompson; Legal Adviser: A. Boyd; Head of Engineering Services: E. Prince; Housing Manager: J. Smith; Public Relations Manager: J. Rigby. Aims to increase the population of Irvine from original 34,000 to a target of 95,000. Population now stands at 58,000. Irvine is Scotland's youngest new town and the only new town by the sea.

J

James Watt College (1973), Finnart Street, Greenock, PA16 8HF. T.-0475 24433. Chairman, College Council: A. Paxton. Principal: R. McAdam; Depute Principal: D. Morrison. College of further education. Six departments integrated into regional consortium with local schools under 16-18 Action Plan. Community organisation as well as a technical/vocational institution; caters for evening and open learning courses as well as day classes.

Jewish Representative Council, Glasgow (1914), 49 Coplaw Street, Glasgow, G42. T.-041-423 8917. President: Kenneth Davidson; Vice President: Dr Walter Sneader; Treasurer: Judith Tankel; Secretary: Dr Kenneth Collins. Representative body of Jewish communal organisations in Glasgow area.

Jordanhill College of Education (1959), Southbrae Drive, Glasgow, G13 1PP. T.-041-959 1232. Chairman, Board of Governors: James L. Brown. Principal: Thomas R. Bone; Vice Principal: James McCall; Secretary: W. Graham Charters; Assistant Principals: Marion Baillie, Robert W. McArthur, William B. Marker, Alasdair G. Nicolson, Stuart M. Niven (Director of School of Further Education), G. Bernard Wright (Director of Scottish School of Physical Education). College for the pre-service and in-service training of teachers (primary, secondary, and further education), social workers, youth and community workers, and speech therapists. Full-time students (pre-service), 1983-84: 1,882.

Judo Federation, Scottish, 8 Frederick Street, Edinburgh, EH2 2HB. T.-031-226 3566. Hon. Secretary: O.J. Clarke; Administrator: Mrs L. Fraser; National Coach: David Starbrook, M.B.E.

Junior Gas Association, Scottish (1904), c/o Scottish Gas, Granton House, 4 Marine Drive, Edinburgh. President, Council: A. Shaw; Vice President: I.F. Hardie; Hon. Treasurer: T. Chambers; Hon. Secretary: A. A. Meenaghan. Professional body for members in the gas industry.

Justices of the Peace, Central Advisory Committee on, St. Andrew's House, Edinburgh, EH1 3DE. T.-031-556 8501. Chairman: Rt. Hon. Lord Wheatley; Members: Colonel B.M. Knox, Major David Butter, Councillor J. Carson, Councillor J. Chatham, Councillor A.M. Craig, Provost J. Swinburne, James B. Highgate, A.B. McLuckie, Terry Grieve, Councillor Gordon Murray, Joyce Shein, James Milne, Dan C. Russell, Edwin G. Smith, Sir William Gray, R.N. O'Sullivan. Secretary: A.F. Reid. To advise the Secretary of State as to problems arising in relation to the appointment and distribution of justices of the peace and work of the justices of the peace in general and of the District Court in particular.

K

Keep Scotland Tidy Campaign, Old County Chambers, Cathedral Square, Dunblane, FK15 OAQ. T.-0786 823202. Director: Douglas S. Wright; General Manager: R.N. Harper; Administration Manager: W.J.C. Rowan; Education Manager: W.S. Hall; Community Manager: C.R. Stewart. National agency for litter prevention. Local projects in most parts of Scotland.

Kennel Club, Scottish (1881), 6B Forres Street, Edinburgh. T.-031-226 6808. Secretary General: I.A. Sim. To promote and encourage the improvement and well-being of dogs; to carry out duties in Scotland on behalf of the Kennel Club.

Kilmarnock and Loudoun Chamber of Commerce. Hon. Secretary: K. Walters, 42 Bank Street, Kilmarnock. T.-Kilmarnock 25104.

Kilmarnock and Loudoun District Council (1974), Civic Centre, John Dickie Street, Kilmarnock, KA1 1BY. T.-0563 21140. Provost: T. Ferguson; Members: R. Brown, I. McAlpine, A. Parker, A. Steele, J. McCrae, J. Buchanan, Mary Porter, J. O'Neil, J. Blaney, R. Stirling, J. Thomson, J. O'Neill, A. Nisbet, J. Mills, G. Turnbull, J. Anderson, J. Campbell. Chief Executive: R.W. Jenner; Depute Chief Executive: A.C. McFadzean; Finance Manager: I.R. Smith; District Chief Environmental Health Officer: J. Riach; District Planner: J.E. Baird; District Engineer: D.T. Maclean; District Architect: A. Innes. District Council. Population of District: 82,000.

Kilmarnock College (1966), Holehouse Road, Kilmarnock, KA3 7AT. T.-Kilmarnock 23501. Principal: P.A. Martin; Depute Principal: J. Cleland; Assistant Principal: M. Aird. Further education college.

Kilmarnock Venture, The (1983), 30 The Foregate, Kilmarnock, KA1 1JH. T.-0563 44602. Chairman: David Adam. Director: Alistair Ferguson. Enterprise trust.

Kincardine and Deeside District Council (1974), Viewmount, Stonehaven. T.-0569 62001. Chairman: D. Mackenzie; Members: A. Grant, Dr G. Walkden, C. Neish, W. Eddie, J.H. McLean, Dr E. Needham, I. Frain, Dr A. Watson, J. Hay, J. Emslie, F. Stothard. Chief Executive and Director of Administration and Finance: T. Hyder; Director of Planning and Development: N.G. Marr; Director of Environmental Health: L. Borthwick; Director of Housing and Property: John D.V. Nicoll; Director of Legal Services: Keith G. Jones. District Council. Population of District: 43,000.

Kincardine and Deeside Tourist Board (1983), 45 Station Road, Banchory, AB3 3XX. T.-03302 2066. Principal Officer of Leisure, Recreation and Tourism, Kincardine and Deeside District Council: J.W. Robertson; Area Tourist Officer: Mrs L. MacInnes. Promotion of tourism.

Kingsway Technical College (1964), Old Glamis Road, Dundee. T.-Dundee 819021. Acting Principal: W. Burnett; Acting Depute Principal: I.A. Madill; Acting Assistant Principal: S.J. Ellacott. Local authority college of further education serving mainly the needs of the city. It comprises eight major departments, catering for a full-time student population of 500 and a part-time complement of 4,500. The College covers the full-range of non-advanced further education with a number of higher level courses, including some at H.N.D. level.

Kirkcaldy College of Technology (1929), St. Brycedale Avenue, Kirkcaldy, KY1 1EX. T.-Kirkcaldy 268591. Principal: D.A. Huckle; Depute Principal: D. Law; Registrar: V. Jeffery. 60% of the College's work is at higher certificate, higher diploma, and post higher diploma level, in engineering, building, management, communications, and science. There are 2,000 students.

Kirkcaldy District Chamber of Commerce (1825), 288 High Street, Kirkcaldy, KY1 1LB. T.-0592 262463. President: R.E. Baker. Secretary: J.W. Brodie, J.P. Promotion and protection of the trade, commerce, and industry of the District.

Kirkcaldy District Council (1974), Town House, Kirkcaldy, KY1 1XW. T.-Kirkcaldy 261144. Convener: Robert King; Members: W.L. Aitken, F. Ballantyne, J.A. Bell, J.W. Brodie, A. Buchanan, Karen Carrick, Catherine Clark, A.H. Dingwall, D. Doig, D. Duffy, J. Ferguson, J. Fitzpatrick, C. Gardner, T. Gray, Maggie W. Henderson, J.J. Herd, J. Jenkins, J. Johnstone, D.C. Leslie, J.G. Lewis, J. Mackie, D. Mason, R. Mays, T. Morrison, G.J. McLaren, R. Nicholson, A.H. Potter, W. Poulton, A. Philp, W.J. Rodger, S. Ronan, T. Smith, R.J. Taylor, D. Watson, Ann M. Watters, Marion Watterston, Hazel M. Weierter, A. Wishart, D. Woolrich. Director of Administration: J. Martin Smith; Director of Finance: Hugh Wilson; Director of Planning: Douglas M. Nelson; Director of Housing: Kenneth G. Fenwick; Director of Architectural and Technical Services: J.I. Brodley; Director of Leisure and Recreation: Alexander Sneddon; Director of Works and Transport: Donald W. Swinney. District Council. Population of District: 149,000.

Knitwear Association, Scottish (1970), 44 Ottoline Drive, Troon, Ayrshire. T.-0292 312478. Chairman: E.T. King. Secretary: B.W.S. Boucher-Myers, D.S.O. To promote, safeguard, uphold, and foster the interests of its members, knitwear manufacturers in Scotland.

Kyle and Carrick District Council (1974), Burns House, Burns Statue Square, Ayr. T.-0292 81511. Provost: G. Macdonald; Members: J. Miller, C. Howie, Alicia Grant, J. Collins, J. Douglas, S. Stevenson, Agnes Davies, J. Keagins, J. Gaw, K. Macdonald, J. Boyle, A. Clarence, Ellen Wyvill, F. Horton, D. McNeill, L. Little, C. Westcott, I. Welsh, Elizabeth Mitchell, T. Macleod, J.A.B. Smyth, J. Taylor, A. Paton, J. Hendry. Chief Executive Officer: I.R.D. Smillie; Director of Finance: J.F. Beaton; Director of Architectural Planning and Technical Services: W. Gilmour; Director of Housing: J.M. Small; Director of Parks and Recreation: D.T. Roy; Director of Environmental Services: J. McVie; Director of Libraries and Museums: P. Hemphill. District Council. Population of District: 112,000.

L

Labour Party, Scottish Council (1907), Keir Hardie House, 1 Lynedoch Place, Glasgow, G3 6AB. T.-041-332 8946. Chairman: Douglas Henderson; Vice Chairman: John Walker; Treasurer: Norman F. Buchan, M.P. Scottish Secretary: Helen Liddell; Scottish Organiser: James Allison. Political party.

Lacrosse Association, Scottish. Secretary: Valerie Veitch, 6 Craigmount Bank, Barnton, Edinburgh, EH4 8HH. T.-031-339 5287.

Ladies Golfing Association, Scottish (1904), 1 Trinity Place, St. Andrews, Fife. T.-0334 76849. Secretary: Mrs F.G. Hood. To further the interests of women's amateur golf in Scotland.

Lanarkshire Health Board (1974), 14 Beckford Street, Hamilton, ML3 0TA. T.-0698 281313. Chairman: Mrs B.M. Gunn, O.B.E., J.P.; Vice Chairman, R.J. Logan, J.P.; Members: Mrs A.P.C.C. Allison, J.P., Dr G.A. Bell, J.P., W. Bertam, M.B.E., F. Campbell J.P., J.A. Campbell, B.E.M., J.P., Dr D. Datta, Mrs A.S. Hinshalwood, Mrs J.H. Holmes, J.P., Dr A.M. Mathewson, D. McClymont, Mrs D.C. McGirr, A.E. McIlwain, A.R. Miller, C.B.E., W.J. O'Brien, J.P., J.P. Robison, J.P., T.S.L. Reid, S.J. Scott, J.P., W. Traynor. Secretary: F. Clark; Treasurer: M. Docherty; Chief Administrative Medical Officer: Dr W.O. Thomson; Chief Area Nursing Officer: Miss E. Hastings. Provision of health service.

Lanarkshire Industrial Field Executive (1983), Old Town Hall, 1/11 High Road, Motherwell, ML1 3HU. T.-Motherwell 66622. Chief Executive: Peter F. Agnew; Business Development Executives: David Hawkes, Terry Currie, Ian Long, Gerry Brough; Company Secretary: Donald Lammie; Marketing Executive: Robert Creighton. Business development agency committed to assist in the creation of new jobs in Lanarkshire by encouraging business start-ups, developing existing companies, and attracting investment into the area from the UK and overseas.

Land Court, Scottish (1911), 1 Grosvenor Crescent, Edinburgh, EH12 5ER. T.-031-225 3595. Chairman: The Hon. Lord Elliott; Members: A. Gillespie. D.D. McDiarmid; A.B. Campbell. Principal Clerk: K.H.R. Graham; Senior Legal Assessors: J.G. Riddoch, J.F. Rankin. The Court considers applications by landlords and/or tenants of any agricultural subjects in Scotland whether these be farms, crofts, or smallholdings, where there is a dispute.

Landowners' Federation, Scottish (1906), 18 Abercromby Place, Edinburgh, EH3 6TY. T.-031-556 4466. President: R.C. Stewart, C.B.E., T.D.; Vice Presidents: The Viscount of Arbuthnott, D.S.C., J.P., Major The Hon. Colin Dalrymple, Col. A.B. Houstoun, O.B.E., M.C., J.P., Lt. Col. J.W. Nicol, D.S.O. Convener: A.R. Trotter; Vice Convener: P.C. Macdonald.

Director: D.J. Hughes Hallett; Legal Adviser: G.W.S. Barry; Journal Editor and Advertising Manager: Mrs D. Graham. To represent the interests of all persons connected with rural land in Scotland; to defend their interests with all relevant authorities; and to further the most efficient system of management of land under private enterprise.

Lands Tribunal for Scotland (1970), 1 Grosvenor Crescent, Edinburgh, EH12 5ER. T.-031-225 7996/7. President: The Hon. Lord Elliott, M.C.; Members: W.D.C. Andrews, C.B.E., William Hall, D.F.C., T. Finlayson, J.P. Clerk to the Tribunal: David McCallum.
Independent judicial body constituted under the Lands Tribunal Act 1949, for the purpose of determining a wide range of questions relating to the valuation of land, compensation for the compulsory acquisition of land, allocation of feu duties, and the discharge or variation of restrictive land obligations. The Act also empowers the Tribunal to accept the function of arbitration under reference by consent. Since 1970, the jurisdiction has been extended by numerous Acts of Parliament. The extended powers include the determination of disputes as to the valuation of land for appeals under the Taxes Acts, appeals against decisions of the Keeper of the Land Register, and disputes over Tenancy-at-will, also disputes arising over the implementation of the Tenants' Rights Etc. (Scotland) Act 1980 concerning council house purchase.

Langside College (1947), 50 Prospecthill Road, Glasgow, G42 9LB. T.-041-649 4991. Chairman, College Council: John H. Jardine. Principal: B.G.F. Guidi; Depute Principal: J. Reilly; Registrar: R. Cruikshank. College of further education with an annual student population of 5,400, of whom 1,400 are full-time. Serves as a local centre for industrial, commercial, general, and continuing education, as well as a community college providing a wide range of vocational and leisure activities by both day and evening. The College is organised in seven departments: building, commerce, engineering, English and general studies, horticulture, modern languages, and tutorial studies.

Lauder Technical College (1899), North Fod, Halbeath, Dunfermline, KY11 5DY. T.-0383 726201. Chairman, College Council: Councillor Mrs J.H. Mackie, J.P. Principal: John Lisgo. Provision of further education to meet the industrial, commercial, and social needs of West Fife. The College is organised into departments of building construction, catering and caring studies, business and general studies, engineering and mining, special programmes, and industrial studies.

Law Commission, Scottish (1965), 140 Causewayside, Edinburgh, EH9 1PR. T.-031-668 2131. Chairman: The Hon. Lord Maxwell; Commissioners (full-time): Dr E.M. Clive, Sheriff C.G.B. Nicholson, Q.C.; Commissioners (part-time): R.D. Bertram, J. Murray, Q.C. Parliamentary Draftsman (full-time): J.F. Wallace; Parliamentary Draftsmen (part-time): G.S. Douglas, Q.C., W.C. Galbraith, Q.C.
To keep under review the law of Scotland, with a view to its systematic development and reform, including in particular its codification, the elimination of anomalies, the repeal of obsolete and unnecessary enactments, the reduction of the number of separate enactments, and generally the simplification and modernisation of the law. The Commission receives and considers proposals for law reform, and provides information and advice to Government departments and other authorities concerned with proposals for law reform. It prepares programmes for the consolidation of enactments, and proposes future programmes, and advises on the putting into effect of

reforms proposed. It is also concerned with the study of foreign legal systems which may be helpful in carrying out its functions. Liaison is maintained with the Law Commission in London, and with relevant professional and academic bodies.

Lawn Tennis Association, Scottish, 12 Melville Crescent, Edinburgh, EH3 7LU. T.-031-225 1284. Secretary: D. Lynd; Development Officer: Ian Woodcraft.

Law Reporting, Scottish Council of (1957), 26 Drumsheugh Gardens, Edinburgh. T.-031-226 7411. Members: Gavin S. Douglas, Q.C., Rt. Hon. Peter Fraser, Q.C., Kenneth J. Cameron, Q.C., Douglas Grant, A.J. Spencer Kennedy, T.G. Ramsay D. Clark, Peter C. Millar, O.B.E., W.D. Prosser, Q.C., The Hon. Lord Ross, The Hon. Lord Grieve, A.R. Brownlie, John Murray, Q.C., John Horsburgh, Q.C. Secretary: Kenneth W. Pritchard. Company limited by guarantee to prepare and publish reports of civil and criminal cases in the High Court of Scotland and The House of Lords in regard to Scottish cases.

Law Society of Scotland (1949), 26 Drumsheugh Gardens, Edinburgh, EH3 7YR. T.-031-226 7411. President: G.R.G. Graham; Vice President: N. M. Stewart; Past President: A.E. McIlwain; Elected Members of Council: H.C. Abram, B.C. Adair, D.R. Anderson, J.C.L. Anderson, V.R.D., J.M. Arnott, T.D., M.J. Bell, D.A. Bennett, T.N. Biggart, C.B.E., J.E. Cameron, K.H. Candlish, J.P., A.C. Clark, I.D. Dunbar, L. Falconer, W.R. Gemmell, A.T.F. Gibb, A.M. Gordon, J.R. Harper, J.D. Keegan, A.J.S. Kennedy, I.D. Kirkpatrick, D.R. Lingard, Professor P.N. Love, C.B.E., A. McArthur, J. McGowan, R.W. McKenzie, D.J. McNeil, J.C.C. McSherry, B.A. Merchant, Alexander D. Millar, Archibald D. Millar, C.B. Miller, H.S. Neilson, I.M.S. Park, C.B.E., I.M. Robertson, G.F. Ritchie, R.M. Ross, D.R. Seagrave, J.M.M. Smith, M.G. Strang Steel, J.A. Wark, M.C. The Secretary: K.W. Pritchard; Senior Deputy Secretary: S.P. Riddell; Senior Deputy Secretary and Secretary, Legal Aid (Scotland): R.H. Gilbert; Secretary Law Reform: N.H. Rose; Secretary Legal Education: Carolyn Slater; Deputy Secretaries: J.G.C. Barr, I. Lamont, P.S.B. Niven, Mrs J.H. Webster, Silvia Whithorn, Keith Marshall; Conference Secretary: Lesley Fenton.
Governing body of the solicitors' branch of the Scottish legal profession. All practising solicitors in Scotland must be members, and the Society maintains the official Roll of Solicitors enabling the public to check a solicitor's credentials to practise. The Society's objects are the promotion of the interests of the profession; and the promotion of the interests of the public in relation to that profession. The Society's functions include education and training, constant review of the charges for solicitors' services, ethics, and the operation of the Guarantee Fund for the public's protection. See also Legal Aid Central Committee.

Lecturers in Colleges of Education in Scotland, Association of. National Secretary: Ian McPherson, Dundee College of Education, Gardyne Road, Dundee, DD5 1NY. T.-0382 453433. Chairman: George Livingstone; Treasurer: Nan Anthony. Professional body.

Legal Aid Central Committee, P.O. Box 123, 41 Drumsheugh Gardens, Edinburgh, EH3 7SW. T.-031-226 7061. Responsible to the Law Society of Scotland for the administration of the Government-funded scheme for the provision of legal aid in the civil and criminal courts.

Leith Chamber of Commerce, 3 Randolph Crescent, Edinburgh, EH3 7UD. T.-031-225 5851. Secretary: D.M. Mowat, J.P.

Leith Enterprise Trust (1984), 25 Maritime Street, Leith, EH6 5PW. T.-031-553 5566. Chairman: R. Bruce Weatherstone. Executive Director: J.A. Prettyman. Committed to encouraging new and expanding business ventures in Leith. The Trust offers business advice and practical assistance.

Leith Nautical College (1908), 24 Milton Road East, Edinburgh, EH15 2PP. T.-031-669 8461. Chairman, Board of Governors: R.S. Salvesen. Principal: Dr A. Watson, T.D.; College Secretary and Treasurer: Miss E. Johnston. The College is recognised by the Department of Transport as a navigation and marine engineering school and by the Home Office as a radio telegraphy school. It is also recognised as a training and examination centre for the Royal Yachting Association/Department of Transport courses leading to all yachtmaster certificates.

Lews Castle College (1953), Stornoway, Isle of Lewis. T.-0851 3311. Principal: John MacLeod, O.B.E.; Depute Principal: Malcolm MacKay. Community/ technical college offering the normal range of post-16 courses up to S.H.N.D. in business and secretarial courses; to H.C. in engineering studies; and a wide range of Y.T.S. and Action Plan modules and C. & G. courses. 160 full-time and 450 part-time students.

Liberal Party, Scottish, 4 Clifton Terrace, Edinburgh, EH12 5DR. T.-031-337 2314. President: Lord Mackie of Benshie. Leader: Russell Johnston, M.P.; Chairman: Ross Finnie; Vice Chairmen: Malcolm Bruce, M.P., J. Wallace, M.P., Ron Waddell. Treasurer: Derek King. General Secretary: David Miller; Assistant Secretary: Helen Grant. Political organisation.

Library Association, Scottish (1908), Motherwell Business Centre, Coursington Road, Motherwell, ML1 1PW. Executive Secretary: R. Craig; Hon. Treasurer: N. Turner. Membership of 2,500 representing all areas of library and information work. Promotion of libraries and librarianship.

Library of Scotland, National (1925), George IV Bridge, Edinburgh, EH1 1EW. T.-031-226 4531. Chairman: M.F. Strachan, C.B.E.; Trustees: Lord President of the Court of Session, Lord Advocate, Secretary of State for Scotland, Dean of the Faculty of Advocates, Minister of the High Kirk of Edinburgh, M.P. for Edinburgh Central, Crown Agent, Lord Provosts of Edinburgh, Glasgow, Dundee, and Aberdeen, Mrs K.J. Anderson, J.A. Ford, C.B., M.C., Ruari McLean, C.B.E., D.S.C., A.C. Murray, D.A.O. Edward, Q.C., R.N.M. MacLean, Q.C., J.T. Cameron, Q.C., J.J. Clyde, Q.C., J.M. Pinkerton, Q.C., Professor A.F. Falconer, V.R.D., H.J. Heaney, J.M. Smethurst, Professor L.G. Whitby, Janet Adam Smith (Mrs John Carleton), O.B.E., Rt. Hon. The Earl of Perth, P.C., Professor D. Hay, A.E. Ritchie, C.B.E., I.K. Murray. Librarian: Professor E.F.D. Roberts; Deputy Librarian: B. G. Hutton; Keepers, Department of Printed Books: W.H. Brown, Dr R. Donaldson, I.D. McGowan, Dr A. Matheson; Keepers, Department of Manuscripts: P.M. Cadell, Dr T.I. Rae; Director, Scottish Library Network: B. Gallivan.
A major British library, containing about 4.5m. printed items and a large collection of manuscripts. A copyright deposit library for U.K. and Irish publications. It is open to the public for reference and research, and is also the administrative centre for inter-library lending in Scotland.

Licensed Trade Association, Scottish (1880), 10 Walker Street, Edinburgh, EH3 7LA. T.-031-225 5169. President: J. Waterson; Vice Presidents: E.P. Watson, J.N. Manson; Treasurer: P.R. McCrudden. Secretary: E.W. Ridehalgh. Association of liquor licensees (excluding registered clubs). To protect and promote the rights and interests of the licensed trade in Scotland.

The Scottish Companion 97

Life Saving Society, Royal (Scottish Region). Secretary: Ms J. Castro, 30 Seres Road, Clarkston, Glasgow, G76 7QF. T.-041-638 8271.

Lilley, F.J.C., plc (1965), 331 Charles Street, Glasgow, G21 2QX. T.-041-552 6565. Chairman: C. White; Managing Director: D.C. Neill. Construction company. Turnover (1984): £230m.

List 'D' School Association, Ballikinrain School, Balfron, By Glasgow. T.-Balfron 40244. President: D.S. McCallum; Co-ordinating General Secretary: D.J. Davies. For managers and headmasters of List 'D' schools.

Literary Studies, Association for Scottish (1970), Department of English, University of Aberdeen, Old Aberdeen, AB9 2UB. T.-0224 40241. President: Thomas Crawford; Secretary: David S. Robb; Treasurer: Dr David S. Hewitt; General Editor: Douglas S. Mack; Chairman, Language Committee: J.D.R. McClure; Chairman, Schools Committee: Ronald Renton; Journal Editor: Kenneth Buthlay; Language Journal Editor: Dr H. Speitel; Reviews Editor: Dr J.H. Alexander; Editors, *New Writing Scotland*: Alexander Scott, Dr James Aitchison. To promote the languages and literature of Scotland, through conferences and publications. Each year, there is a conference devoted to a major figure, period, or topic from the Renaissance to the present day. For the year's subscription, each member receives an annual volume (a new edition or an out of print work of Scottish literature), the *Scottish Literary Journal*, and a newsletter.

Livingston Development Corporation (1962), Sidlaw House, Almondvale, Livingston, West Lothian. T.-0506 414177. Chairman: R.S. Watt; Deputy Chairman: W. Percy. Chief Executive: J. Wilson; Secretary and Legal Adviser: J. Ritchie; Chief Finance Officer: A. Kinnear; Commercial Director: J. Pollock. Development of new town.

Local Administration in Scotland, Commissioner for (The Ombudsman), 5 Shandwick Place, Edinburgh, EH2 4RG. T.-031-229 4472. Commissioner: Eric Gillett; Secretary: K. Bratton. Investigation of complaints from the public of injustice attributed to mal-administration in local government.

Local Authorities, Convention of Scottish (1975), 16 Moray Place, Edinburgh, EH3 6BL. T.-031-225 1626. President: Councillor R. Stewart; Vice President: Councillor K. Fagan. Secretary and Treasurer: G.H. Speirs.
The Convention was created after the reform of local government in Scotland to protect the interests of the new regional, district, and islands authorities in matters of national concern. It considers legislation before Parliament on matters of local government interest. It negotiates and consults with other national bodies whose work affects local authorities or who look to local government for financial support. The most significant negotiations are with civil servants and Ministers on levels of public expenditure and the amount of Exchequer grant payable to local authorities in each financial year. It also submits evidence on behalf of local authorities to Royal Commissions and Committees of Inquiry and is available to guide member councils on any matter where a uniform approach by individual authorities is desirable.

Local Authorities Special Housing Group, Scottish (1963), 53 Melville Street, Edinburgh, EH3 7HL. T.-031-226 3376. Chairman of Council: Councillor W. Wilson. Director: P.H. Stringer. To encourage better housing through common development of all matters relating to housing plans – the provision, management, and maintenance of the housing stock and the continuing welfare of the tenant.

Local Authority Accounts in Scotland, Commission for, Miller House, 18 George Street, Edinburgh, EH2 2QU. T.-031-226 7346. Chairman: John R. Small;

Deputy Chairman: P.M. Robertson; Members: J.D.S. Bennett, R.A. Dingwall-Smith, R. Gordon, B. Grosset, J.C. Macfarlane, Sir Charles O'Halloran, A.M. Pelham Burn, B.C. Ritchie. Controller of Audit: J.W. Troman; Depute Controller of Audit: R.K. Simpson; Assistant Controllers of Audit: N. Docherty, T. Irvine, J.H. Winter; Secretary: N.P. Carpenter. The major part of the Commission's work is to secure the audit of the accounts of the regional, islands, and district authorities and of a number of associated joint committees and ad-hoc boards.

Local Government Boundary Commission for Scotland (1975), New St. Andrew's House, Edinburgh. T.-031-556 8400, Ext. 4848. Chairman: R.A. Bennett, Q.C.; Deputy Chairman: A.A.L. Evans; Members: Miss J. Forbes, G. Carlton, O.B.E., S. McDowall. Secretary: I.A. McLeod. The Commission has two main functions: that of reviewing the areas of local authorities in Scotland; and of reviewing the electoral arrangements for local government areas.

Local Health Councils, Association of Scottish, 21 Torphichen Street, Edinburgh. Secretary: Linda Headland.

Locate in Scotland, 120 Bothwell Street, Glasgow, G2 7JP. T.-041-248 2700. Part of the Industry Department for Scotland; responsible for inward investment.

Lochaber District Council (1974), Lochaber House, High Street, Fort William, Inverness-shire. T.-0397 3881. Chairman: Colin Neilson; Vice Chairman: Jessie M. MacInnes; Members: J.R. Campbell, A. Kitson, J.K. MacKay, R.E. Hervo, B.J. Murphy, Mrs A.S. Forbes, D.P. MacFarlane, T. Brogan, Mrs J.A. Fraser, C. King, D. MacGillivray, Miss C.L. Maclean of Ardgour, A.B. Robertson. Chief Executive: D.A.B. Blair; Depute Chief Executive: A.J. Jackson; Director of Finance: N.A. MacKenzie; Director of Environmental Health Services: J. Cormack; Director of Housing: J. MacLeod; District Architect: M. McGruer. District Council. Population of District: 20,000.

Loch Lomond, Stirling and Trossachs Tourist Board (1983), P.O. Box 30, Stirling. T.-Stirling 70945. Chairman: Councillor Norman McEwan. Tourism Manager: James Fraser. Promotion of tourism within the District Council areas of Dumbarton, Stirling, and Clackmannan.

Lord Lyon, Court of the, H.M. New Register House, Edinburgh, EH1 3YT. T.-031-556 7255. Lord Lyon King of Arms: Malcolm R. Innes, C.V.O.; Islay Herald, Lyon Clerk and Keeper of the Records: John I.D. Pottinger, M.V.O.; Procurator Fiscal: Ivor R. Guild; Albany Herald: Sir Iain Moncreiffe of that Ilk, C.V.O., Q.C.; Marchmont Herald: Major David M. Maitland-Titterton, T.D.; Carrick Pursuivant: John A. Spens; Unicorn Pursuivant: Sir Crispin Agnew of Lochnaw, Bt.; Dingwall Pursuivant: Charles J. Burnett. The Court of the Lord Lyon is a court of law responsible for the administration of heraldry in Scotland and for the recording of all arms and bearings in Scotland. It is also responsible for the organisation of all ceremonies of State in Scotland. Like any other court of law, the public has direct access.

Lothian Community Relations Council (1971), 12A Forth Street, Edinburgh, EH1 3LH. T.-031-556 0441. Chairman: M. Yousaf Inait. Senior Community Relations Officer: Mohammed Akram. Voluntary body which aims to eliminate racial discrimination and promote better relationships between people of different origins. These objectives are pursued through education, community work, and non-party political activities.

Lothian Health Board (1974), 11 Drumsheugh Gardens, Edinburgh, EH3 7QQ. T.-031-225 1341. Chairman: A. Findlay; Members: Mrs P. Bell, Dr I. Capperauld, A.T. Clark, Mrs W.E. Donaldson, G.S. Douglas, Dr A.R. Milne, J.I. Thomson, Mrs M.H. Waterston, R.B. Weatherstone, Mrs G. Barton, A.B. Dunlop, Dr R.J. Kellett, J.M. MacNeill, E.A. Matthews, D. Molloy, E.J. Rawlings, A.H. Russell, A.G. Smart, Professor J. Williamson. Secretary: Ross Mitchell; Treasurer: Derek F. Hardman; Chief Administrative Medical Officer: C. Brough; Chief Area Nursing Officer: Miss M.W. Nimmo; Chief Administrative Dental Officer: J.W. Craig; Chief Administrative Pharmaceutical Officer: T.R. Lowther. Provision of health service.

Lothian Regional Council (1974), Regional Headquarters, George IV Bridge, Edinburgh, EH1 1UQ. T.-031-229 9292. Convener: B.A. Meek; Vice Convener: I.A. Cramond; Members: D.R.W. Alexander, A. Bell, I.J. Berry, P.C. Boyes, D.A.P. Buchanan, I.H. Buchanan, B.J. Cavanagh, J. Cook, C.D.S. Cowan, M.J. Coyne, I.M. Crosbie, A.M. Darling, M. Docherty, Mrs W.E. Donaldson, W. Drummond, E.B. Fallon, H.D.G. Fraser, K.T. Geddes, J. Gilchrist, D.C.E. Gorrie, J.M. Gray, I.R. Hoy, Mrs A. Huggins, J.R.S. Kelly, R.M. Knox, A.H. Lester, N. Lindsay, J.R. McLaren, G.F. McNeill, E. Milligan, J.W. Moffett, Mrs M. Monies, R. Muir, J.P. Mulvey, R.C.M. Morton, J. Hill, P.W. Nolan, W.R.V. Percy, D.H. Ramsay, W.G. Rankine, J. Scott, K. Simpson, W.J. Stoddart, D.O. Thomson, K.F. Ward, J.M. Wesley. Chief Executive: R.G.E. Peggie; Director of Planning: G. Bowie; Regional Secretary: R.L. Cowan; Director of Manpower Services: G.A. Lister; Director of Architectural Services: T.R. Hughes; Assessor and Electoral Registration Officer: J.S. Gardner; Director of Trading Standards: J. Short; Director of Water and Drainage: L.K.W. Richards; Director of Education: W.D.C. Semple; Firemaster: W. Kerr; Director of Highways: P.J. Mason; Chief Constable: W.G.M. Sutherland; Director of Social Work: R.W. Kent; Director of Transport: C. Evans; Children's Hearings Reporter: A.F. Finlayson; Industrial Development Manager: P. Richardson; Estates Surveyor: J.D.C. Simpson; Medical Adviser: Dr J.N. Gray; Regional Analyst: M.F. Godfray; Chief Registrar: G.W. Robertson; Regional Solicitor: G.F.G. Welsh. Scotland's second largest regional authority.

Low & Bonar PLC (1912), Bonar House, Faraday Street, Dundee, DD1 9JA. T.-0382 818171. Chairman: Sir Dermot de Trafford; Managing Director: R.J. Jarvis; Deputy Managing Director: H.C. Bowron; Finance Director: W.L. Telfer; Non-Executive Directors: G.C. Bonar, B.H. Lewis, Sir J. Stewart-Clark. Regional Chief Executive, American Region: E.G. Campbell; Regional Chief Executive, African Region: L.A. Williams. Holding company with interests in textiles, engineering, travel, and packaging. Operations in North America, Africa, and Australia. Turnover (1984): £175m.

Low & Company PLC, William (1868), P.O. Box 73, Baird Avenue, Dryburgh Industrial Estate, Dundee. T.-0382 814022. Chairman: J.P. Rettie; Deputy Chairman: I.W. Stewart; Managing Director: J.L. Millar; Marketing Director: C.C.R. Mitchell; Finance Director: H.L. Findlay. Supermarket retailers operating 45 supermarkets and 16 freezer centres throughout Scotland. Turnover (1984): £132m.

Lyceum Theatre Company, Royal (1965), Grindlay Street, Edinburgh, EH3 9AX. T.-031-229 7404. Chairman, Board of Directors: Ludovic Kennedy;

The Scottish Companion

Members: Councillor Donald Gorrie, O.B.E., Dr Roger Savage, Ian
Robertson, Sir Frederick O'Brien, K.B., Q.C., John Barr, Callum Mill,
Patrick Rayner, James Service, Councillor Paulo Vestri, Councillor George
Kerevan, Councillor Gertrude Barton, Councillor Robert Cairns, Councillor
Frances Wood. Artistic Director: Ian Wooldridge; General Manager: Roger
Spence. To present major dramatic works from the whole spectrum of world
theatre at the highest possible international standards to as large and varied
an audience as possible.

M

Macaulay Institute for Soil Research (1930), Craigiebuckler, Aberdeen, AB9 2QJ. T.-0224 38611. Council of Management: G.I. Lumsden, Professor G.A. Sim, Professor Lord Tedder, Professor H.M. Keir, Professor C.H. Gimingham, Professor J.W. Parsons, W.J. Ferguson, G.J.F. Copeman, Dr J.H. Topps, Professor J.E. Smith, Professor N.F. Robertson, C.B.E., A.J. Grayson, M. Mackie, jnr., Professor J.D. Matthews. Director: Dr. T.S. West; Deputy Director: Dr G. Anderson; Heads of Departments: Dr M.J. Wilson (Mineral Soils), R.A. Robertson (Peat and Forest Soils), Dr A.M. Ure (Spectrochemistry), Dr G. Anderson (Soil Organic Chemistry),A.E.S. Macklon (Plant Physiology), Dr J.F. Darbyshire (Microbiology), R.H.E. Inkson (Statistics), J.S. Bibby (Soil Survey); Secretary: Miss E.A. Piggott. The Institute combines practical studies of the soils of Scotland, designed to improve their fertility, with related research into various branches of soil science.

Macintosh Society, Charles Rennie (1973), Queen's Cross, 870 Garscube Road, Glasgow, G20 7EL. T.-041-946 6600. Chairman: Dr Frank A. Walker; Hon. Secretary: Patricia Douglas. To foster interest in the work of the Scottish architect. The Society is restoring Queen's Cross Church in Glasgow, an important Macintosh building, as a meeting place.

Management, British Institute of (1947), 15 Woodside Terrace, Glasgow, G3 7XH. T.-041-333 0707. Director, Scotland and Northern Ireland: John Lambert, F.B.I.M.; Administrative Assistant: Eleanor Murdoch. Professional body for practising managers. It has a membership of 9,000 organisations and 75,000 individuals in the U.K. In Scotland, 600 organisations and 4,000 individuals. Main activities are information (library) and advisory services, together with conferences and seminars.

Manpower Services Commission (1974), Office for Scotland, 9 St. Andrew Square, Edinburgh, EH2 2QX. T.-031-225 8500. Committee for Scotland: Dr James Munn, O.B.E. (Chairman), G.R. Carter, J. Davidson, Councillor R. Gould, W. Hughes, A. Inglis, J. Milne, J. Morrell, J.D. Pollock, Councillor Mrs B. Vaughan. Director, Scotland: P. Mackay; Assistant Director: A.I. Randall; Employment Manager, Scotland: J.G. Duncan; Operations Manager, Skillcentre Training Agency, Scotland: D.M. Dickson. The M.S.C. runs the public employment and training services and advises the Government on manpower policies. The Commission is accountable to the Secretary of State for Scotland for its operations in Scotland, on which it spends about £200m. per year. Its three operating divisions – Employment, Training, and the Skillcentre Training Agency – run the network of local job centres, area offices, professional and executive recruitment offices, employment rehabilitation centres and skillcentres, through which the

Commission provides a wide range of advisory services and schemes to help employers train and obtain workers and to assist people – including those in special groups such as school leavers, disabled people, and the long-term unemployed – to choose, train for, and obtain employment.

Marine Biological Association, Scottish (1914), P.O. Box 3, Oban, PA34 4AD. T.-0631 62244. Director: Professor Ronald I. Currie, C.B.E. Marine research covering most scientific disciplines concerned with the sea, physics, chemistry, biology, etc. Undertakes contract work relating to marine environment.

Marriage Guidance Council, Scottish (1948), 26 Frederick Street, Edinburgh, EH2 2JR. T.-031-225 5006. Chairman: Dr J. Douglas Haldane. Director: David Clark; Secretary: John G.M. Watt. To foster the success and stability of marriage as the foundation of family life and the well-being of society, by providing a confidential counselling service. There are 18 local M.G.C.s in Scotland and more than 50 counselling centres.

Master Bakers, Scottish Association of (1891), 19 Atholl Crescent, Edinburgh, EH3 8HJ (from March 1985: 4 Torphichen Street, Edinburgh). T.-031-229 1401. President: G.A. Robertson. Director: John Lefley. Trade association representing and promoting the interests of its members, who cover the vast majority of firms in the bakery and allied trades in Scotland.

Master Printers of Scotland, Society of (1910), Edinburgh House, 3-11 North St. Andrew Street, Edinburgh, EH2 1JU. T.-031-557 3600. President: R.B.R. Walker; Vice President: C.I. McAulay. Director: J.B. Raeburn; Director, Manpower: W. Kidd; Secretary: R.M. Jeffrey. Employers' organisation and trade association representing the interests of the printing industry in Scotland.

Meat and Livestock Commission (1967), Scottish Headquarters, 3 Atholl Place, Perth, PH1 5ND. T.-0738 27401. Scottish Commissioners: J. Forbes, J.F. Royan. Chief Officer for Scotland: A. Donaldson; Chief Livestock Officer: G.M. McPherson; Chief Fatstock Officer: I.S. Wiggins. To improve the production and marketing of British cattle, sheep, and pigs, and the meat they produce. The Commission provides services, information, and advice for livestock producers, auctioneers, slaughterers, wholesalers, manufacturers, retailers, caterers, and consumers. It is funded by statutory levies on all slaughter stock, fees as agents for the Intervention Board for Agricultural Produce and the Ministry of Agriculture, and payment received for services and publications.

Meat Traders' Associations, Scottish Federation of (1918), 3 Kinnoull Street, Perth, PH1 5EN. T.-0738 37785. Secretary: Mrs Moira Brady. Represents the retail meat trade in liaison with Government bodies, with particular regard to proposed legislation. Advises and helps retail meat traders with everyday problems, including wage negotiations.

Medical Association, British (1832), 7 Drumsheugh Gardens, Edinburgh, EH3 7QP. T.-031-225 7184. Chairman, Scottish Council: Dr A.G.R. Law; Deputy Chairman: Dr J.A. Ford. Scottish Secretary: Dr Derek Buchanan; Assistant Secretary (Scotland): Miss E.M. Campbell. Voluntary body of 8,000 members of the medical profession in Scotland (65,000 in U.K.), representing the collective and individual interests of its members. Sole medical body recognised by Government in negotiation with Government departments in Scotland (and in the U.K. as a whole).

Medico-Chirurgical Society of Glasgow, Royal (1814). Hon. Secretary: John W. Turner, Institute of Neurological Sciences, Southern General Hospital,

Glasgow, G51 4TF. T.-041-445 2466, Ext. 3743. To advance knowledge of and promote research in medicine, surgery, and allied sciences.

Memorial to David Livingstone Trust, Scottish National (1926), David Livingstone Centre, Blantyre, Glasgow, G72 9BT. T.-0698 823140. Chairman: Frederick McDermid; Vice Chairmen: Elspeth J. Murdoch, Rev. Neil C. Bernard; Secretary: Alex. M. Ferguson; Treasurer: Donald J. MacLeod. Warden: William Cunningham; Education Officer: Susan Middleton. Preservation, as a visitor centre, of the tenement building in which David Livingstone was born; and maintenance of the building and surrounding parkland as a memorial/museum illustrating the life of Livingstone.

Mental Health, Scottish Association for, 40 Shandwick Place, Edinburgh, EH2 4RT. T.-031-225 3062. Chairman: Rt. Rev. M.G. Hare Duke; Vice Chairman: Dr R.A.Y. Stewart. Director: Peter J. Clarke. Independent organisation concerned with people who experience mental illness. Seeks to develop voluntary action and influence policy.

Mental Welfare Commission for Scotland (1962), 22 Melville Street, Edinburgh, EH3 7NS. T.-031-225 7034. Chairman: P.C. Millar, O.B.E.; Commissioners: Professor Annie T. Altschul, C.B.E., Professor T.D. Campbell, R.G. Davis, Mrs J.B.M. Ellis, O.B.E., Ms A.M. Green, Mrs A.I. Huggins, D.A. Macdonald, O.B.E., Mrs H.S. Mein, Dr A.F. Rodger, Dr H.S. Ross, H.F. Smith, M.B.E., J.G. Sutherland. Medical Commissioners: H.C. Fowlie, W.D. Boyd; Medical Officers: Dr J. Connaughton, Dr B. Hamilton, Dr A.E. Weatherhead; Secretary: Mrs D. Mellon.
Established under the Mental Health (Scotland) Act 1960, as amended by the Mental Health (Scotland) Act 1984. The Commission exercises protective functions in respect of persons who may, by reason of mental disorder, be incapable of adequately protecting their persons or their interests. Where those persons are liable to be detained in hospital, or subject to guardianship under the provisions of the Act, the Commission's functions shall include, in appropriate cases, the discharge of such patients.

Mentally Handicapped, Scottish Society for the (1954), 13 Elmbank Street, Glasgow, G3 4QA. T.-041-226 4541. Chairman, Scottish Council: T. Boyle; Vice Chairmen: Mrs M. Birss, R. MacCallum, P. Bruce, M.B.E.; Treasurer: Dr M.J. Tomkinson. General Secretary: Iain M. McMurray; Assistant General Secretary: Hugh W.L. Stewart. Concerned with all aspects of the welfare of mentally handicapped people and their families. Founded by parents, the Society has almost 80 branches in all parts of Scotland, providing a range of services.

Menzies plc, John (1833), Hanover Buildings, Rose Street, Edinburgh, EH2 2YQ. T.-031-225 8555. Chairman: J.M. Menzies; Managing Director: T.P. Callaghan. Wholesale and retail newsagents, booksellers, and stationers, and providers of library services. Turnover (1984): £461m.

Methodist Church, Synod in Scotland. Chairman: Rev. Alan P. Horner. Secretary: Rev. E. Raymond Watker, 62 Newton Street, Greenock, PA16 8SP. T.-0475 22706.

Mid-Argyll, Kintyre & Islay Tourist Organisation, The Pier, Campbeltown, Argyll, PA28 6EF. T.-0586 52056. Area Tourist Officer: L. MacKinnon. Promotion of tourism.

Midlothian District Council (1974), 1 White Hart Street, Dalkeith, EH22 1DE. T.-031-663 2881. Convener: W. Steele; Members: M. Moore, D. Lennie, D.F. Molloy, S. Campbell, J.G. Hope, J. Murray, T. Darby, J. Green,

Thelma Lennie, R. Small, A.R. Fraser, D.G. McDonald, Ellen Leary, D.R. Smith. Chief Executive and Director of Administration: D.W. Duguid; Director of Finance: W.W. Lang; Director of Planning and Building Control: R.W. Maslin; Director of Technical Services: T. Steele; Director of Recreation and Leisure: J.A.L. Gilfillan; Director of Environmental Health and Cleansing: I.F. Florence; Director of Housing: A.S. Adams. District Council. Population of District: 83,000.

Midwives, Royal College of, Scottish Board (1881), 37 Frederick Street, Edinburgh. T.-031-225 1633. Secretary/Treasurer: Mrs S. Davidson. To advance the art and science of midwifery and maintain high professional standards.

Milk Marketing Board, Scottish (1933), Underwood Road, Paisley, PA3 1TJ. T.-041-887 1234. Chairman: A.L. Howie; Vice Chairman: W. Weir; Members: G.A. Anderson, T. Brewster, J.A. Brown, Mrs C. Campbell, J.P., H.B. Christie, A. Gray, J.A. McIntyre, D. Yellowlees. Managing Director: I.A. McAlpine; Secretary: W. Davidson; Marketing Director: Dr J.D.W. McQueen; Director of Creameries: A.S. McCartney; Finance Director: J.M.S. Pirie.
The Board is responsible for the administration of the Scottish Milk Marketing Scheme, under which all milk to be marketed by dairy farmers in the Board area from Montrose to the Solway must be sold to the Board, apart from about 2% which the Board licences for direct sale. It sells 1,100m. litres of milk with a value of £200m. per annum to achieve the highest possible return for its registered milk producers; operates six transport depots and six creameries as a Commercial Division, purchasing about 25% of all milk to manufacture into a wide range of milk products with a turnover of £60m. per annum; provides a wide range of producer services, either on a commercial basis or in a free advisory capacity.

Milk Records Association, Scottish (1903), Underwood Road, Paisley, PA3 1TJ. T.-041-887 1234. Director of Milk Recording Services: B.R. Speight. The Association co-ordinates the official milk recording service for individual cows in Scotland.

Monklands District Council (1974), Municipal Buildings, Dunbeth Road, Coatbridge, ML5 3LF. T.-Coatbridge 24941. Chairman: Provost Edward Cairns, J.P.; Vice Chairman: Henry Mallon; Members: Florence Inglis, M.B.E., Arthur Fitzpatrick, Hugh Kearns, Robert Gilson, Jim Smith, John Dillon, William Ferguson, James Logue, George Orr, Agnes Gordon, Eric Burns, John Love, Martin Dempsey, Samuel Gordon, Betty Leitch, James Brooks, Hugh Lucas, Thomas Somers. Chief Executive and Director of Finance: J.S. Ness; Director of Administration and Legal Services: B. Devine; Director of Technical Services: T. Linney; Director of Planning and Development: A.I. Cowe; Director of Leisure and Recreation: M.C. Barron; Director of Environmental Services: C.A. Thomson; Director of Housing: T. McKenzie. District Council. Population of District: 110,000.

Moray College of Further Education, Hay Street, Elgin, IV30 2NN. T.-0343 3425. Principal: Donald MacPhail. College of further education.

Moray District Council (1974), District Headquarters, High Street, Elgin. T.-Elgin 3451. Chairman: E. Aldridge, J.P.; Members: A.A. Anderson, J.P., A. Farquharson, Mrs R.L. Hossack, J.P., J.A. Proctor, J.P., A.R. Slorach, R.G. Cochrane, D.M.A. Thompson, J.P., R.M. Murdoch, J.M. Mustard, J.P., Mrs J.M. Shaw, J.M. Watt, F.W. Anderson, G.S. Innes, J.P., T.A. Howe, J.P., L. Mann, J.P., W.P. Watt, J.P., Mrs M.W. Marshall.

Chief Executive and Director of Law and Administration: J.P.C. Bell; Depute Chief Executive and Depute Director of Law and Administration: J.A. Sword; Director of Housing and Technical Services: I.F. Potter; Director of Environmental Health: W. Stables; Director of Physical Planning and Development: R.A. Stewart; Director of Finance: I.J. Stuart; Director of Recreation: R. Cherry; Director of Libraries: Miss M. Innes. District Council. Population of District: 84,000.

Moray Firth Radio (1982), P.O. Box 271, Inverness. T.-0463 224433. Directors: D. Alistair Gardner (Chairman), Douglas Graham (Deputy Chairman), Thomas Prag (Managing), Sandy Cameron, R. Glen Grant, Steuart Henderson, Derick Henry, Charles MacRae, Mrs Christine MacWilliam, O.B.E., Dr Samuel Marshall, Anthony Mollett, William Phillips, Donald Waters. News Editor: Mike Hurry; Programme Organiser: Brian Anderson. Independent local radio station covering Moray Firth area from Wick to Fraserburgh. Audience research shows that the station is listened to every week by 56% of the local population.

Moray House College of Education, Holyrood Road, Edinburgh, EH8 8AQ. T.-031-556 8455. Principal: Gordon Kirk; Vice Principal: Bernard Thompson; Assistant Principal and Director Secondary Studies: Pauline E. Brown; Assistant Principal and Director In-Service Studies: Hugh E. Perfect; College Secretary: Stewart Dowie. The College offers a wide range of pre-service and in-service courses for a number of related professions: teaching, social work, community education, and educational psychology. **Scottish Centre for Education Overseas.** Director: Alexander McLellan.

Motherwell College, Dalzell Drive, Motherwell, ML1 2DD. T.-0698 59641. Principal: Alex. Money. College of further education.

Motherwell District Council (1974), Civic Centre, Motherwell, ML1 1TW. T.-0698 66166. Provost: J. McGhee. Members: H. Curran, H. McGuigan, A. Allan, A. Craig, V. Mathieson, Wilma Angus, James Fairley, J. Frew, J. Foley, Agnes Knighton, J. Gallacher, J. Sneddon, P. Hoey, J. McNeil, W. Wilson, J. Thomson, H. McMahon, Isabella Money, J. Moran, J. McCormack, D. McKendrick, J.E. McLellan, F. Johnston, P.J. Cullinan, R. Lyle, W. Graham, F. Gormill, J. Armstrong, J. McDonald. Chief Executive and Director of Administration: J. Bonomy; Director of Finance: J. Milne; Director of Technical Services: Alexander R. Stewart; Director of Housing: R. Thomson; Director of Environmental Health: J.M. Brownlie; Director of Planning: S. Cook. District Council. Population of District: 150,000.

Motherwell Enterprise Trust (1983), 28 Brandon Parade, Motherwell, ML1 1UJ. T.-0698 69333. Chairman: H. Porter, O.B.E.; Hon. Secretary: I. Livingston; Hon. Treasurer: E. McDaid. Executive Director: E. MacAulay. Private/public sector sponsored organisation promoting business enterprise and job creation in Motherwell District.

Motor Trade Association, Scottish (1903), 3 Palmerston Place, Edinburgh, EH12 5AQ. T.-031-225 3643. President: Anthony Charnell; Vice President: John Livingstone. Secretary: John Boyes. Formed to encourage, promote, and protect the retail motor trade. Has more than 1,600 garages in membership. The Association offers numerous services to members, including advice on current legislation and negotiations with manufacturers, oil companies, trade unions, etc., on behalf of the trade. All member firms have to be adhere to the Association's code of practice, which has been approved by the Office of Fair Trading. A customer complaint service is provided by which the motoring public can have disputes with member garages settled speedily without charge.

Mountaineering Council of Scotland (1971), South Tillysole Cottage, Kinnaird Park, Brechin, Angus, DD9 6TX. T.-Brechin 3480. President: Robin N. Campbell; Vice President: Paul Howgate; Hon. Secretary: Christopher J. Eatough; Hon. Treasurer: David J. Foster. To foster and promote mountaineering in Scotland. 85 member clubs.

Mountain Rescue Committee of Scotland. Secretary: M. Duckworth, 5 Westfield Terrace, Aberdeen. T.-0224 646995.

Museum, Royal Scottish (1854), Chambers Street, Edinburgh, EH1 1JF. T.-031-225 7534. Director: Dr Robert Anderson; Keepers: Ms D. Idiens (Art and Archaeology), Dr M. Shaw (Natural History), Dr C.D. Waterston (Geology), J.D. Storer (Technology and Science); Head of Education and Public Relations: Dr S. Brock; Head of Exhibitions and Design: H. Fernandez; Keeper, Scottish United Services Museum: S. Wood.
The Royal Scottish Museum is the largest comprehensive museum under one roof in Britain. It has wide-ranging collections of national importance covering the decorative arts of the world, Ethinography, Natural History, Geology, Technology and Science. Temporary exhibitions, programmes of lectures and films, and other educational activities for adults and young people at advertised times. The Museum attracts 600,000 visitors every year.

Museums Council, Scottish (1984), County House, 20/22 Torphichen Street, Edinburgh, EH3 8JB. T.-031-229 7465. Chairman: Colin Thompson, C.B.E. Director: Graeme Farnell; Depute Director: Timothy Ambrose. Aims to improve the quality of local museum and gallery provision in Scotland. Conservation work, touring exhibitions, information service.

Music Archive, Scottish (1968), 7 Lilybank Gardens, Glasgow, G12 8RZ. T.-041-334 6393. Chairman: Professor Ian Sneddon; Director: Professor Hugh Macdonald. Secretary and Librarian: Paul Hindmarsh. Centre for the study and promotion of Scottish music. The Archive has a reference library of scores, books, and information, including a major collection of 20th century music; microfilm collections of surviving sources of pre-Reformation Scottish music; and collections of 18th and 19th century printed editions. Its publications include a catalogue of published and unpublished music and lists of recent acquisitions.

Music Association, Scottish Amateur (1956), 7 Randolph Crescent, Edinburgh, EH3 7TH. T.-031-225 7592. Hon. President: Philip Ledger; Vice Presidents: Mrs Helen B. Davidson, Professor D.R. Kimbell; President: David G. Robertson; Chairman: George C. McVicar; Hon. Secretary: Alex. A. Soutar. The Association provides a common meeting place for discussion of the promotion and stimulation of local musical effort; encourages such effort; assists in the formulation of policy for the promotion of musical activity and for the furtherance of new and extended advisory services.

Musicians' Benevolent Fund, Scottish (1918), 9 Branziert Road, Killearn, Glasgow, G63 9RG. T.-0360 50413. Hon. President: Sir Alexander Gibson, C.B.E.; Hon. Vice President: Ian B. Rodger, O.B.E.; Hon. Trustees: Dame Jean Roberts, D.B.E., J.P., J.M. Turnbull, David G. Laurie, Neil B. Aitken; Hon. Solicitor: I. Rosslyn Mitchell; Hon. Secretary/Treasurer: Rodney Mount. To assist Scottish musicians and/or their dependants in need.

N

Nairn District Council (1974), The Court House, High Street, Nairn, IV12 4AU. T.-0667 52056. Provost: Lt. Col. H. McLean, M.B.E.; Members: A. Miller, J.W. Campbell, A.I. Finlayson, Christine Ellen, Margaret Anderson, S.A. Macarthur, J.H. Cattanach, R.G. King, H.J. Fraser. Director of Law and Administration: Allan Kerr; Director of Finance: W.J. Anderson; Director of Technical Services, Housing and Environmental Health: Andrew M. Cook. District Council. Population of District: 10,000.

Napier College of Commerce and Technology (1964), Colinton Road, Edinburgh, EH10 5DT. T.-031-447 7070. Chairman, College Council: Professor R.C.B. Aitken. Principal: W.A. Turmeau; Depute Principals: K.J. Anderson, I.H. Marker; Assistant Principals: A. Barron, D. Leach, J. Murray, M. Wright; Secretary and Academic Registrar: R.W. Stevenson. College of further education offering a wide range of courses at degree and diploma level. Most of the courses are vocationally orientated. There are 3,800 full-time and 3,300 part-time students.

National Party, Scottish (1928), 6 North Charlotte Street, Edinburgh, EH2 4JH. T.-031-226 3661. President: Rt. Hon. Donald Stewart, P.C., M.P.; Vice Presidents: Winifred Ewing, M.E.P., Janette Jones, Councillor Hamish Watt; Chairman: Gordon Wilson, M.P.; Senior Vice Chairman: Margaret Ewing; Executive Vice Chairmen: Tom McAlpine (Administration), Councillor Jim Mitchell (Local Government), Ron Wyllie (Organisation), George Leslie (Policy), Colin Bell (Publicity); Ordinary Members, N.E.C.: Jim Fairlie, Provost Andrew Welsh, Alex. Salmond, Isobel Lindsay, Jim Sillars, Jenny Herriot, Kenneth MacAskill, William McRae, James Halliday, Dr Allan Macartney. Headquarters Director/National Organiser: A. McKinney. Political party dedicated to self-government for Scotland and the furtherance of all Scottish interests.

Nature Conservancy Council (1973), Headquarters for Scotland, 12 Hope Terrace, Edinburgh, EH9 2AS. T.-031-447 4784. Director for Scotland: Dr J.M. Francis; Deputy Director for Scotland: J. McCarthy. Government body responsible for nature conservation in Britain. Establishment of nature reserves, as well as advisory and research work.

NESDA (1969), 8 Albyn Place, Aberdeen. T.-Aberdeen 643322. Director: David Ross; Depute Director: Ian Mackay. Development department of Grampian Regional Council, offering a free and confidential business advice and information service.

Network Scotland Ltd. (1984), 74 Victoria Crescent Road, Glasgow, G12 9JQ. T.-041-357 1774. Chairman: Alex. Inglis; Secretary: Michael W. Russell; Members, Board of Directors: John McCormick, Angela Mason, Professor Lalage Bown, Ian Young, Alexander Watson, Dr Elisabeth Gerver, George

108   The Scottish Companion

Paton. Executive Director: Michael W. Russell; Depute Director: Anne
Docherty; Organiser: Kathleen Z. Grieve, M.B.E. Scottish broadcasting
support and referral service (originally the Scottish Telephone Referral
Service), acting as the principal provider of support materials and services
both to Scottish radio and television, and to a number of UK projects. It
undertakes programme and materials research, materials production, and a
complete range of telephone and mail support services. In addition, Network
operates a definitive Scottish educational information service, providing for
telephone and mail inquiries information on adult and continuing education
opportunities in Scotland and elsewhere.

Newbattle Abbey College (1937), Dalkeith, Midlothian, EH22 3LL. T.-031-663
1921/2. Chairman, Board of Governors: Miss C. Morgan. Principal:
Alexander D. Reid; College Secretary: Stuart W. Mair. Residential college
for adults. It offers one and two year courses in liberal studies, and its
diploma is recognised by the S.U.C.E. as satisfying general entrance
requirements. It also offers short courses especially during the Easter and
summer periods, and houses conferences of an educational nature.

New Lanark Conservation Trust (1974), Counting House, New Lanark, Lanark,
ML11 9DG. T.-0555 61345. Manager: J. Arnold. The objective of the Trust
is to 'revivify' the historic village of New Lanark. Help is given to a local
housing association, and in 1983 the industrial area of the village, including
the cotton mills, was taken over by the Trust. It is planned to bring the entire
village back to life as part of an integrated scheme.

Newspaper Proprietors' Association, Scottish, Edinburgh House, 3-11 North St.
Andrew Street, Edinburgh, EH2 1JU. T.-031-557 3600. President: K.
Whitson; Senior Vice-President: I. Romanes; Junior Vice-President: D.
Smail. Director: J.B. Raeburn; Director-Manpower: W. Kidd; Secretary:
R.M. Jeffrey. Employers' organisation and trade association representing the
interests of the weekly newspaper industry in Scotland.

Nithsdale District Council (1974), Municipal Chambers, Buccleuch Street,
Dumfries, DG1 2AD. T.-0387 53166. Provost: K. Cameron; Members: J.H.
Lockhart; P.S. Deegan, Jean McMurdo, W. Little, D.P. Grant, J.H. Dalziel,
R.S. Wilson, Jane Robison, R.J. Jardine, Margaret McMurdo, W.G.
Carmichael, A. Morton, Earl of Dalkeith, J. Cotts, P.R. Rennie, R.C.
Watson, D.F. Sutherland, A. Saunders, W.M. Copeland, Heather Cross,
Shona Hyslop, J. Watson, Fiona Patterson, E.D. Gibson, T.A. McAughtrie,
D. Stewart, T.B. McCallum. Chief Executive: William W. Japp; Director of
Administration: Ian W. Watson; Director of Finance: K.C. Brown; Director
of Environmental Health: K. Stewart; Director of Technical Services and
Housing: E.D. Denholm. District Council. Population of District: 56,000.

North Country Cheviot Sheep Society (1945), The Cottage, Reay, Thurso,
Caithness, KW14 7RE. T.-084781 202. President: Robert M. Cowan;
Secretary: Edward H. McDonald. Breed society.

North East Fife District Council (1974), County Buildings, St. Catherine Street,
Cupar, Fife. T.-Cupar 53722. Chairman: D.A. Barrie, J.P.; Vice Chairman:
Mrs A.J. Gardner, M.B.E., J.P.; Members: Dr C.R. Sneddon, E.J.
Titterington, W. McCallum, R.W. Nairn, E. Garrett, H. Gray, D. Niven,
J.P., W. Allen, W.R.S. MacKenzie, A.J. Mackenzie, J. Braid, J.P., A.F.
Gilmour, J.P., Mrs I.K. Bell, Mrs I.M. Cater, D.P. Hamilton, J.P., P.
Regent, J.P. Chief Executive and Director of Administration: David W.
Anderson, C.B.E.; Depute Chief Executive: Robin G. Brotherton; Director
of Finance: Michael C. Dyke; Director of Planning and Building Control:

Philip J. Hutchinson; Director of Environmental Health: Ross J. Vettraino; Director of Housing: Michael B. Stanley; Director of Technical Services: Robin M. Hastie; Works Manager: Mark Nicol; Director of Recreation: Andrew C. Kydd; District Librarian: Ian Copland. District Council. Population of District: 62,000.

North East River Purification Board, Woodside House, Mugiemoss Road, Persley, Aberdeen, AB2 2UQ. T.-0224 696647. River Inspector: F.J. Little.

North of Scotland College of Agriculture (1904), School of Agriculture Building, 581 King Street, Aberdeen, AB9 1UD. T.-0224 40291. Chairman, Board of Governors: N.S. Thornton-Kemsley; Vice Chairman: W.J. Ferguson. Principal: Professor G.A. Lodge; Deputy Principal: Professor A. Martin; Secretary: Mrs S.S. Hannabuss. Courses leading to B.Sc. (Agr.) degrees, both honours and designated, and opportunities for study and research leading to the degrees of M.Sc. and Ph.D. The courses prepare students for the diploma and higher diploma in agriculture. In addition, a one year post diploma course in farm business organisation and management is offered. The College is responsible for the advisory services to the farming community in the area. It has 13 area offices and four farms scattered throughout the North of Scotland.

North of Scotland Grassland Society (1961), c/o Grassland Division, School of Agriculture, 581 King Street, Aberdeen. T.-0224 40291. Chairman: H. Jackson; Secretary/Treasurer, C.K. Mackie. To encourage research and practice in grassland husbandry leading to its more efficient use. The Society brings together farmers, research workers, and technical members of the agricultural industry.

North of Scotland Hydro-Electric Board (1943), 16 Rothesay Terrace, Edinburgh, EH3 7SE. T.-031-225 1361. Chairman: M. Joughin, C.B.E.; Deputy Chairman and Chief Executive: K.R. Vernon, C.B.E.; Members: C.A. MacLeod, C.A.M. Davis, M.G.N. Walker, Rear Admiral D.A. Dunbar Nasmith, C.B., D.S.C., D.J. Miller, A.T.H. Tulloch, C.S. MacPhie. Chief Engineer: A.T.L. Murray; Chief Commercial Officer: M.C. Whitfield; Chief Financial Officer: A.D. Stewart; Chief Personnel Officer: W.M.M. Harrison; Secretary: J.E.M. Watts; Computing and Services Controller: A.A. Robertson.
The Board, an autonomous nationalised industry, is responsible to the Secretary of State for Scotland for the generation, transmission, distribution, and retail sale of electricity in the North of Scotland. The Board's district comprises Scotland to the north and west of a line roughly joining the Firths of Clyde and Tay, including all the island groups extending to the Outer Hebrides, Orkney and Shetland; it covers one quarter of the land area, and contains about two per cent of the population of Great Britain. Almost 100 per cent of potential customers in the Board's district have been provided with a supply. The Board was set up under the Hydro-Electric Development (Scotland) Act 1943 to exploit the water power resources of the Highlands. The Board operates hydro and pumped storage, steam, diesel, and gas turbine stations.

North of Scotland Milk Marketing Board (1934), Claymore House, 29 Ardconnel Terrace, Inverness, IV2 3AF. T.-0463 232611. Chairman: J. Clark; Vice Chairman: M.W.T. Wood. Managing Director: J.A. Anderson; Financial Director: W.L. Anderson. Marketing of milk; operation of manufacturing creameries.

Northern Lighthouses, Commmissioners of (1786), 84 George Street, Edinburgh, EH2 3DA. T.-031-226 7051. Commissioners: (ex officio) Lord Advocate, Solicitor General, the six Sheriffs-Principal for Scotland, the Lord Provosts of Edinburgh, Glasgow, and Aberdeen, the Provost of Inverness, and the Chairman of Argyll and Bute District Council; (appointed by the Secretary of State for Transport and nominated by the Lieutenant Governor of the Isle of Man): an Isle of Man representative; (five other members elected by the Board) William D.H. Gregson, C.B.E., Captain John A. MacLeod, Captain Alexander F. Dickson, O.B.E., Rev. Captain Albert W.G. Kissack, Alastair J. Struthers. General Manager: Cdr. J.M. Mackay, M.B.E.; Secretary: J.R. Welsh; Engineer-in-Chief: J.H.K. Williamson. The Board is responsible for the superintendence and management of all lighthouses, buoys, and beacons throughout Scotland and adjacent seas and islands and the Isle of Man. In addition, through its administration, professional, and technical staff, the officers and crews of its lighthouse supply ships, and its lightkeepers, the Board provides and maintains the lights, fog signals, radio and radar beacons, lighted buoys and unlighted buoys and beacons required for general navigation in its area of jurisdiction.

Northern Studies, Scottish Society for (1967), c/o School of Scottish Studies, 27 George Square, Edinburgh, EH8 9LD. T.-031-667 1011. Chairman: Dr Barbara Crawford; Hon. Secretary: Morag Macleod. Provides a meeting ground for people interested in the cultural, historical, and literary links between Scotland and Scandinavia.

Northsound Radio (1981), 45 King's Gate, Aberdeen, AB2 6BL. T.-0224 632234. Chairman: A.D.F. Lewis; Managing Director: J.Q. Macfarlane; Directors: Miss M. Hartnoll, Professor A.G. Kemp, W. McKinlay, J. Wheeler, D.H. Young. Head of Finance: John Martin; Head of Sales: Gloria Taylor; Chief Engineer: Bob Barrow; News Editor: Rob Maclean; Head of Music: Graeme Moreland. Independent Local Radio station for Aberdeen and North East Scotland.

Nursery Nurses' Examination Board, Scottish (1967), 38 Queen Street, Glasgow, G1 3DY. T.-041-248 7900. Chairman: Dr W.W. Easton. Secretary: D. Hemingway. Provides courses of education and training for nursery nurses in Scotland, assesses students' attainments, and makes awards.

Nursing, Midwifery and Health Visiting for Scotland, National Board for (1983), 22 Queen Street, Edinburgh, EH2 1JX. T.-031-226 7371. Chairman: Miss C.A. Asher. Chief Executive Officer: Margaret W. Thomson; Principal Professional Adviser: Anne M. Calderwood; Principal Administrative Officer: Peter S. Taylor. Provision of training courses leading to registration as a nurse, midwife, or health visitor, and further training for those already registered; provision of examination structure to enable persons to become registered or to obtain additional qualifications; investigation of allegations of misconduct against nurses, midwives, and health visitors.

Nursing, Royal College of, of the United Kingdom, Scottish Board, 44 Heriot Row, Edinburgh, EH3 6EY. T.-031-225 7231. Chairman: Miss E.M. Smith; Secretary: Elizabeth McLaren.

O

Observatory, Royal, Edinburgh (1896), Blackford Hill, Edinburgh, EH9 3HJ. T.-031-667 3321. Director of the Observatory, Astronomer Royal for Scotland, and Professor of Astronomy at the University of Edinburgh: Professor Malcolm S. Longair; Deputy Director of the Observatory: Russell D. Cannon. Primarily a pure research establishment (now part of the Science and Engineering Research Council). There is a visitor centre.

Oatridge Agricultural College (1973), Ecclesmachan, Broxburn, West Lothian. T.-0506 854387. Principal: L. Coutts; Deputy Principal: C. Nixon. Provides further education in agriculture, horticulture, agricultural engineering, and forestry, up to diploma level, for South East and Central Scotland.

Oban, Mull and District Tourist Board, Tourist Information Centre, Argyll Square, Oban. T.-Oban 63122. Chairman: Ian Nicholson. Area Tourist Officer: Jane Johnson. Promotion of tourism.

Open Learning, Scottish Committee on (1983), Dowanhill, 74 Victoria Crescent Road, Glasgow, G12 9JN. T.-041-334 9314. Chairman: Ian Collie. Secretary and Development Officer: Peter Gartside. Open Learning is an approach to learning which emphasises the needs and convenience of the learner. Its aim is to reduce or remove barriers to access to education and training opportunities. S.C.O.L. aims to act as a national voice for open learning, identifying priorities, encouraging research, helping to arrange training, and publishing information.

Open University in Scotland (1969), 60 Melville Street, Edinburgh, EH3 7HF. T.-031-226 3851. Scottish Director: G.K.W. Arkieson, D.F.C. The Open University was set up to provide higher education by distance teaching methods for adults in full-time employment or who work in the home. No academic qualifications are required for entry. More than 57,000 have graduated. Continuing Education programme offers a variety of single courses, both on academic subjects and vocational updating and professional training, as well as self-contained learning packages and short courses on matters of everyday concern.

Opera, Scottish (1962), 39 Elmbank Crescent, Glasgow, G2 4PT. T.-041-332 3321. Chairman, Board of Directors: J.R. Johnstone; Vice Chairman: Hon. J.M.E. Bruce; Members: J.N. Anderson, G. Boyd, C.B.E., Sheriff J.S. Boyle, A. Clark, R.R. Dalgety, M. Everist, P.S. Ledger, A.J. Murray, Professor H. Macdonald, L.J. Paterson, W. Proudfoot, P.W. Simpson, Dr J. Smith, Professor M. Tilmouth. Artistic Director: Sir Alexander Gibson, C.B.E.; General Administrator: J. Cox; Financial Controller: R. Stenhouse; Production Controller: J.L. Graham; Production Director: G. Vick; Planning Controller: S. Playfair; Head of Music: I. Robertson; Publicity

Director: R. Witts; Development Director: J. Penney; Orchestra Manager: R. Brown; Company Manager: P. Heselton. International opera company based in Glasgow. Tours Scotland, north of England, and abroad. Extensive education programme.

Ophthalmic Opticians, Scottish Committee of (1934). Secretary and Treasurer: A.M. Thomson, 179 West George Street, Glasgow, G2. T.-041-221 8395. Represents ophthalmic opticians in all matters affecting them.

Orchestra, Scottish National (1950), 3 La Belle Place, Glasgow, G3 7LH. T.-041-332 7244. Acting Chairman: R. Williamson; Vice Chairman: William Gregson, C.B.E.; Secretary: G.K.V. Clarke; Directors: Diana Balfour, Councillor R. Ball, Councillor Tom Barrie, Richard Chester, Ian R. Clark, D.W.A. Donald, O.B.E., Morrison Dunbar, Christie Duncan, Robert Gardiner, Colonel Allan M. Gilmour, O.B.E., M.C., James Harter, Councillor N.K.P. Jamieson, Councillor T. Lenehan, J.P., D. Miller, James Milne, D.G. McDonald, Councillor W.G. Rankine, Councillor Bruce Salter, Councillor David Sanderson, Ian Smith, Councillor David Webster, Harold Whitson, C.B.E. Musical Director: Neeme Jarvi; General Administrator: Fiona Grant.
The Scottish National Orchestra gives more than 150 concerts in Scotland each year, and makes regular tours to Europe and North America. Its work also includes gramophone recordings and performances for radio and television.

Ordnance Survey, 160 Causewayside, Edinburgh. T.-031-668 3180. Manager (Scotland): J.G. Price; Area Manager (North): R.H. Brett; Area Manager (South): E. Pearson. Scottish office of national mapping agency of Great Britain. The organisation is entrusted with the task of maintaining the mapping of Great Britain up to date, and providing related services to the public and business.

Orienteering Association, Scottish. Secretary: Miss L. Cooper, 34 Burnbutts Crescent, Cove Bay, Aberdeen, AB1 4NU. T.-0224 897425.

Orkney Council of Social Service, Unit 9, Quest Building, Mounthoolie Lane, Kirkwall, Orkney. T.-0856 2897. President: Lady Laura Grimond; Chairman: J. Rendall. Co-ordinator: Mrs V.C. Reynolds. Voluntary organisation offering services to groups throughout Orkney.

Orkney Health Board (1974), Health Centre, New Scapa Road, Kirkwall, Orkney. T.-0856 2763. Chairman: J.D.M. Robertson; Vice Chairman: A.H. Bevan; Members: B.M. Clark, F.J. Groundwater, J. Leslie, J.W.R. Moar, J.S. Walker, J.C. Bevan, J. Flett, J.M.F. Groat, W. Groundwater, Mrs E.M. Street, J. Towrie, R.T. Tullock. Chief Administrative Medical Officer: Dr J.I. Cromarty; Chief Area Nursing Officer: Mrs D.E. Hudson; Chief Administrative Dental Officer: C.J. Booth; Secretary: J.A. Muir; Treasurer: A.F. Preen. Provision of health service in Orkney.

Orkney Islands Council (1974), Council Offices, Kirkwall, Orkney, KW15 1NY. T.-0856 3535. Convener: E.R. Eunson; Members: I.W. Argo, J.C. Brown, Mrs M.J.B. Crichton, W. Dass, J.D.C. Groat, H. Halcro-Johnston, E.S.H. Harcus, J.C. McRae, Mrs J. Marwick, C.T. Rioch, Mrs B.M. Robertson, J.R.T. Robertson, S.J. Rosie, A.J.B. Scholes, E.F. Scott, J. Scott, J. Sinclair, C.K. Soames, A.W. Stanger, G. Stevenson, J.A. Tait, T.A. Taylor, J. Towrie. Chief Executive: R.H. Gilbert; Director of Administration and Legal Services: R. McCallum; Director of Engineering: J.C. McIntosh; Director of Physical Planning and Development: M. Sargent; Director of Education: A. Bain; Director of Social Work: H. MacGillivray; Director of

Harbours: Captain D.O. Robertson; Director of Environmental Health: A.E. Leslie; Director of Architectural Services: M.M. Gilbertson. Islands Council. Population of Islands: 19,000.

Orkney Tourist Board (1969), Tourist Information Centre, 6 Broad Street, Kirkwall, Orkney, KW15 1NX. T.-Kirkwall 2856. Chairman: Kenneth Anderson. Secretary: Josh Gourlay. Promotion of tourism.

Ornithologists' Club, Scottish (1936), 21 Regent Terrace, Edinburgh, EH7 5BT. President: Dr Ivan T. Draper; Vice President: John M.S. Arnott; Law Agent: Dougal G. Andrew; Hon. Treasurer and Librarian: W.G. Harper; Editor: Valerie M. Thom. Secretary: John C. Davies. The Club was formed to encourage the study of ornithology in Scotland. It has 3,000 members and 13 branches in Scotland. Its offices, the Waterston Library, and the Bird Bookshop are located in Edinburgh's New Town. The Club publishes a quarterly journal, *Scottish Birds*, and the annual *Scottish Bird Report*.

Outer Hebrides Tourist Board, 4 South Beach Street, Stornoway, PA87 2XY. T.-0851 3088. Promotion of tourism.

Overseas Development Studies, David Livingstone Institute of (1974), University of Strathclyde, 16 Richmond Street, McCance Building, Glasgow, G1 1XQ. T.-041-552 4400. Director: Professor James Pickett. Research activities specialising in technology and development of less developed countries. Postgraduate training leading to M.Sc. and Ph.D. degrees.

P

Painters in Water-Colours, Royal Scottish Society of (1878), 12 Sandyford Place, Glasgow, G3 7NE. T.-041-248 7411. President: William J.L. Baillie; Vice Presidents: James Cumming, William Littlejohn; Treasurer: John B. Fleming. Secretary: John G. Barclay. Promotes annual exhibition of water-colours in the Royal Scottish Academy galleries.

Paisley Chamber of Commerce, 51 Moss Street, Paisley, PA1 1DS. T.-041-889 6244. (Nil Return).

Paisley College of Technology (1897), High Street, Paisley, PA1 2BE. T.-041-887 1241. Chairman, Board of Governors: Aubrey E. Harper; Vice Chairman: James M. McLaren. Principal: Thomas M. Howie; Vice Principal: Thomas C. Downie; Secretary and Registrar: John M. Oswald. Scottish Central Institution offering a wide range of undergraduate and postgraduate degrees with 3,000 students undertaking courses in science and technology, engineering, management, and social studies.

Paisley Daily Express (1874), 14 New Street, Paisley, PA1 1YA. T.-041-887 7911. Evening newspaper for Paisley and district.

Paraplegic Association, Scottish (1960), 3 Cargil Terrace, Edinburgh, EH9 2AW. T.-031-552 8459. General Secretary: Rosina Lamont. Welfare and sporting activities.

Parole Board for Scotland (1968), St. Margaret's House, London Road, Edinburgh, EH8 7TQ. T.-031-661 6181. Chairman: Mrs J.D.O. Morris, M.B.E.; Vice Chairman: Dr D. Chiswick; Members: The Hon. Mrs M. Corsar, The Hon. Lord Cowie, E.M. Dalglish, O.B.E., Dr E.E. Gavin, Rev. F.S. Gibson, R.F. Hendry, Sheriff A.C. Horsfall, D.M. Lowson, Mrs J.I. Miller, O.B.E., Dr J. Milne, J.M. Scott, T.B. Skinner, Dr G.S. Stirling. Secretary: I.C. Stewart.
Advises the Secretary of State for Scotland on the release of prisoners under licence, on the conditions of such licences, the revocation of such licences, and allied matters.

Patriots, The Scottish (1946), 76 Constitution Street, Edinburgh, EH6 6RP. T.-031-554 7951. Hon. President: Robert M. Robertson; Vice President and Secretary: Violet MacInnes; Treasurer: Robina Wood; Editor: Iain MacGregor. Independent independence movement founded by the late Wendy Wood, devoted to maintaining Scotland's identity in politics and culture.

Pension Appeal Tribunals (Scotland) (1943), 20 Walker Street, Edinburgh, EH3 7HS. T.-031-225 4734. President: D. Bruce Weir; Secretary: Miss E. Wilson. To hear appeals against rejection of war pension claims made by members of the forces.

Perth and Kinross District Council (1974), Council Chambers, 3 High Street, Perth. T.-Perth 21161. Provost: John M. Mathieson, J.P.; Members: Henry T. Beattie, O.B.E., Lorraine H. Caddell, Ewen W. Cameron, O.B.E., J.P., Hugh D. Campbell, J.P., Thomas Campbell, John B.F. Coutts, Robert A. Cromb, Dr Peter Dallas Ross, James Doig, J.P., Thomas Drane, J.P., James H. Ferguson, Mrs C.E.W. Ferrand, William Henry, Margaret R. Hockey, J.P., John M. Howe, Mrs J.E.W. McCormack, Roy A. McLean, Margaret Martin, Stewart O. Miller, William A. Morrison, Alexander Murray, Michael O'Malley, Brian McK. Scotland, J.P., Kathleen Scott, Alastair J. Stuart, David White, B.E.M., J.P., W.O. Wilson, J.P., Peter M. Young. Chief Executive: J.E.D. Cormie; Director of Finance: H. Robertson; Director of Planning: D.R. Penman; Director of Technical Services (Acting): J.J. Turnbull; Director of Environmental Health: W.A. Dunlop; Director of Housing: G. Black; Director of Leisure and Recreation: M.B. Wood; District Personnel Officer: G. Wallace; District Librarian: F.J. Guthrie; Curator of Museum and Art Gallery: J.A. Blair. District Council. Population of District: 119,000.

Perth College of Further Education, Brahan Estate, Crieff Road, Perth, PH1 2NX. T.-0738 27044. Principal: W. McNeill. College of further education.

Perth Repertory Theatre (1935), 185 High Street, Perth, PH1 5UW. T.-0738 38123. Chairman: Charles Lang. Artistic Director: Joan Knight, O.B.E.; General Manager: David J. Bonnar. Perth Theatre is the oldest established repertory theatre in Scotland. It operates seasons of plays and hosts visits from arts companies during the annual Perth Festival. Its objective is to provide a balanced and entertaining programme of events throughout the year.

Perthshire Chamber of Commerce (1871), 16 Dunkeld Road, Perth, PH1 5RW. T.-Perth 37626. President: T.A.S. Robinson; Vice President: R.W. Dunbar. Secretary/Treasurer: H.D. Ruthven.

Perthshire Tourist Board (1982), P.O. Box 33, George Inn Lane, Perth. T.-0738 27958/9. Chairman, Management Committee: Norman T. Renfrew. Director of Tourism: John L. Grainger. Promotion and development of tourism throughout Perthshire. During 1983, two million visitors came to Perthshire and spent £60m.

Pharmaceutical Federation, Scottish (1919), 135 Buchanan Street, Glasgow, G1 2JQ. T.-041-221 1235. Chairman: P. Gilbride. Secretary and Treasurer: Robert H. Stewart. Employers' association representing the commercial interests of retail pharmacists.

Pharmaceutical General Council (Scotland), 34 York Place, Edinburgh, EH1 3HU. T.-031-556 2076. (Nil Return).

Physical Education Association, Scottish. Secretary: Mrs J. Thompson, Balcanquhal Cottage, Glenfarg, Perth, PH2 9QD. T.-05773 414.

Physical Education, Scottish Council of. Hon. Secretary: G.M. Donald, Regional Council Office, Newtown St. Boswells, TD6 OSA. T.-08352 3301.

Physicians and Surgeons of Glasgow, Royal College of (1599), 234-242 St. Vincent Street, Glasgow, G2 5RJ. T.-041-221 6072. Registrar: John W. Robb. 4,500 Members and Fellows in many countries. Sets examinations and maintains standards of practice in all medical specialties.

Physicians of Edinburgh, Royal College of (1681), 9 Queen Street, Edinburgh, EH2 1JQ. T.-031-225 7324. President: Professor R.H. Girdwood, C.B.E.; Treasurer: Dr I.D. Campbell; Secretary: Dr T.M. Chalmers; Registrar: Dr J.L. Anderton. Maintenance of specialist standards amongst physicians in the

U.K. and overseas. Award of basic registrable qualifications and postgraduate diplomas in medicine, pharmaceutical medicine, and community child health. Dissemination of medical knowledge by meetings and publications.

Pipe Band Association, Royal Scottish (1930), 45 Washington Street, Glasgow, G3 8AZ. T.-041-2221 5414. President: Robert J. Black; Chairman, John W. Smith. Executive Officer: Robert Nichol. Aims to promote fellowship among all pipebandsmen; organises and promotes the Pipe Band College; organises pipe band competitions.

Pipers' Society, Royal Scottish (1881), 127 Rose Street Lane South, Edinburgh. T.-031-225 4123. Hon. Secretary: J.J. Burnet. Encourages the playing of the Highland Bagpipe among amateurs.

Pitlochry and District Tourist Association (1954), 22 Atholl Road, Pitlochry, Perthshire, PH16 5BX. T.-0796 2751. Tourist Director: Kyle N. Mackay. Promotion of Pitlochry and District, including operation of tourist centre, marketing, entertainments. Accommodation bookings third highest in Scotland. Only directly operated Bureau de Change in Scotland. Largest tourist association in Scotland.

Pitlochry Festival Theatre (1951), Port-na-Craig, Pitlochry, PH16 5DR. T.-0796 3054. Chairman, Board of Governors: Charles G. Findlay; Members: W.R. Douglas, G. Hallewell, Lt. Col. J.J. Lamb, O.B.E., Barbara M. Liddell, Professor Jan McDonald, P.B. Mackenzie Ross, A.G. Thomson, H. Young, J.P., Provost J.M. Mathieson, J.P., Councillors H.D. Campbell, N.K.P. Jamieson, J.S. MacKay, B. Mackie, A. Murray, Kathleen Scott. Administrator: Stephen Lawrence; Artistic Director: Sue Wilson; General Manager: Roy Wilson. Theatre for the presentation of drama, music, and art. Established in its famous 'tent' theatre for 30 years, it is now housed in a new building on the banks of the River Tummel.

Planning Exchange, The, 186 Bath Street, Glasgow, G2 4HG. T.-041-332 8541. Chairman: W.L. Taylor, C.B.E.; Vice Chairmen: Councillor C. Gray, Dr Derek Lyddon, C.B. Director and Secretary: Tony Burton; Associate Director: Tom Duncan. Independent body which acts as a centre for information, research, training, and publications on housing, planning, economic development, and finance and administration. It operates an extensive library.

Playing Fields Association (Scotland), National (1926), 12 Manor Place, Edinburgh, EH3 7DD. T.-031-225 4307. President: Rt. Hon. Lord Clydesmuir, K.T., C.B., M.B.E., T.D.; Chairman: W.F.E. Forbes; Deputy Chairman: Brian M. Simmers. Director: M.R.S. Cunningham, M.B.E. To encourage the provision and development of recreational and sporting facilities for the benefit of young people. Since 1946, the Scottish Branch has offered £225,000 to assist nearly 2,000 projects covering a wide variety of sports within voluntary clubs, organisations, and communities. In addition, grants of almost £95,000 have been allocated to the establishment of 84 King George V Memorial Fields.

Playwrights, Scottish Society of (1973), 37 Otago Street, Glasgow, G12 8JJ. T.-041-339 1787. Chairman: Ian Brown; Vice Chairman: Eric MacDonald; Secretary: Hector MacMillan; Treasurer: A.J. Stewart; Members of Council: Anne Downie, Carl MacDougall, John McGrath, Alan Richardson, Charles Palliser, Liz Lochhead. Administrator: Charles Hart. Formed by a group of playwrights to promote the development and production of theatre writing in Scotland and to help playwrights in all matters affecting them.

Plumbing Employers' Federation, Scottish and Northern Ireland (1923), 2 Walker Street, Edinburgh, EH3 7LB. T.-031-225 2255. Director: W. Todd Soutar; Secretary: Robert D. Burgon. Trade association for plumbing and domestic central heating firms. Membership of more than 1,000. It operates a code of fair trading and provides lists of local members on request.

Poetry Library Association, Scottish, Tweeddale Court, 14 High Street, Edinburgh, EH1 ITE. T.-031-557 2876. Director: Tessa Ransford. The Association has established the Scottish Poetry Library, opened in 1984. As well as being a lending and reference library, it is a centre of activity where everyone with an interest in poetry can come to browse, study, or listen to poetry on tape. A postal lending service is available.

Police Advisory Board for Scotland (1965), c/o Scottish Home and Health Department, St. Andrew's House, Edinburgh. T.-031-556 8501. The function of the Board is to advise the Secretary of State for Scotland on non-negotiable matters affecting the police in Scotland (i.e., matters other than hours of duty, leave, pay and allowances, or issue, use and return of police clothing, personal equipment and accoutrements). The Board comprises representatives from the Association of Chief Police Officers (Scotland), the Association of Scottish Police Superintendents, the Scottish Police Federation, C.O.S.L.A., and five independent members. It meets at least once annually.

Police College, Scottish, Tulliallan Castle, Kincardine-on-Forth, by Alloa, FK10 4BE. T.-0259 30333. Commandant: Major-General D.C. Alexander, C.B.

Police (Scotland) Examinations Board (1922), c/o Scottish Home and Health Department, St. Andrew's House, Edinburgh, EH1 3DE. T.-031-556 8501. Chairman: J. Dunning, C.B.E.; Vice Chairman: Dr W. Easton. To conduct the qualifying examinations or such other examinations in connection with the promotion or recruitment of constables, as designated by the Secretary of State.

Police Federation, Scottish (1919), 5 Woodside Place, Glasgow, G3 7PD. T.-041-332 5234; 041-332 6268. Chairman: Patrick Kennedy. General Secretary: Alexander Gowl. Staff association for members of the federated ranks of the Scottish police service.

Polo Association, Scottish. Secretary: Captain M. Fox-Pitt, The Grange, Cupar, Fife. T.-Gauldry 234.

Postal Board, Scottish, West Port House, 102 West Port, Edinburgh, EH3 9HS. T.-031-228 7200. Chairman: Ian Barr. Secretary: Martin Cummins. Provides Royal Mail letter, parcel, and counter services throughout Scotland.

Postgraduate Medical Education, Scottish Council for (1970), 8 Queen Street, Edinburgh, EH2 1JE. T.-031-225 4365. Chairman: Professor E.M. McGirr, C.B.E. Secretary: K.M. Parry, O.B.E.; Deputy Secretary: R.G. Cairncross; Administrative Officer: Annette Todd. The Council's terms of reference are to co-ordinate and stimulate the organisation and development of postgraduate medical and dental education and training in Scotland; to provide a national forum for discussion of matters relating to such education and training; and to provide the Government with an authoritative source of advice on these matters.

Post Office Users Council for Scotland (1969), Alhambra House, 45 Waterloo Street, Glasgow, G2 6AT. T.-041-248 2855. Chairman: G.C.C. Duncan; Members: W.J. Brown, M.B.E., T.D., Mrs J. Forbes Sempill, J.D.M. Hardie, W.J. Humphries, B.E.M., C.J. MacDonald, Mrs I.E. McGowran, Dr C. McLean, A.J. Paterson, T.J. Ransley, Mrs P.M.N. Stewart, D.G.

118 The Scottish Companion

Walker, J.G. Watson, J.P. Secretary: M. McNab; Assistant Secretary: Miss M. Barrett. Set up by Act of Parliament, and completely independent of the Post Office and British Telecom. The Council's job is to make sure customers have a voice in matters affecting them, such as the standard of quality of the service. The Council receives complaints from customers who have been unable to obtain satisfaction from the Post Office or British Telecom. It also takes the initiative in proposing changes in policies and practice where it considers such changes would further customers' interests.

Poultry Research Centre (1947), Roslin, Midlothian, EH25 9PS. T.-031-440 2726. Director: Dr D.W.F. Shannon. Established by the Agricultural and Food Research Council. Research at the Centre is aimed at increasing the biological efficiency of poultry production while maintaining and improving poultry welfare. This is facilitated by basic and applied research in various fields.

Press & Journal, The (1748, as *Aberdeen Journal*), P.O. Box 43, Lang Stracht, Mastrick, Aberdeen, AB9 8AF. T.-0224 690222. Editor: Peter Watson. Morning newspaper serving Aberdeen, Grampian and Tayside, and parts of the Highlands.

Prevention of Accidents, Royal Society for the (1924), Scottish Office, 41 South West Thistle Lane, Edinburgh, EH2 1EW. T.-031-226 6856. Director for Scotland: A. Fraser Dryburgh. R.O.S.P.A. is Europe's largest and most comprehensive safety organisation. It is a completely independent professional body drawing on a wealth of voluntary expertise available to it through its national committees. Much of its work is educational, teaching children how to avoid accidents in all environments. Specialist training to combat accidents at work is available at the Society's training centre in Birmingham or at venues throughout the country.

Prevention of Cruelty to Animals, Scottish Society for (1839), 19 Melville Street, Edinburgh, EH3 7PL. T.-031-225 6418. Chairman: Neil McCall Smith, J.P.; Vice Chairman: Peter Simpson; Members, Board of Directors: Mrs M.D. Fergusson, P. Murray, V.R.D., A.G.S. Bryson, Mrs M.S. Dewar, Mrs P. Evans, Mrs P.M. Guild, C. Husker, P.J.A. Leggate, J.P., Mrs Hope of Luffness, Mrs C.M. MacDonald, Mrs L.M. Shearer, Miss S. Rowan-Hamilton, Mrs J. Stuart, W.A.H. Johnston, R.C. Turcan, Mrs R.K.B. Cole-Hamilton, W. McLennan, D.K. Swan, G.F.S. Brian, J. Lamond. Chief Executive: Sir Cameron Rusby, K.C.B., M.V.O.; Treasurer: J.D.M. Watson.

Represents animal welfare interests to government, local authorities, and others; maintains inpectorate to patrol and investigate and to advise owners of their responsibility for the welfare of animals in their care; educates the young to realise their responsibilities.

Prevention of Cruelty to Children, Royal Scottish Society for (1884), Melville House, 41 Polwarth Terrace, Edinburgh, EH11 1NU. T.-031-337 8539. President: H.R.H. The Princess Margaret, Countess of Snowdon. Chairman, Executive Committee: Rev. H.M. Ricketts. General Secretary: A.M.M. Wood; Administrative Officer: D.L. Cowie; Organising Secretary: Mrs M. Mackay; Promotions Organiser: D. Turner; Social Work Executive Officer: R. Starrs; Training Officer: Mrs S. Davidson; Research/Information Officer: R. Irvine.

1984 marked one hundred years of child protection through the R.S.S.P.C.C. The objectives of the Society are: to promote and develop the social welfare of abused and neglected children; to protect the rights and interests of children; to prevent unnecessary suffering caused by private and public wrongs; in influence public policy to achieve these aims; and to undertake experimental or innovative activities for the benefit of children and their families. A team of 56 inspectors and caseworkers provide a round-the-clock service throughout Scotland, dealing with some 4,500 calls a year affecting more than 10,000 children.

Prevention of Vivisection, Scottish Society for the (1912), 10 Queensferry Street, Edinburgh, EH2 4PG. T.-031-225 6039. Director: Clive Hollands; Assistant Director: Leslie Ward. Animal welfare society concerned with the protection of animals from cruelty, the prevention of the infliction of suffering, and the abolition of vivisection. **St. Andrew Animal Fund** (1969). Established to undertake the purely charitable activities of the S.S.P.V. Seeks to promote humane attitudes towards animal life and the development of a proper understanding and appreciation of all living things. **Committee for the Reform of Animal Experimentation** (1977). The S.S.P.V. provides a secretariat for the Committee, which is drawn from both Houses of Parliament and the fields of science and medicine, as well as animal welfare. Devoted to the reform of the law relating to the use of animals for research experiments and other laboratory purposes. **Scottish Grey Seal Group** (1981). Chairman: Clive Hollands. Represents the Scottish viewpoint on the conservation and protection of the grey seal.

Princess Louise Scottish Hospital (Erskine Hospital) (1916), Bishopton, Renfrewshire, PA7 5PU. T.-041-812 1100. President: Rt. Hon. The Lord Provost of Glagow. Chairman: Sir Eric G. Yarrow, M.B.E.; Vice Chairman: Brigadier Alastair S. Pearson, C.B., D.S.O., O.B.E., M.C., T.D. Commandant: Colonel W.K. Shepherd; Assistant Commandants: Major C.A. MacDonald Gaunt, Sqn. Ldr. A.F. Shaw; Senior Medical Officer: Dr T. McFadyen; Matron: Mrs M.E. Lundie, J.P.; Treasurer: I.W. Grimmond; Secretary: A.O. Robertson, 179 West George Street, Glasgow. Founded by public subscription, initially to care for the limbless from the 1914-1918 War, subsequently accepting ex-servicemen from all three services (including the Merchant Navy) with all types of disability, illness, and injury, whether caused in peace or war. More than 50,000 have been cared for in the last six decades. The Hospital provides long or short stay and convalescent hospital facilities and opportunities for rehabilitation, training, and paid employment in the sheltered workshops and market garden. It is the largest ex-service hospital in the U.K. (300 beds), and is outwith the N.H.S. Annual running costs are some £3m., and after taking into account all public grants, investment income, and board charges, the Hospital requires more than £1m. annually to meet ordinary expenditure.

Prison Service, Scottish, St. Margaret's House, 151 London Road, Edinburgh, EH8 7TQ. T.-031-661 6181. Director: A.M. Thomson; Deputy Directors: D.M. MacIver (Operations and Industries), R.C. Allan (Administration), R.D. Jackson (Personnel and Services). Administration of prisons and other types of penal establishments in Scotland.

Procurator Fiscal Service. *Glasgow and Strathkelvin Region,* Custom House, 298 Clyde Street, P.O. Box 185, Glasgow. T.-041-204 2855. Regional Procurator Fiscal: J.M. Tudhope. *Lothian and Borders Region,* 3 Queensferry Street, Edinburgh. T.-031-226 4962. Regional Procurator Fiscal: J.D. Allan. *Grampian, Highlands and Islands Region,* T.-0224 654132. Regional Procurator Fiscal: M.T. MacNeill. *Tayside Central and Fife Region,* T.-0382 27535. Regional Procurator Fiscal: D.R. Smith. *North Strathclyde Region,* T.-041-887 5225. Regional Procurator Fiscal: J.B.R. Mackinnon. *South Strathclyde, Dumfries and Galloway Region,* T.-0698 284000. Regional

Procurator Fiscal: S.W. Lockhart. The Procurator Fiscal is the public prosecutor in the local Sheriff and District Courts. He is subject to directions from the Lord Advocate (see also Crown Office).

Procurators Fiscal Society (1930), Sheriff Court, 149 Ingram Street, Glasgow. T.-041-552 3434. President of Council: N.G. O'Brien; Treasurer: W.G. Carmichael; Secretary: L.A. Higson. Represents and promotes the career interests of members of the Procurator Fiscal Service; considers all subjects connected with the law of Scotland, the administration of justice, and the efficiency and conditions of the Service.

Procurators in Glasgow, Royal Faculty of (1796), 62 St. George's Place, Glasgow, G2. T.-041-332 3593. Dean: Duncan J. McKichan; Clerk, Treasurer, and Fiscal: J.H. Sinclair. To represent the interests of solicitors practising in the Glasgow area.

Protection of Birds, Royal Society for the (1889), 17 Regent Terrace, Edinburgh, EH7 5BN. T.-031-556 5624. Chairman, Scottish Regional Committee: N.J.O. Graham. Director (Scotland): Frank Hamilton. The R.S.P.B. acquires and manages nature reserves (100 in the U.K., including 35 in Scotland); carries out research; monitors land use practices and pollution affecting birds; protects and assists in the enforcement of the law relating to birds; conducts an extensive programme of formal education in schools and colleges and informal activity through the 90,000-strong Young Ornithologists' Club; produces and distributes its own bird films; and has an extensive publication department. The Society's membership in the U.K. is 375,000 adults.

Protection of Rural Scotland, Association for the (1926) 14A Napier Road, Edinburgh, EH10 5AY. T.-031-229 1898. President: Sir Ilay Campbell of Succoth, Bt. Chairman: Donald A. Reid; Vice Chairman: P. Playfair-Hannay; Members of Council: Mrs J. Hunter Blair, Lt. Cdr. H. Campbell-Gibson, R.N. (Rd.), S. Tod, G.R. Curtis, Robert Close. Director: Robert L. Smith, O.B.E., J.P. Central organisation to protect rural Scotland. Its objectives are: to stimulate and guide public opinion for the protection of the Scottish countryside; to act as a centre for giving advice and information on matters affecting the general welfare of rural areas, including towns and villages; and to encourage appropriate development in the countryside.

Public Transport, Scottish Association for (1964), 11 Queen's Crescent, Glasgow, G4 9AS. President: Professor Arnold Hendry; Chairman: Dr Morris Bradley. Promotion of the value of public transport to the community, and of improvements and developments in public transport.

Publishers Association, Scottish (1974), 25a South West Thistle Street Lane, Edinburgh, EH2 1EW. T.-031-225 5795. Chairman: Colin Kirkwood; Vice Chairman: Stephanie Wolfe Murray; Treasurer: Richard Drew; Secretary: Neville Moir. Administrative Executive: Judy Moir. To foster the growth of Scottish publishing by assisting member publishers in all aspects of publishing activity, particularly the joint promotion and marketing of members' publications. Membership of the Association is 60.

Q

Queen Margaret College (1875, as Edinburgh School of Cookery and Domestic Economy), Clerwood Terrace, Edinburgh, EH12 8TS. T.-031-339 8111. Principal: Miss C.L. Morgan. Scottish Central Institution offering degree courses in dietetics, home economics, speech pathology and therapy, nursing, and communication studies. Courses in health visiting, clinical nusing education, district nursing, and drama are also available. There are 1,100 full-time students.

Queen's College, Glasgow, The (1908), 1 Park Drive, Glasgow, G3 6LP. T.-041-334 8141. Chairman, Governing Body: Ian S. Hutchison, O.B.E., J.P.; Vice Chairman: Ethel M. Gray, C.B.E., J.P. Principal: Geoffrey A. Richardson; Vice Principal: Anthony Milson; Secretary and Treasurer: H.F.A. Rose. Provision of vocationally orientated higher education in the fields of catering, home economics, health sciences, and social work.

Queen's Hall (Edinburgh) Ltd. (1978), 5 Hope Park Crescent, Edinburgh, EH8 9NA. T.-031-668 2117. Chairman: Kenneth Newis, C.B., C.V.O. Administrator: Ursula M. Richardson. Owns and manages The Queen's Hall, a concert hall used by a wide variety of artistic organisations.

Queen's Nursing Institute, Scotland (1888), 31 Castle Terrace, Edinburgh. T.-031-229 2333. Chairman and Trustee: The Hon. Lord McDonald, M.C.; Vice Chairman: Dr A.D. Mitchell; Trustee: J.A. Dick Peddie; Hon. Treasurer and Trustee: P.W. Simpson; Hon. Secretary: Mrs G.S. Russell. Secretary and Treasurer: C.C. McInroy. Promotion of home nursing for the benefit of the sick; the stimulation of interest in District Nursing.

Queen's Own Highlanders (Seaforth and Camerons), Regimental Headquarters Cameron Barracks, Inverness. T.-Inverness 224380. Colonel of the Regiment: Major General J.C.O.R. Hopkinson, C.B. Regimental Secretary: Lt. Col. A.A. Fairrie; Assistant Regimental Secretary: Major A.F. Blincow, M.B.E. Regimental business on behalf of the Colonel of the Regiment, including Regimental Museum (at Fort George, by Inverness).

R

Radio Clyde plc (1973), Clydebank Business Park, Clydebank, G81 2RX. T.-041-941 1111. Chairman: F.I. Chapman; Managing Director: James Gordon, C.B.E.; Directors: William Brown, C.B.E., Kenneth McKellar, A.R. Macmillan, A.J. Murray, David Nickson, C.B.E., Sir Charles O'Halloran, Sir Iain Stewart. Programme Controller: Alex. Dickson; Chief Accountant: Norman Quirk; Chief Engineer: G. Allan; Sales and Marketing Controller: Geoffrey Holliman. Independent Local Radio station.

Radio Forth Ltd. (1975), Forth House, Forth Street, Edinburgh, EH1 3LF. T.-031-556 9255. Chairman: L.M. Harper Gow, M.B.E.; Managing Director: R. Findlay; Financial Director: A.R. Wilson; Programme Director: T.G. Steele; Directors: J. Romanes, K. MacFie, W. Blakey, J. Currie, R. MacPherson, D. Ford, K. Baker, A. McEwan. Sales Manager: G. Wilson; News Editor: D. Johnston; Topical Programmes Editor: M. MacDonald; Sports Editor: V. Wood. Independent Local Radio station serving Edinburgh and East Central Scotland.

Radio Nan Eilean, Rosebank, Church Street, Stornoway, Lewis. T.-0851 5000. BBC radio station for the Western Isles.

Radio Tay (1980), P.O. Box 123, Dundee, DD1 9UF. T.-0382 29551. Chief Executive: Allen R. Mackenzie. Independent Local Radio station for Dundee/Perth.

Railway Path and Cycle Route Project, Scottish (1980), 180 High Street, Edinburgh, EH1 1QS. T.-031-226 3971. Director: John Grimshaw. Community project to establish the feasibility of a network of safe routes for the use of cyclists and pedestrians.

Railway Preservation Society, Scottish (1961), Union Street, Bo'ness, EH51 0AD. T.-0506 822298. Chairman: Angus E. Rex; Secretary: Peter R. Ovenstone. Preservation of Scotland's railway heritage in general, and specifically the establishment and operation of the Bo'ness Steam Railway.

Ramblers' Association (Scotland) (1965). Hon. Secretary: R. Riddell, 3 Coats Place, Dundonald, Ayrshire. T.-0563 850406. To encourage rambling and mountaineering; to foster a greater knowledge, love, and care of the countryside; to work for the preservation of natural beauty and for the provision of access to open country.

Record Office, Scottish, H.M. General Register House, Edinburgh, EH1 3YY. T.-031-556 6585. Keeper of the Records of Scotland: J. Imrie; Deputy Keeper of the Records: A.L. Murray; Curator of Historical Records: J.D. Galbraith; Secretary, National Register of Archives (Scotland): P.D. Anderson.
The Scottish Record Office is responsible for the safe custody and

preservation of public and historical records relating to government, administration, and life in Scotland, and for providing services to facilitate their use by lawyers, historians, and the general public. The National Register of Archives (Scotland), which is a branch of the Scottish Record Office, carries out surveys of archives in private hands and advises and assists owners.

Records Association, Scottish (1977), University Library, Dundee, DD1 4HN. T.-0382 23181. Chairman: Dr Grant Simpson; Treasurer: Dr Ishbel Barnes; Secretary: Mrs Joan Auld. Concerned with the preservation and use of public and private records in Scotland. Promotes public interest in the subject, and offers a forum for communication between owner, custodian, and user of records.

Record Society, Scottish (1897). Hon. Secretary: Dr James Kirk, c/o Scottish History Department, University of Glasgow, Glasgow. President of Council: Professor Gordon Donaldson; Hon. Treasurer: Rev. Dr Duncan Shaw; Chairman: Dr Athol Murray. Publishes volumes of calendars and indices of public records and private muniments relating to Scotland.

Recreational Land Association, Scottish (1972), 18 Abercromby Place, Edinburgh, EH3 6TY. T.-031-556 4466. President: The Duke of Atholl; Vice President; Professor J.T. Coppock. Secretary: D.J. Hughes Hallett; Convener: J.P. Grant. Encourages and assists owners and occupiers of land in Scotland to provide facilities for public recreation, by giving specialist help and advice on the practical, legal, and commercial aspects of recreational land use.

Red Cross Society, British, Scottish Branch (1907), Alexandra House, 204 Bath Street, Glasgow, G2 4HL. T.-041-332 9591. Chairman, Scottish Council: The Marquis of Lothian, K.C.V.O.; Vice Chairman: Mrs I.R. Readman. General Secretary: Col. D.A.W. Lochhead; Assistant General Secretary: Colin W. Newman. Charity caring for people in need in Scotland. Also offers training in first aid, nursing, and welfare, and co-ordinates international appeals on behalf of the Red Cross in Scotland.

Red Deer Commission, The (1959), Knowsley, 82 Fairfield Road, Inverness, IV3 5LH. T.-0463 231751. Chairman: I.K. MacKenzie; Vice Chairman: R.W.K. Stirling; Members: Professor F.T. Last, D.J. Harrison, R.R. Balfour, Lord Dulverton, H.A. Waterson, J. Lammie, J.E. McNaughton, Lt. Col. L.G. Gray-Cheape, W.G. MacLeod, J.M. McDiarmid, W. Lindsay. Secretary: N.H. McCulloch; Assistant Secretary: G. Motion; Senior Deer Officer: L.K. Stewart; Deer Officer: R.W. Youngson.
To further the conservation and control of red and sika deer in Scotland and to keep under review matters relating to all species of deer. The Commission conducts an annual red deer census and advises on deer management, venison dealing, and the prevention of illegal taring and killing of deer.

Reformation Society, Scottish (1850), 17 George IV Bridge, Edinburgh, EH1 1EE. T.-031-225 1836. Chairman: Rev. James Crichton; Vice Chairman: Rev. David L. Wright; Hon. Treasurer: A. Fraser Maclennan. Secretary and Lecturer: Rev. A. Sinclair Horne. Interdenominational organisation set up to promote a witness to the Reformed heritage of Scotland stemming from the Scottish Reformation and subsequent events. Publications, lectures, tours of places of interest.

Reformed Presbyterian Church of Scotland (1743), 17 George IV Bridge, Edinburgh, EH1 1EE. Synod Clerk: Rev. A. Sinclair Horne. Presbyterian church.

Registers of Scotland, Department of the (1868), Meadowbank House, 153 London Road, Edinburgh, EH8 7AU. T.-031-661 6111. Keeper: W.S. Penman; Deputy Keeper: W. Russell; Senior Assistant Keepers: P.G. Skea, T.M. Nichol, J. Robertson. Registration of a wide range of legal documents, including those relating to transactions in land. The most important of these documents are the General Register of Sasines and the Land Register of Scotland, which concern rights in land and other heritable property. The Department also registers many other types of legal documents. These are kept in separate registers which still retain their ancient names, such as the Register of Hornings, Inhabitions and Adjudications, the Service of Heirs, the Great Seal, the Prince's Seal, and the Cachet Seal.

Regular Forces Employment Association, Scottish Society (1886), New Haig House, Logie Green Road, Edinburgh, EH7 4HQ. T.-031-557 1747. Chairman: Colonel H.F.O. Bewsher, O.B.E.; Vice Chairman: Flt. Lt. F. Roberts. Secretary and Employment Officer: Ft. Lt. F. Roberts. Helps find employment for ex-servicemen and women.

Reid Kerr College, Renfrew Road, Paisley, PA3 4DR. T.-041-889 4225. Chairman, College Council: J. McGuire. Principal: Frederick Sharples; Depute Principal: William Morrison; Registrar: J.A. Donnelly. College of further education.

Religious Education, Scottish Joint Committee on, c/o 46 Moray Place, Edinburgh, EH3 6BH. T.-031-225 6244. Joint Conveners: Rev. William Henney (Churches), Archibald Armour (Teachers). Joint Secretaries: Rev. Alasdair J. Morton (Churches), Frederick L. Forrester (Teachers). Joint Committee of the Educational Institute of Scotland and the various interests concerned with religious education.

Renfrew District Council (1974), Municipal Buildings, Cotton Street, Paisley, PA1 1BU. T.-041-889 5400. Provost: Walter McCready; Vice Chairmen: Agnes Allison, William Orr; Members: Thomas Williams, Thomas Wilkie, Olga Clayton, Irene Gilgallon, Robert MacAulay, Norman MacDonald, Walter Lucas, George Logie, Margaret Pollock, Alexander Morton, James Peden, Charles Bryce, George Murray, James Mitchell, Elizabeth McFaull, Henry Dean, Michael O'Sullivan, Richard Manser, George Farquharson, Ian Forbes, Agnes McKinnon, Owen Taylor, Daniel Collins, Joseph Reilly, James Harkins, Gordon McMaster, Sheila Fogg, Robert Stevenson, William Turner, Elizabeth McIntosh, Archibald Driver, Georgina Notman, Lawrence Millar, James Rutherford, Robert Cowper, Alexander Clark, Peter Fogg, Ian Taylor, Hugh Henry, Anne McOuat, James Waddell, Ruth Tait. Chief Executive and Director of Administration: William McIntosh; Director of Finance: Robert L. Ballantyne; Director of Technical Services: Ronald A.S. Rattray; Director of Physical Planning: Charles D. Begg; Director of Housing: James J.S.S. Maltman; Director of Leisure and Recreation: Iain C. McAdam; Director of Personnel and Management Services: Peter F. Waddell; Director of Cleansing: Stanley J. Dagg; Director of Environmental Health: Bernard J. Forteath; Chief Librarian: Joseph D. Hendry; Chief Curator of Museums and Art Galleries: David R. Shearer. District Council. Population of District: 206,000.

Research in Education, Scottish Council for (1928), 15 St. John Street, Edinburgh, EH8 8JR. T.-031-557 2944. Chairman: Gordon Kirk; Chairman, Finance Committee: John Hume; Chairman, Communications Committee: John Perry; Chairman, Research Committee: Margaret Cameron-Jones;

Members: William R. Dunn, Dr David A. Kennedy, Frank Pignatelli, Bernard M. Scott, D.I.M. Sutherland, William A. Illsley, James M. Ewing, Dr Leo B. Hendry, Dr J. David Hartley, Dr George O.B. Thomson, Melville R.M. Hendry, Thomas M. Linton, William Shaw, George Rubienski, Joyce J.M. Armstrong, Harry A. Ashmall. Director: Dr W.B. Dockrell. Semi-autonomous body funded by grants from the Scottish Education Department, local authorities, and teachers' associations, and through commissioned projects. In addition to undertaking research, and assisting others involved in research, it publishes reports and organises workshops and conferences. It also provides information in response to inquiries about educational issues.

Retirement Council, Scottish (1959), 212 Bath Street, Glasgow, G2 4HW. T.-041-332 9427. Director: S. Graham Hoey. To co-ordinate and organise education and preparation for retirement; to promote occupational activities for people in retirement; to provide information and advice on retirement.

Rights of Way Society, Scottish (1845), 28 Rutland Square, Edinburgh, EH1 2BW. T.-031-447 9242. Chairman: Dr Ian S. Fraser; Hon. Secretary: Robert A. Dickson; Hon. Treasurer: James S. Anderson. Preservation, maintenance, and defence of rights of way throughout Scotland. The Society keeps a watchful eye open for possible encroachment on the rights of the public, and aims at signposting all major cross-country routes in Scotland.

River Purification Boards' Association, Scottish (1957), City Chambers, Glasgow, G2 1DU. T.-041-221 9600. Secretary: I.G. Fraser. Protects the interests, rights, and privileges of River Purification authorities, and facilitates the exchange of ideas and discussion of common problems.

Robert Gordon's Institute of Technology (1903), Schoolhill, Aberdeen, AB9 1FR. T.-Aberdeen 633611. Chairman: Robert L.C. Hunter; Vice Chairman: James T.C. Hay. Principal: Dr Peter Clarke, C.B.E.; Vice Principal: Brian L. Gomes da Costa; Secretary: David C. Caldwell; Heads: Professor R.T. Hart (Business School), Professor C.N.C. Drey (School of Chemistry), Professor F.G. McIntosh (School of Electronic and Electrical Engineering), A.F. Flattely (Gray's School of Art), Armand Borisewitz (School of Hotel and Institutional Management), Dr Roderick Bennett (School of Home Economics), J.M. Orr (School of Librarianship and Information Studies), Dr J.R. Usher (School of Mathematical Sciences and Computer Studies), Professor Blyth McNaughton (School of Mechanical and Offshore Engineering), Professor D.M.S. Livingston (School of Nutritional Science), Dr Daniel Edwards (School of Pharmacy), Professor N.H. Langton (School of Physics), R.G.M. Webster (Scott Sutherland School of Architecture), C.W. Ellis (School of Social Studies), S.H. Baxter (School of Surveying). Scottish Central Institution providing degree, postgraduate, and post-experience vocational courses in architecture, art, business, chemistry, computer studies, design, electronic and electrical enginering, health visiting, home economics, hotel and catering management, information studies, librarianship, management studies, mathematics, mechanical and offshore engineering, nutrition, personnel management, pharmacy, physics, public administration, regional planning, social studies, social work, surveying, and urban design.

Rock Garden Club, Scottish (1933), 21 Merchiston Park, Edinburgh, EH10 4PW. T.-031-229 8138. Hon. Secretary Miss K.M. Gibb. Club of alpine gardening enthusiasts (3,500 in Scotland, the rest of the U.K., and overseas), who hold lectures, demonstrations, and competitive shows.

Roman Catholic Church. *Archdiocese of St. Andrews and Edinburgh.*
Archbishop: His Eminence Cardinal Gordon Gray, St. Bennet's, 42
Greenhill Gardens, Edinburgh, EH10 4BJ. T.-031-447 3337. *Diocese of
Aberdeen.* Bishop: Rt. Rev. Mario J. Conti, Bishop's House, 156 King's
Gate, Aberdeen, AB2 6BR. T.-0224 39154. *Diocese of Argyll and the Isles.*
Bishop: Rt. Rev. Colin MacPherson, Bishop's House, Esplanade, Oban,
PA34 5AB. T.-0631 62010. *Diocese of Dunkeld.* Bishop: Rt. Rev. Vincent
Logan, Bishop's House, 29 Roseangle, Dundee, DD1 4LX. T.-0382 24327.
Diocese of Galloway. Bishop: Rt. Rev. Maurice Taylor, Candida Casa, 8
Corsehill Road, Ayr, KA7 2ST. T.-0292 266750. *Archdiocese of Glasgow.*
Archbishop: Most Rev. Thomas J. Winning, 40 Newlands Road, Glasgow,
G43 2JD. T.-(Diocesan Centre, 18 Park Circus, Glasgow, G3 6BE) 041-332
9473. *Diocese of Motherwell.* Bishop: Rt. Rev. Joseph Devine, Viewpark
Road, Motherwell, ML1 3ER. T.-0698 63715. *Diocese of Paisley.* Bishop:
Rt. Rev. Stephen McGill, Bishop's House, Porterfield Road, Kilmacolm,
PA13 4PD. T.-Kilmacolm 2494. R.C. National Commissions:*Vocations
Commission,* St. Vincent's Centre, Langbank, PA14 6XA. T.-047 554 248.
Secretary: Rev. H.J. McEwan. *Liturgy Commission.* Secretary: Rev. J.A.
McKelvie, Chaplain's Residence, St. Andrew's College of Education,
Bearsden, Glasgow, G61 4QA. *Education Commission,* 43 Greenhill Road,
Rutherglen, Glasgow, G73 2SW. T.-041-647 2986. Secretary: James
McGrath. *Theology Commission.* Secretary: Rev. J. Cunningham, St.
Francis', Auchenbothie Road, Port Glasgow, PA14 6JD. T.-0475 43222.
Commission for Christian Unity, Diocesan Centre, Coursington Road,
Motherwell, ML1 1PW. Secretary: Rev. J. Quinn. *Communications
Commission,* 5 St. Vincent Place, Glasgow, G1 2DH. T.-041-221 1168.
General Secretary: Rev. T. Connelly. *Social Welfare Commission,* 18 Park
Circus, Glasgow, G3 6BE. T.-041-332 9473. *Justice and Peace Commission,*
28 Rose Street, Glasgow, G3 6RE. T.-041-333 0238. Secretary: Rev. W. J.
Slavin. *Catholic Heritage Commission.* Secretary: Rev. John McIntyre, Blairs
College, Aberdeen, AB9 2LA. *Joint Commission of Bishops and Council of
Major Religious Superiors,* 94 Dixon Avenue, Glasgow, G42 8EJ. Secretary:
Sister M. Slaven. T.-041-423 3634. *Scottish Catholic International Aid Fund,*
43 Greenhill Road, Rutherglen, Glasgow, G73 2SW. T.-041-647 2986.
Secretary: Duncan MacLaren. *Scottish Catholic Tribunal,* 22 Woodrow
Road, Glasgow, G41 5PN. T.-041-427 4212.
Scotland's estimated Catholic population is 814,000. There are two
archdiocese and six diocese and a total of 476 parishes.

Ross and Cromarty District Council (1974), County Buildings, Dingwall.
T.-0349 63381. Convener: G.D. Finlayson; Members: M.M.G. MacLennan,
R.W.K. Stirling, R. MacLennan, A.I. MacArthur, E.L. Simpson, S.M.M.
Newton, N. McKechnie, H. Fraser, A.J. Cameron, T. Anderson, J.C.
Stewart, Valerie Maciver, E.M. Wilson, R. Mardon, J.C. Mitchell, R.R.
Ruddie, Isobel C. Rhind, A.H.D.C. Ralph, Mrs E. Wilkerson, H. Miller,
E.R. Stone. Chief Executive: Alex. Cuthbertson; Director of Finance: J.I.
Glashan; Director of Environmental Health: G. Lemon; Director of
Housing: W.A. Gillies; Director of Architectural Services: G.B. Smith;
Director of Administration: D.J. Davidson; Director of Legal Services: I.
Robertson; Director of Leisure and Recreation: J. Watt. District Council.
Population of District: 47,000.

Ross and Cromarty Tourist Board (1981), North Kessock, Black Isle, Ross-
shire. T.-046373 505. Chairman: I. McCrae. Area Tourist Officer: Mrs E.
Allan. Promotion of tourism.

Ross Hall Hospital (1981), The Glasgow Independent Hospital Ltd., 221 Crookston Road, Glasgow, G52 3NQ. T.-041-810 3151. Chairman, Board of Directors: Sir William Gray. Hospital Director: Stuart Byron; Director of Nursing: Christeen Mundell; Director of Finance: Stephen Payne; Director of Marketing and Development: Lynda M. Somerville. Provider of health care services to the West of Scotland community.

Rothesay and Isle of Bute Tourist Board (1978), The Pier, Rothesay, Isle of Bute, PA20 9AQ. T.-0700 2151. Chairman: Mrs Irene Pincott. Area Tourist Officer: J.S. McMillan. Promotion of tourism.

Rowett Research Institute (1913), Greenburn Road, Bucksburn, Aberdeen, AB2 9SB. T.-0224 712751. Chairman, Governing Body: Principal G.P. McNicol; Vice Chairman: Professor H.M. Keir. Director: Professor W.P.T. James; Deputy Director: Dr A.S. Jones; Senior Staff: Dr P.J. Garlick (Director's Unit), Dr C.F. Mills (Inorganic Biochemistry), Dr P.N. Hobson (Microbial Biochemistry), Dr J.C. MacRae (Energy Metabolism), Dr B.F. Fell (Experimental Pathology), Dr R.N.B. Kay (Physiology and Veterinary Services), Dr A. Smith (Chemical Analysis), S.A. Abel (Engineering/Maintenance). The Institute is funded almost entirely by the Department of Agriculture and Fisheries for Scotland. It is considered to be the prime nutrition institute in the agricultural research service, and while the emphasis has been on animal nutrition in recent years, there is now a renewed interest in human nutrition. The total staff is 320, of whom 205 are in the science category.

Rowing Association, Scottish Amateur. Secretary: P.G. Morrison, 46 Churchill Drive, Bridge of Allan, Stirling, FK9 4TJ. T.-0786 833029.

Roxburgh District Council (1974), District Council Offices, High Street, Hawick, TD9 9EF. T.-0450 75991. Chairman: J.R. Irvine; Members: D. Rixham, Sarah Gillie, J. Murray, A. Middlemass, R. Jack, Mary Clark-Hutchison, G. Yellowlees, J. Scott, C. Wilson, Margaret Galloway, R. Campbell, Mary Turnbull, G. Turnbull, W. Douglas, J. Hamilton. Principal Officer and Director of Administrative and Legal Services: K.W. Cramond; Director of Finance: I.C. MacKerron; Director of Housing and Development: R.M. Johnson; Director of Technical Services: T. Armstrong. District Council. Population of District: 35,000.

Royal and Ancient Golf Club (1745), St. Andrews, Fife. T.-0334 72112. Secretary: M.F. Bonallack; Deputy Secretary: W.G. Wilson; Championship Secretary: D. Hill; Secretary, Rules of Golf and Amateur Status: J. Glover; Administration Secretary: T.B. Forrester. Governing authority for rules of golf in all countries of the world except U.S.A., Canada, and Mexico. Organisers of the Open Championship, Amateur Championship, Seniors, Youths, and Boys Championships, and Walker Cup matches in Great Britain.

Royal Bank of Scotland plc (1727), P.O. Box 31, 42 St. Andrew Square, Edinburgh, EH2 2YE. T.-031-556 8555. Chairman: Sir Michael Young-Herries, O.B.E., M.C.; Vice Chairmen: Peter E.G. Balfour, C.B.E., L.M. Harper Gow, M.B.E.; Directors: W. Jan Collins, Maurice H. Davenport, Robert G. Duthie, C.B.E., Ian F.H. Grant, J.P., Angus M.M. Grossart, Alexander M. Hamilton, C.B.E., J.P., J.C. Roger Inglis, John S.G. Kirkland, Douglas G. MacDonald, W. Robert McKim, Robert M. Maiden, Sidney Procter, Dennis Rebbeck, C.B.E., J.P., Sir Iain M. Stewart, William R.E. Thomson, Charles M. Winter (Managing Director). Senior General Manager (Banking): Alexander J. Reid; General Managers (Banking):

Andrew S. Buchan (Central Region), James Grier (Glasgow), Joseph M. Macdonald (Northern Region), Lewis S. McGill (Southern Region), John Sinclair (London); General Managers: David C. Arbuthnott (Staff), Donald A. Cameron (Trustee and Investment), Norman M. Irvine (Electronic Data Processing), Alexander McAndrew (Administration), John M. Mather (International), Robert H. Smith (Corporate Finance).

The Royal Bank transacts all customary banking business and operates almost 600 branches in Scotland, England, and overseas. It has correspondents throughout the world.

Royal Highland Fusiliers (Princess Margaret's Own Glasgow and Ayrshire Regiment), Regimental Headquarters, 518 Sauchiehall Street, Glasgow, G2 3LW. T.-041-332 5639; 041-332 0961. Regimental Secretary: Lt. Col. J.M.R. Fleming. Regimental business, including maintenance of Regimental Museum.

Royal Scots, The, Regimental Headquarters, The Castle, Edinburgh, EH1 2YT. T.-031-336 1761, Ext. 4265. Regimental Secretary: Lt. Col. J.L. Wilson Smith, O.B.E. The Regimental Museum of The Royal Scots (The Royal Regiment) contains records of 350 years of service, and attracts half a million visitors each year.

Royal Society of Edinburgh (1783), 22/24 George Street, Edinburgh, EH2 2PQ. T.-031-225 6057. President: Sir John Atwell, C.B.E.; Vice Presidents: Professors W. Cochran, C. Kemball, C. Blake, W.W. Fletcher, J. McIntyre, L.G. Whitby; General Secretary: Professor R.M.S. Smellie; Secretaries to the Ordinary Meetings: Professor R.J. Knops, Emeritus Professor A.M. MacLeod; Treasurer: I.A. Forbes; Curator of the Library and Museum: Professor D.M. Henderson; Councillors: A.J. Hale, Professor E.M. McGirr, D.H. Pringle, Professor V.B. Proudfoot, Professor D.M. Walker, Q.C., Sir Roger Young, E.J. Balfour, C.B.E., Professor P.E. Brown, Professor A.S.G. Curtis, Professor D. Hay, Professor J.C. Smith, Professor Lord Tedder. Executive Secretary and Librarian: William H. Rutherford.

Established under a Royal Charter granted by George III. Its origins can be traced to a number of scientific, medical, philosophical, and literary societies that were active in Edinburgh during the period of the Scottish Enlightenment. The principal functions of the Society have been the promotion of all branches of scholarship through the organisation of meetings, the publication of journals, and the maintenance of its library. Although the Society was founded and is based in Edinburgh, its Fellows, from the earliest days, have been drawn from all parts of Scotland and beyond, and have included scholars of all disciplines.

Rugby Union, Scottish (1873), Murrayfield, Edinburgh, EH12 5PJ. T.-031-337 2346. President: J.W.Y. Kemp; Vice Presidents: G. Burrell, Dr D.W.C. Smith; Secretary: I.A.L. Hogg; Treasurer: I.A. Forbes; Administrative Secretary: J.D. Cockburn; Technical Administrator: J.H. Roxburgh. National sporting organisation. There are 104 clubs and five District Unions in membership of the S.R.U. and 145 clubs in membership of the District Unions.

Rutherford House (Scottish Evangelical Research Trust) (1982), Claremont Park, Edinburgh, EH6 7PJ. T.-031-554 1206. Chairman: Rev. Martin Allen; Secretary and Hon. Administrator: Derrick Dawson; Treasurer: Duncan Martin. Warden: Rev. Dr Nigel M. de S. Cameron; Librarian: N.R. Needham; Administrative Secretary: Mrs R.M. Michell. Residential theological research library, established upon a conservative evangelical doctrinal basis. It sponsors research and co-ordinates study projects, publishes several journals as well as booklets and monographs, arranges lecture tours, and provides reading accommodation for students, academics, and ministers in its Library. The House is inter-denominational, although it maintains a special interest in the Church of Scotland.

S

Sabhal Mor Ostaig (1973), Teanga, An t-Eilean, Sgitheanach, Alba, IV44 8RQ. T.-04714 280. Chairman: Rev. Jack MacArthur; Vice Chairman: Allan Campbell. Principal: Sean F. O Drisceoil; College Secretary: Norman N. Gillies. Registered educational charity offering a unique two year H.N.D. course in business and Gaeltachd studies, taught through the medium of Gaelic and specifically designed for people wishing to make their livelihood in the Highlands and Islands of Scotland. Short courses are offered in Gaelic language, culture, piping, computing, accountancy, and management.

Salmon Angling Federation, Scottish. Secretary: G.W.S. Barry, 18 Abercromby Place, Edinburgh, EH3 6TY. T.-031-556 4466.

Saltire Society, The (1936), Saltire House, Atholl Crescent, Edinburgh, EH3 8HA. T.-031-228 6621. President: Professor Emeritus David Daiches; Immediate Past President: Sir Kenneth Alexander; Chairman of Council: Dr Jean O. Lindsay; Vice Chairmen: Dr G. Bruce, P.H. Scott, Margaret F. Sievwright, Margaret Street; Hon. Treasurer: Marjorie A. Matheson; Hon. Secretary: Ian A.G. Kinniburgh. Administrator: Kathleen Austin. Formed by a group of people who were anxious to see Scotland restored to its proper position as a cultural entity. The Society is concerned with all things Scottish, past, present, and future. It seeks to preserve all that is best in Scottish tradition and to encourage developments which can strengthen and enrich the country's cultural life.

Salvation Army in Scotland (1879), Houldsworth Street, Glasgow, G3 8DU. T.-041-221 3378. Territorial Commander: Colonel B. Wesley Harris; General Secretary: Lt. Col. W. Bramwell Baird; Field Secretary: Lt. Col. A. Thompson Wood; Financial Secretary: Major William Banks; Territorial Youth Secretary: Major Keith Banks. The objects of the Army are the advancement of the Christian religion, by the advancement of education, the relief of poverty, and other charitable objects beneficial to society or the community of mankind. It has 147 centres in Scotland, including 22 social service establishments, more than 200 full-time officers, 400 employees, and some 5,000 voluntary paying members.

School Broadcasting Council for Scotland, BBC, Broadcasting House, 5 Queen Street, Edinburgh, EH2 1JF. T.-031-225 3131. Chairman: Dr F. Macintosh, C.B.E. Secretary/Senior Education Officer: Jacqueline Johnston; Education Officers: Donald Gunn (North of Scotland), Dr Alastair Noble (West of Scotland). To advise the B.B.C. on the provision of appropriate educational broadcasts to Scotland; to conduct research, issue publications, and generally act as the official link between the educational world and the BBC.

Schoolmasters, National Association of, and Union of Women Teachers (Scotland) (1933), 4th Floor, 34 West George Street, Glasgow, G2 1DA.

T.-041-332 2688. President: S.A. Hood; National Executive Member: P. O'Donnell; Scottish Secretary: J. Duffy. Scottish Regional Official: James O'Neill. Part of a national trade union covering teachers throughout the U.K.

Schools Science Equipment Research Centre, Scottish (1965), 103 Broughton Street, Edinburgh, EH1 3RZ. T.-031-556 2184; 031-557 1037. Secretary: Dr R.G. Musgrave. Director: John Richardson; Depute Director: Allen Cochrane.

SCOPE in Scotland (formerly Scottish Pre-School Playgroups Association) (1969), 16 Sandyford Place, Glasgow. T.-041-221 4148/9. Executive Officer/ Company Secretary: Frances Love. SCOPE (Scottish Council for Opportunity in Play Experience) promotes awareness of the importance of play experience in a child's development.

Scotch Quality Beef and Lamb Association Ltd. (1974), 17 Grosvenor Crescent, Edinburgh, EH12 OPQ. T.-031-226 3797. Chairman: J.E. McNaughton; Vice Chairman: J.G. Ewing. Director and Secretary: M.W. Morris. Established by the national organisations representing Scottish farmers, meat wholesalers, livestock auctioneers, and butchers. Promotes Scotch beef and lamb.

Scotland-U.S.S.R. Society (1945), 8 Belmont Crescent, Glasgow, G12 8ET. T.-041-339 3008. President: Lady Ritchie-Calder; Vice President: William Taylor, C.B.E.; Chairman: Robert Brown; General Secretary: George McAlister. The promotion of peace, understanding, and friendship between the peoples of Scotland and the U.S.S.R.

Scotsman, The (1817), 20 North Bridge, Edinburgh, EH1 1YT. T.-031-225 2468. Editor: Eric B. Mackay. National morning newspaper.

Scottish and Newcastle Breweries plc, (1960), Abbey Brewery, Holyrood Road, Edinburgh, EH8 8YS. T.-031-556 2591. Chairman: David Nickson; Managing Director: Alick Rankin. Brewers, public house owners, and hoteliers. Turnover (1984): £692m.

Scottish Council (Development and Industry) (1946), 23 Chester Street, Edinburgh, EH3 7ET. T.-031-225 7911. Highland Office: 77 Church Street, Inverness. T.-0463 231878. North-East Office: 15 Union Terrace, Aberdeen, AB1 1NJ. T.-0224 642798. Glasgow Office: 87 St. Vincent Street, Glasgow, G2 5TF. T.-041-221 0200. President: Rt. Hon. Lord Clydesmuir, K.T., C.B., M.B.E., T.D. Chairman: P.E.G. Balfour, C.B.E. Members of Council: (nominated by the Association of Scottish Chambers of Commerce) W. Low, C.B.E., J.P., H.B. Johnson; (nominated by S.T.U.C. General Council) J. Morrell, J. Milne; (nominated by the Scottish Banks) C.M. Winter, D.B. Pattullo, A.R. Cole-Hamilton; (nominated by C.O.S.L.A.) Councillors D.R.W. Alexander, J.M. Askew, E.R. Eunson, Dr W.K. Fitzgerald, E.P. Harrison, R. King, Mrs J. McFadden, L. McGarry, D.J. McPherson, A.G. Sellar, T.G. Simpson, J. Wyness; (Representatives of corporate members) Sir Kenneth Alexander, K.J. Evans, J.D.H. Hume, H.B. Macnee, M.J. Moran, K.D.L. Risk; (Representatives of ex officio and private members): Hon. James Bruce, J. Foss Finnie, T. McAlpine, Dr R.D. McIntyre, D.J. Mackay; (nominated by the Secretary of State for Scotland): Professor Norman C. Hunt, C.B.E., W.B. Miller, O.B.E., Rt. Hon. Viscount Weir; (Representatives of Standing Committees): Rt. Hon. Lord Balfour of Burleigh, John G. Bridges, O.B.E., C.G. Carnie, E. Dietlicher, Sir James Farquharson, K.B.E., J.D. Hardie, L.M. Harper Gow, M.B.E., J. Langan, Sir William Lithgow, Bt., C.A.

Oakley, Sir D. McDonald, C.B.E., K.J. Peters, C.B.E., J.P., W.T. Stevenson, D.A. Ross Stewart, Rt. Hon. Lord Taylor of Gryfe; Co-opted members: R.W. Colvil, P. De Vink, D.B. Gillan, G.A. Hepburn, Dr T.L. Johnston, A.S. Kyle, J. Mather, D.W. Mitchell, J.A. Riddell-Webster, M.C., G.B. Thomson, C.B.E.
Chief Executive: H.R. Morrison; Operations Director: A. Wilson; Director, Policy Research: R.C. Campbell; Director, International Forum: J. Saunders; Secretary: H. Hunter.
The Council is a voluntary organisation supported by Scottish industry, banks, local authorities, and trades unions, founded to advance the industrial and social development of Scotland by helping to stimulate growth in the economy and in employment.

Scottish Office, New St. Andrew's House, Edinburgh, EH1 3SK. T.-031-556 8400. Secretary of State: Rt. Hon. George Younger, M.P.; Minister of State for Agriculture and Fisheries: Lord Gray of Contin; Minister for Industry and Education: J. Allan Stewart, M.P.; Minister for Health and Social Work: John J. MacKay, M.P.; Minister for Home Affairs and the Environment: Michael Ancram, M.P. Permanent Under-Secretary of State: Sir William Fraser, G.C.B.; Deputy Secretary (Central Services): I.D. Penman.
The Scottish Office consists of five departments: Department of Agriculture and Fisheries for Scotland; Industry Department for Scotland; Scottish Development Department; Scottish Education Department; and Scottish Home and Health Department. (See separate entry for each). These Departments (plus a group of Central Services divisions including the Solicitor's Office, the Scottish Information Office, the central Statistical Unit, and the Inquiry Reporters) are collectively known as the Scottish Office, which administers the Secretary of State's statutory functions.

Scout Association, The (1908), Scottish Headquarters, 18 Hanover Street, Edinburgh, EH2 2QN. T.-031-226 7375. Chief Commissioner of Scotland: W. Garth Morrison. Secretary: R. Hendy Procter; Executive Commissioner: David C. Jefferies. To encourage the physical, mental, and spiritual development of young people so that they may take a constructive place in society. Provides an enjoyable and attractive scheme of progressive training in a wide variety of pursuits and adventurous activities based on the Scout promise and law and guided by adult leadership.

Scripture Union – Scotland (1867), 280 St. Vincent Street, Glasgow, G2 5RT. T.-041-221 0051. Chairman: W.G. Johnston; Hon. Treasurer: J.H. Beattie. General Secretary: Rev. J.M.F. Butler; Schools Director: Miss E.T.M. Clark; Camps Director: Graham D. Wilson. Christian evangelism and nurture through camps, missions, school groups, and literature.

Sea Anglers, Scottish Federation of (1961), 18 Ainslie Place, Edinburgh, EH3 6AU. T.-031-225 7611. President: M.L. Rowlands; Secretary: Cath Watson.

Sea Fish Industry Authority (1981), Sea Fisheries House, 10 Young Street, Edinburgh, EH2 4JQ. T.-031-225 2515. Chairman: J.P. Rettie, T.D.; Deputy Chairman: B. Davies; Members: A.M. Bannerman, A.J. Bolt, S.C. Craigs, O.B.E., G. Crawford, O.B.E., J.R. Crook, M. Gallin, M.B.E., W. Hay, M.B.E., J.M. Keenan, Professor D.I. MacKay, I.C. Wood, C.B.E. Chief Executive: J.C.H. Richman; Secretary: R.A. Davie; Finance Director: A. Downie; Technical Director: P.D. Chaplin; Marketing Director: R.M. Kennedy.
Statutory body for the purpose of promoting the efficiency of the sea fish industry having regard to the interest of consumers of sea fish and sea fish

products. The Authority has power to carry out research and development, provide training, promote the marketing and consumption of sea fish and sea fish products, and provide financial assistance to construct or improve fishing vessels and plant for making ice or processing sea fish.

Secondary Teachers' Association, Scottish (1946), 15 Dundas Street, Edinburgh, EH3 6QG. T.-031-556 5919; 031-556 0605. President: D. Campbell; Vice President: D.C. Halliday. General Secretary: A.A. Stanley; Assistant General Secretaries: A.C. Duncan, A.M. Lamont; General Treasurer: J.R. McKelvie. Independent organisation of secondary teachers in Scotland. Its objects are to advance education in Scotland with particular regard to secondary education, and to safeguard and promote the interests of Scottish secondary teachers in all matters. The Association is a registered, independent trade union affiliated to the S.T.U.C., but does not maintain a political fund. Current membership is 7,200.

Seed and Nursery Trade Association, Scottish (1917), 12 Bruntsfield Crescent, Edinburgh, EH10 4HA. T.-031-447 1035. Secretary and Treasurer: J.R.L. Cruickshank. Trade association.

Seed Potato Development Council, Scottish (1981), 10 Rutland Square, Edinburgh, EH1 2AS. T.-031-228 6768. Chairman: John Fotheringham, O.B.E.; Workers' Representative: Henry Crawford, M.B.E.; Producers' Representatives: A.A. Arbuckle, W.H. Porter, J.A. McLaren, A.J. Roy, W.L. Gill, J. Jeffrey; Merchants' Representatives: J.H. Barr, J.E. Cook, J.O. Robertson, D.A. Lawson, R.G. Ramsay, I.R. McKenzie, R. Doig. Chief Executive: John Bethell. Established by the Secretary of State for Scotland with the aim of achieving the maximisation of profitability of the seed potato industry in Scotland.

7:84 Theatre Company Scotland (1973), 31 Albany Street, Edinburgh, EH1 3QN. T.-031-557 2442. Artistic Director: John McGrath; General Manager: Kate Craik; Assistant General Manager: John Wood. The company's first production was *The Cheviot, The Stag and The Black, Black Oil*. Since then, it has performed more than 20 productions throughout Scotland. 7:84 has established a theatre in Scotland which presents the realities of working class life and history directly to working class audiences. It has its roots in the popular tradition of entertainment.

1745 Association (1947). Hon. Secretary: Miss C.W.H. Aikman, Ferry Cottage, Ardgour, Fort William. Chairman: Alastair Livingstone; Hon. Treasurer: Rev. K.E. Wigston. Study of the history of the House of Stuart and the Jacobite period.

Shelter-Scottish Campaign for the Homeless (1968), 65 Cockburn Street, Edinburgh, EH1 1BU. T.-031-226 6347. Chairman, Scottish Advisory Council: Dr Peter Robson; Members: John Maxton, M.P., Anna McCurley, M.P., Councillor Val Woodward, Ian Gracie, Mary Brailey. Director: Noel Dolan; Depute Director: Martyn Evans. Campaigning organisation on behalf of Scotland's homeless and badly housed. Uses the casework experience of Shelter's three housing aid centres; develops local projects; conducts research and educational work.

Shetland Chamber of Commerce (1936), 122 Commercial Street, Lerwick, ZE1 OEX. T.-Lerwick 4739. Chairman: J.H. Ferris. Secretary: Mrs V.J. Cousins.

Shetland Health Board (1974), 28 Burgh Road, Lerwick, ZE1 OQP. T.-0595 5678. Chairman: R. Adair; Vice Chairman: W.A. Smith; Members: R.R. Bentley, A.G. Flaws, A.H. George, Mrs F.B. Grains, Dr M.D. Hunter, R.

Leask, J.A. Leslie, R.L.C. Manson, Mrs J.K. Sandison, J.M. Sinclair, Mrs
L.A. Stout, Mrs M. Williamson, S.A. Zaman. Secretary: David C. March;
Treasurer: David P.P. Eva; Chief Administrative Medical Officer: Dr Jill
MacDonald; Chief Administrative Dental Officer: John F. Allan; Chief Area
Nursing Officer: Merryn S. Henderson. Provision of health service in
Shetland.

Shetland Fishermen's Association (1947), 14 Alexandra Buildings, Lerwick,
Shetland. T.-0595 3197. Secretary: J. Goodlad. Represents all full-time
fishermen in Shetland. **Shetland Fish Producers Organisation Ltd.** (1982).
Primarily concerned with administering the E.E.C. market support system.

Shetland Islands Council (1974), Town Hall, Lerwick, ZE1 OHB. T.-0595 3535.
Convener: A.I. Tulloch; Vice Convener: E. Thomason; Members: W.A.
Anderson, R.R. Bentley, M.S. Bray, A.J. Cluness, W.A. Cumming, C.J.
Dowle, C.R.H. Eunson, J.L.W. Eunson, A.B. Fraser, J.J. Graham, R.S.
Gray, L.G. Groat, J.A. Hunter, P.B.A. Hunter, J.C. Irvine, D.J. Johnston,
Miss A. Manson, T.M.Y. Manson, Mrs J. McLeod, W.A. Smith, H.A.
Stewart, W. Tait, G.A. Walterson. Chief Executive: Michael A. Gerrard;
Director of Finance: Malcolm E. Green; Director of Administration: Patrick
B. Regan. Islands Council. Population of Islands: 22,000.

Shetland Pony Stud-Book Society (1890), 8 Whinfield Road, Montrose, Angus.
T.-0674 73148. Secretary and Treasurer: D.M. Patterson. Breed society.

Shetland Tourist Organisation (1969), Information Centre, Lerwick, ZE1 OLU.
T.-0595 3434. Chairman: E. Cope. Director of Tourism: M.S. Mullay.
Promotion of tourism.

Shooting Council, Scottish. Secretary: Dr G. Webb, 39 Pelstream Avenue,
Stirling, FK7 OBG. T.-0786 75769.

Single Homeless, Scottish Council for (1974), 4 Old Assembly Close, Edinburgh,
EH1 1QX. T.-031-226 4382. Chairman: Sandy Murray; Vice Chairman:
Sheila Campbell; Hon. Treasurer: David D. Duncan. Director: Laurie M.
Naumann; Administrative Secretary: Allison T. Bertram. Campaigns on
behalf of single homeless people in Scotland and aims to promote their social
welfare. It provides information and advice, and carries out research on
housing and allied welfare needs. The Council also deals with the broader
issues relating to housing for single people. It encourages and co-ordinates
collaboration with other organisations, including both voluntary agencies and
statutory authorities, influencing legislation and policy developments which
have a bearing on single persons' housing needs nationally and, where
appropriate, locally.

Single Parents, Scottish Council for (1944), 13 Gayfield Square, Edinburgh, EH1
3NX. T.-031-556 3899. Chairman: Mrs A.R. Turnbull; Vice Chairmen: Mrs
N. Campbell, Mrs M. Walker. Director: Miss J.A. MacQueen, O.B.E.;
Training Officer: Ms S. Robertson. The Council is a co-ordinating body of
organisations concerned with one parent families, be they separated,
divorced, unmarried, or bereaved. It aims to bring about improvements in
the lives of single parents and their children, by stimulating new ventures,
undertaking research, publishing information, organising study days, and
acting as a consultative body.

Ski Council, Scottish National, 110a Maxwell Avenue, Bearsden, Glasgow, G61.
T.-041-943 0760. Secretary: Catherine Legget.

Skye and Lochalsh District Council (1974), District Council Offices, Park Road,
Portree, Isle of Skye, IV51 9EP. T.-Portree 2341. Chairman: John F. Munro;

Vice Chairman: Alexander M. Munro; Members: Murdoch J. MacLeod, Olive Parker, Alistair W. Langlands, Donald M. MacKenzie, Peter Fulton, Farquhar M. MacLennan, George Sutherland, Donald Cameron. Chief Executive: David H. Noble; Director of Finance: Kenneth G. Goddard; Director of Environmental Health: Norman M. Gillies; Housing Manager: Graham Ross; Building Services Manager: Andrew R. MacLaren. District Council. Population of District: 10,000.

Skye and South West Ross Tourist Board, Isle of, Tourist Information Centre, Portree, Isle of Skye, IV51 9BZ. T.-0478 2137. Chairman: Jonathan MacDonald. Secretary to the Board and Area Tourist Officer: Peter H. Turner. Promotion of tourism.

Social Democratic Party, Scottish Office, 5 Royal Exchange Square, Glasgow, G1 3AH. T.-041-221 8871. Chairman, Council for Scotland: Peter Wilson; Secretary: Moira Craig. Scottish Organiser: John Best. Political organisation.

Solicitors Discipline Tribunal, Scottish (1934), 5 Rutland Square, Edinburgh. Clerk: John M. Barton. Judicial tribunal operating under the provisions of the Solicitors (Scotland) Act 1980 and empowered principally to hear complaints of professional misconduct against solicitors enrolled in the register of solicitors in Scotland.

Solicitors in the Supreme Courts of Scotland, Society of (1784), S.S.C. Library, Parliament House, Edinburgh, EH1 1RF. T.-031-225 6268. President of Council: John G. Gray; Vice President: A.P. Laird; Treasurer: D.A. Lamb; Librarian: C.W. Palmer; Fiscal: N.H. Rose and Messrs J.M. Reid, J.H. Crawford, A.J. Robertson, R.M. Harley, N.M. Stewart, P. Wheatley, A.G. McCulloch; Secretary: Alistair R. Brownlie, 2 Abercromby Place, Edinburgh, EH3 6JZ. Keeper of the Library: Andrew Gill; Assistant Keeper: Hugh Cameron. The Society consists of some 250 solicitors, mostly but not all in the vicinity of Edinburgh, whose work lies principally in the Supreme Courts of Scotland – the Court of Session and the High Court of Justiciary. As a part of the College of Justice in Scotland, the Society encourages the development of Scots law, the practice of the law, and the contribution of solicitors to law and public life.

Solway River Purification Board (1954), Rivers House, Irongray Road, Dumfries, DG2 OJE. T.-0387 720502. Chairman: Col. Sir William E. Jardine of Applegirth, Bt., O.B.E., T.D. Director: C.P. James; Depute Director: W.T. Welsh. Formed under the terms of the Rivers (Prevention of Pollution) (Scotland) Act 1951 and reconstituted in 1975 under the Local Government (Scotland) Act 1973. The Board is a pollution prevention authority and also the hydrological authority for its area.

South of Scotland Chamber of Commerce (1861), 19 Buccleuch Street, Hawick, Roxburghshire. T.-0450 72267/8. Secretary: A.L. Rintoul; Assistant Secretary: T. Young.

Spastics, Scottish Council for (1946), 22 Corstorphine Road, Edinburgh, EH12 6HP. T.-031-337 9876. President: Rt. Hon. Lord Clydesmuir, K.T., C.B., M.B.E., T.D.; Honorary Vice Presidents: Admiral Sir Nigel S. Henderson, G.B.E., K.C.B., A. Stone, Mrs M.T. Fraser. Executive Committee: Chairman: G.A. Pollock, O.B.E.; Vice Chairmen: T.E. Woodsend, J.P., K.G. Hooper; Members: J. Anderson, C.B.E., J.C.M. Cormie, W. Drysdale, Miss J.M. Errington, M.B.E., J.M. Findlay, V.R.D., K.E. Guest, G.D. Holmes, C.B., Dr J.M. MacArthur, Sheriff J.L.M. Mitchell, Dr J.A.L. Naughton, M.C., J. Oswald, M.B.E., J.G. Paul, R. Pettie, M.S. Preston, T.D., J.L. Richardson, Miss D.D. Smith, M.C.B. Ward, Mrs A. Watson.

Director: Commander A. Cameron, O.B.E., D.S.C., R.N. (Rd.); Depute Director/Personnel Officer: A.M. Brown; Finance Officer: R.I.H. Scott; Appeals Manager/Public Relations Officer: A.D.J. Dickson. The principal purpose of the Council is to plan, initiate, promote, or assist schemes and activities directed towards the well-being of persons suffering from cerebral palsy and allied conditions and/or from any other illness, disease, or accident causing physical handicap or disablement whether or not accompanied by mental handicap or sensory loss. The Council manages various special establishments and services, including schools, adult employment centres, adult residences, therapeutic services, and social services.

Special Housing Association, Scottish (1937), 15/21 Palmerston Place, Edinburgh, EH12 5AJ. T.-031-225 1281. Chairman, Council of Management: Derek S. Mason, J.P.; Deputy Chairman: Charles Snedden, O.B.E., J.P.; Members: Tom Begg, A. Bryan Broomfield, Mrs A.T. Cruickshank, Ian Stevenson, Tom McCalmont. General Manager: F.C. Marks, O.B.E.; Director of Technical Services: J.H. Fullarton; Secretary and Director of Administration: R.O. Stevenson; Director of Finance: I.G. Ireland; Director of Housing Management: L. Ferguson, M.B.E.
The S.S.H.A. is a Government sponsored body which designs, builds, and manages houses on a non-profit-making basis. Set up to build houses in the Special (or 'Distressed') Areas, the Association's function was extended after the War to provide houses for any local authorities requiring assistance with their housing problem. It has developed into an organisation employing some 2,000 people and has built more than 110,000 houses – one tenth of the public sector houses in Scotland. Houses have been built from Shetland to the Borders and many thousands of houses have been modernised. Since 1979, the sale of houses to sitting tenants has become a major role.

Spina Bifida Association, Scottish (1966), 190 Queensferry Road, Edinburgh, EH4 2BW. T.-031-332 0743. Executive Officer: A.D. Smith. To improve quality of life for those of all ages with spina bifida and/or hydrocephalus and allied disorders. National information service; counselling; group and family holidays; sports training courses; self-management courses.

Sports Association for the Disabled, Scottish. Hon. Secretary: Bill Fenwick, 14 Gordon Court, Dalclaverhouse, Dundee. T.-0382 40263.

Sports Council, Scottish (1972), 1 St. Colme Street, Edinburgh, EH3 6AA. T.-031-225 8411. Chairman: Peter Heatly, C.B.E.; Vice Chairman: Dr Valerie J. Marrian; Members: M.C. Barron, Miss M.B. Burns-Greig, E.W. Cameron, O.B.E., J.P., Professor J.T. Coppock, Mrs A.M. Gulland, G.A. Hunter, O.B.E., W. McAllister, J. Mclean, R.C. Miquel, C.B.E., Dr P.F. Radford, R.B. Rafferty, R.A. Robertson, The Hon. Mrs Sandeman, J.M. Souness, A. Stuart, Miss M. Urquhart. Chief Executive: J.K. Hutchison; Deputy Chief Executive: R. McDonald; Head of Administrative Division: N.T. Harvey; Head of Facilities Planning Division: Dr I.G. Davies; Head of Sports Development Division: D.G. Casey; Head of Information Services Dept.: G. Shepherd.
The Council was established by Royal Charter with the objects of fostering the knowledge and practice of sport and physical recreation among the public at large in Scotland and the provision of facilities. It receives annual grant-in-aid from the Government from which it provides financial assistance to governing bodies of sport – for coaching, administration, and international events; to local sports clubs – for playing and associated facilities; and to local authorities and others – for sports projects including national and prototype facilities. The Council also undertakes research, provides information and advisory services, and operates three national sports training centres:

Glenmore Lodge, National Outdoor Training Centre, Aviemore, Inverness-shire. T.-Aviemore 86256. Principal: F.W.J. Harper.
Inverclyde National Sports Training Centre, Largs, Ayrshire. T.-Largs 674666/7.
Cumbrae National Water Sports Training Centre, Largs, Ayrshire. T.-Largs 674666/7. Principal (Inverclyde and Cumbrae): M.R. Barratt.
The Council has established a **Scottish Sports Association** (formerly Scottish Standing Conference of Sport), membership of which is open to all the governing bodies of sport and physical recreation in Scotland and other appropriate organisations. Its functions include acting as a consultative body to the Scottish Sports Council.

Sports Aid Foundation, Scottish 11 Market Street, Edinburgh, EH1 1DE. T.-031-663 9239; 031-225 5484. Chairman, Committee of Governors: R.C. Miquel, C.B.E.; Governors: P. Heatly, C.B.E., The Duke of Hamilton, W.M. Campbell, G.A. Hunter, O.B.E., A. Gibson, J. Loughray, B. Marshall. Administrator: D.J O'Brien. Autonomous fund-raising Foundation, which awards grants to competitors, preferably young, who represent Scotland or are deemed to have the ability to represent Scotland, at any sport. Grants are to assist with the costs of extra coaching, or for travel to competition away from home.

Springburn College (1965), 110 Flemington Street, Glasgow, G21 4BX. T.-041-558 9001. Principal: A.J. Ironside; Depute Principal: N. MacNicol; Registrar: R.S. Masson. Originally a specialist college of engineering, the College is now developing over a broader base, with particular emphasis on meeting the needs of the local community.

Squash Rackets Association, Scottish (1936), 18 Ainslie Place, Edinburgh, EH3 6AU. T.-031-225 2502. Secretary: Brenda Carmichael. National Coach: Robin Smeaton. To foster the playing of the game at all levels.

St. Andrew's Ambulance Association (1882), St. Andrew's House, 48 Milton Street, Glasgow, G4 OHR. T.-041-332 4031. President: The Duke of Buccleuch and Queensberry, K.T., V.R.D.; Vice Presidents: The Lord Provost of Glasgow, The Convener of Strathclyde Regional Council, Dr H.R.F. Macdonald, O.B.E., John Blair, A.B. Robertson, B.E.M., D. Strachan, O.B.E., James Magee, M.B.E. Chairman of Council: Dr H.R.F. Macdonald, O.B.E. Director General and Secretary: J.W.R. Cunningham; Director (Administration): J. Jackson; Director (Training): G.A. Watt. Provides training and qualifications in first aid and home nursing, and equipment in these fields. Through a corps of trained volunteers, the Association also provides first aiders to assist at public occasions and events as community service.

St. Andrews and North East Fife Tourist Board, 2 Queens Gardens, St. Andrews, Fife. T.-0334 74609. Chairman: Councillor D. Niven. Tourism Manager: Miss S.L. Grandison. Promotion of tourism.

St. Andrew's College of Education (1981), Bearsden, Glasgow, G61 4QA. T.-041-943 1424. Chairman, Board of Governors: Rt. Rev. Joseph Devine. Principal: Sister Margaret Sheridan; Vice Principal: Bartholomew J. McGettrick; Assistant Principals: Sister Dorothea M.E. Sweeney, Teresa Gourlay. Formed as the result of a merger between Notre Dame and Craiglockhart Colleges of Education, to become Scotland's national Catholic College for the training of teachers.

St. Andrew Society, The, P.O. Box 84, Edinburgh. T.-031-228 1902. President: Cecil G. McGregor; Chairman: Dr W.J.A. Macartney; Secretary: William McIntyre; Treasurer: Elizabeth Wark. To uphold the rights and privileges of

Scotland and the Scottish people, encourage the celebration of St. Andrew's Day and the study of Scottish literature, arts, music, and customs, and maintain connections with affiliated societies abroad.

St. Andrews, University of (1410), College Gate, St. Andrews, Fife KY16 9AJ. T.-0334 76161. Chancellor: Sir Kenneth James Dover; Rector: Katharine Whitehorn; Principal and Vice Chancellor: John Steven Watson; Secretary and Registrar: Dr Martin J.B. Lowe; Quaestor and Factor: Charles P. Gordon; University Librarian: Alexander G. Mackenzie.
Senatus Academicus: Professorial Members: Professors M.A. Jeeves, D. Brynmor Thomas, William McKane, R.M.M. Crawford, J.A. Whyte, D.W.N. Stibbs, R.B. Dingle, Lord Tedder, R.F. Christian, S.N. Curle, Peter Robson, P.A.H. Wyatt, E.K. Walton, M.S. Laverack, J.F. Lamb, J.H. Brumfitt, A.J. Cole, J.M. Howie, J.K. Cameron, F.D. Gunstone, D.H.N. Spence, A.H.T. Levi, R.M. Cormack, D.D.R. Owen, D.A. Bullough, I.G. Kidd, V.B. Proudfoot, D.H. Reid, R.J. Adam, D.J. Gifford, T.S. Blyth, S.S.B. Taylor, D.E.R. Watt, P.C. Bayley, C.J.G. Wright, J.F. Cornwell, D.R.B. Kimbell, P.H. Grinyer, D.W.D. Shaw, P.J. Branscombe, A. Serafini-Fracassini, T.C. Smout, J.W. Allen, J.P. Kenyon, M.J. Kemp, G.E. Rickman, N.G. Parker, E.R. Priest, A.F. Upton, R.S. Furness, A.K.G. Paterson, W.C. Russell, P.J.B. Slater, G.A. Cottrell.
The University was inaugurated in 1410, incorporated in 1412, and granted the full privileges of a university in 1413. It comprises the United College of St Salvator and St Leonard, and St Mary's College. There are three faculties: Arts; Divinity; and Science.

St. Andrews, University of, Department of Adult Education and Extra-Mural Studies, Mansefield, 3 St. Mary's Place, St. Andrews KY16 9UY. T.-0334 73429. Director: Clarke Geddes; Assistant Director: Dr John C. Horobin. Provision of a programme of courses on behalf of the University for adults in St. Andrews and Fife Region. It organises an extensive summer residential programme for adults and families, and an Easter residential programme for families and for pre-university school leavers.

Stationery Office, H.M. – Scotland, Government Buildings, Bankhead Avenue, Sighthill, Edinburgh EH11 4AE. T.-031-453 5610. Director: G.A. Turner.

Steel Corporation, British (1957), Ravenscraig Works, Motherwell, ML1 1SW. T.-Motherwell 66211. Works Director: J.G. Dunbar. Iron and steel manufacturers.

Stevenson College of Further Education, Bankhead Avenue, Edinburgh, EH11 4DE. T.-031-453 6161. College of further education.

Stewartry District Council (1974), Council Offices, Kirkcudbright, DG6 4PJ. T.-0557 30291. Convener: John Nelson; Vice Convener: Charles Devlin; Members: Jock Purdie, A.P. Davidson, James Ewart, Donald M. Kerr, J.F.S. Lyon, Elizabeth J. Smith, John L. Maxwell, Nigel Hesketh, Agnes R. Murdoch, Dr Peter Pearce. Chief Executive and Director of Administration: W.L. Dick-Smith, O.B.E.; Director of Finance and Housing: J.C. Howie; Director of Technical Services: A. Strachan; Director of Environmental Health: W.P. Davidson. District Council. Population of District: 22,000.

Stirling District Council (1974), Municipal Buildings, Stirling, FK8 2HU. T.-0786 73131. Convener: J. Wyles; Members: R. Govan, J. Paterson, P. Stuart, A. Ritchie, M. Connarty, Catherine Organ, Ann Dickson, Patricia Greenhill, Helen Scott, J. Hendry, F. Riddell, Margaret Brisley, Blanche Carmichael, J. McConnell, E. Carrick, T. Brookes, N. MacEwan, G. Watt, T. Barlow. Chief Executive: J. Cairns; Director of Finance: R.A. Bryson;

Director of Development: M.N. Dobson; Director of Environmental Health: C. Gibson; Director of Leisure and Recreation: S.D. Mackenzie; Director of Housing: D. Johnstone. District Council. Population of District: 80,000.

Stirling, University of (1967), Stirling, FK9 4LA. T.-0786 73171. Chancellor: Sir Montague Finniston; Principal and Vice-Chancellor: Sir Kenneth Alexander; Deputy Principals: Professor J. Trainer, Professor W.R.A. Muntz; University Secretary: R.G. Bomont, J.P.; Deputy Secretary (Registrar): F. Smyth; Librarian: P.G. Peacock. University Court: The Principal and Deputy Principals; Dr R.D. McIntyre; Dr A.C. Chitnis, Dr L.G. Jillings, Professor P.D. Jimack, Professor M.F. Thomas, Professor C. Turner, Dr I.C. Walker, Mrs D. Littlejohn, J.A.M. Mitchell, G.R. Simpson, Chairman of Stirling District Council, Convener of Central Regional Council, Hon. President of the Students' Association, President of the Students' Association, I.M. Collie, A. MacDonald, P.J. Wordie.
Senior Academic Staff: Professors J.P. Dickinson, D.H. Patz, J. Milnes Holden, R.J. Roberts, W.R.A. Muntz, T. Cannon, J.A. Dawson, J.M.G. Cowie, L.B. Wilson, P. Henderson, C.V. Brown, J.H. Duthie, T.A. Dunn, A.N. Jeffares, M.F. Thomas, H.A. Hetherington, P.D. Jimack, S.I.J. Lockerbie, J. Trainer, D.A.G. Waddell, D.H. Allen, D.A.R. Wallace, N.W. Tennant, H.R. Wilson, H.J.W. Kleinpoppen, K.N. Medhurst, Ivana Markova, D.W.G. Timms, C. Turner.

St. Margaret of Scotland Adoption Society, 274 Bath Street, Glasgow, G2 4JR. T.-041-332 8371. Chairman: Rev. William Mone; Vice Chairperson: Sister Catherine Mulligan; Secretary: Philip Rooney; Treasurer: Brian Hay. Principal Social Worker: May McGhee; Senior Social Worker: Mrs E. Kearney. Catholic voluntary agency which offers a comprehensive service by social workers engaged in the following: assessment of prospective adopting parents; counselling and continuing support of natural parents; placement of babies, older children, and those with special needs; a growing commitment to families and individual adoptees who seek counselling.

Stock Exchange, Scottish (1973), 69 St. George's Place, Glasgow, G2. T.-041-221 7060. Chairman: Andrew Forrest; Vice Chairman: William B. Carmichael. General Manager: J.H.B. Adams. Maintains the Scottish trading floor of The Stock Exchange.

Stow College (1934), 43 Shamrock Street, Glasgow, G4 9LD. T.-041-332 1786. Principal: David W. Snaith; Depute Principal: John H. Shankland; Registrar: Samuel Stevenson. College of further education offering a wide range of full-time, block-release, and part-time courses.

Strathclyde Passenger Transport Executive (1973), Consort House, 12 West George Street, Glasgow, G2 1HN. T.-041-332 6811. Director General: Alan R. Westwell; Director of Finance, Personnel, and Integrated Operations: W. Norman Stirling; Secretary and Legal Adviser: Gavin Mason. Co-ordination of public transport in Strathclyde; operation of the Glasgow bus and underground system.

Strathclyde Regional Council (1974), Strathclyde House, 20 India Street, Charing Cross, Glasgow, G2 4PF. T.-041-204 2900. Convener: James Burns; Vice Convener: James Jennings; Leader of the Council: Richard Stewart, C.B.E.; Depute Leader of the Council: Charles Gray; Members: Jean Armstrong, James P. Bannerman, O.B.E., Joseph Barrett, Thomas Barrie, James M. Boyd, James Boyd, Robert Campbell, Ronald Carson, Thomas Colyer, Ian Davidson, John Donnelly, James F. Dunnachie, W. Peter Edmondson, Andrew Ferguson, John Fitch, David Fulton, James Fyfe, B.E.M., James Gibson, Stan Gilmore, William Goudie, Robert Gould,

140   The Scottish Companion

Thomas Graham, Elliot Gray, John Gray, Dr Malcolm Green, Robert M. Greig, James Hanlon, William J. Harley, Douglas Hay, Charles B. Hebenton, Helen Hodgins, John Hunter, James Irvine, Joseph Knox, Rev. David D. Laing, Archibald Lambie, Adam Lawson, Peter E.M. Leggat, Albert J. Long, C.B.E., Thomas McAvoy, John McCorkindale, Iain MacDonald, John McDowell, Peter McEachran, Laurence McGarry, William M. McGill, Andrew McGowan, Gerald McGrath, James McGuire, James McInnes, James W. Mackechnie, Agnes McLean, Alexander MacLean, Joseph F. McLean, Daniel McMillan, James McMillan, Niall MacNeill, John Mair, Vera A. Marvin, Dr Christopher M. Mason, Jeanette M. Mason, James Meldrum, Duncan Mills, John G. Mullin, Thomas Murphy, Gordon S. Murray, Kenneth J. Murray, Edward Myles, William M. Perry, William Petrie, Thomas Rae, Henry Revie, Elspeth W. Riddell, Robert Robertson, C.B.E., James P. Robison, David M. Sanderson, Bernard M. Scott, David Scott, Robert Scott, May Smith, David Stewart, James D. Taylor, William M. Timoney, Charlotte Toal, Patrick Trainer, Malcolm Turner, O.B.E., Alexander Viola, Helen Walker, James Walsh, Patrick Watters, Malcolm Waugh, David Webster, Bernard Whelan, Richard M. Wilkinson, Robert B. Wilson, Anthony Worthington, James Wray, Ronald G. Young.
Chief Executive: Robert Calderwood; Senior Depute: Ian S. McFarlane; Deputes: Peter M. Howitt, Iain M. Stuart, Michael J. Wilkinson; Solicitor to the Council: Walter O. Lunn; Director of Architectural and Related Services: Jack C. McDougall; Assessor and Electoral Registration Officer: J.W. Wood; Regional Chemist, Public Analyst and Agricultural Analyst: Ronald S. Nicolson; Head of Computer Services: James Semple; Head of Consumer and Trading Standards: Clive A. Howard-Luck; Chief Constable: Sir Patrick Hamill; Head of Direct Works: Campbell J. McKelvie; Director of Education: Edward Miller; Head of Estates: Neil G. MacFarlane; Director of Finance: Kenneth R. Paterson; Firemaster: Clive B. Halliday; Head of Management Services: George McGowan; Director of Manpower Services: Robert M.O. McCulloch; Director General, Passenger Transport Executive: Alan R. Westwell; Director of Physical Planning: Robert G. Maund; Head of Public Relations: Henry D.M. Dutch; Reporter to Children's Panel: F.J. Kennedy; Director of Roads: William S. McAlonan; Director of Sewerage: William T. Greer; Director of Social Work: Frederick E. Edwards; Head of Supplies: Archibald Muirden; Head of Internal Transport: Richard S. Housley; Director of Water: William T. Devenay.
In the west of Scotland, Strathclyde Regional Council is responsible for providing major local authority services to 2,383,000 people, just under half the population of Scotland. With 103 elected members and a staff of 110,000, it is the largest Regional Council in the country. Its 1984-85 budget is £1,680m., more than half of which is spent on education, the Council's biggest service. Other major responsibilities include highways and transportation, social work, and police and fire. The political composition of the Council is: Labour, 79; Conservative, 15; Alliance, 4; S.N.P., 3; Independent, 2.

Strathclyde, University of (1964), 16 Richmond Street, Glasgow, G1 1XQ. T.-041-552 4400. Chancellor: The Rt. Hon. Lord Todd of Trumpington; Principal and Vice Chancellor: Dr Graham Hills; Vice Principal: Professor Hamish C.S. Wood; Deputy Principals: Professor David J. Tedford; Professor Michael J. Baker, T.D. Chairman, University Court: Gavin Boyd, C.B.E.; Members: (ex officio) The Chancellor, Principal and Vice Chancellor, Vice Principal, Deputy Principal; (appointed by Glasgow

District Council) Baillie Robert Innes, J.P.; (appointed by Strathclyde Regional Council) Councillor Malcolm R. Green; (Convocation) Gavin Boyd, C.B.E., H.R. Crone, James Munn, O.B.E., James Sutherland, C.B.E.; (Senate) Professor Gordon S.G. Beveridge, Professor Alexander T. Florence, Dr George Gordon, Dr Thomas G.F. Gray, Professor Lewis A. Gunn, Dr Christopher N. Larsson, Professor George M. Maxwell, Professor Peter L. Pauson, Dr Joseph L. Smyrl, Andrew Wilkin; (Graduates Association) Emeritus Professor John F.T. MacLaren; (Students Association) James Lee, Bruce M. Wilson; (Co-opted by Court) Sir Lawrence Boyle, J.P., Donald McLean, Stephen P. Newall, Sir Patrick M. Thomas, F. Olaf Thornton, O.B.E., Colin Young.
The Senate: Professorial Members: Hamish C.S. Wood, James L. Alty, William Anderson, Derek Attridge, Michael J. Baker, T.D., David I.H. Barr, John R.S. Beavis, Henry B. Bell, Gordon S.G. Beveridge, Angela M. Bowey, William C. Bowman, Roy H. Burdon, Campbell B. Burns, Clifford R. Burrows, David S. Butler, John Butt, Thomas F. Carbery, O.B.E., John G. Clark, Anthony I. Clunies-Ross, Andrew J.T. Colin, Brian Culshaw, William A. Donaldson, O.B.E., George Eason, Edward Eisner, Alexander T. Florence, John Gennard, Neil B. Graham, Michael J. Grimble, Lewis A. Gunn, Anthony J. Harper, Brian Henderson, Michael L. Hitchman, Neil Hood, G. Melvyn Howe, John Hughes, Gustav Jahoda, David J. Jeffries, O.B.E., Chengi Kuo, Frank M. Leslie, J.P., Colin M.J. MacCabe, James W. McGilvray, David G. McKinlay, Iain A. MacLeod, Thomas A. Markus, Robin D. Marshall, Thomas W. Maver, George M. Maxwell, John M. Midgley, Fikry N. Morcos-Asaad, William R. Morrison, Christopher W. Nobes, David H. Owens, James R. Parratt, Alan A. Paterson, John P. Paul, Peter L. Pauson, Peter G. Perkins, Jeremy J. Richardson, Brian D. Ripley, Gary F. Roach, Richard Rose, Aeneas M. Rosie, Donald S. Ross, Michael J. Russell, H. Rudolph Schaffer, William Scott, Robert K. Shaw, John N. Sherwood, David R.F. Simpson, Hugh C. Simpson, Anthony L.S. Smith, John E. Smith, Keith Smith, John Spence, William H. Stimson, Andrew J.M. Sykes, David J. Tedford, Joseph M. Thomson, William J. Tilstone, Urlan A. Wannop, John T. Ward, John T. Webster.
The University is a leading centre of education and research in engineering, science, and business studies. It actively supports industrial regeneration in Scotland and the U.K. There are more than 7,000 full-time students, and an additional 5,000 part-time students.

Strathkelvin District Council (1974), P.O. Box 4, Council Offices, Kirkintilloch, G66 1PW. T.-041-776 7171. Provost: Robert M. Coyle, J.P.; Members: William Kemmett, J.P., James Hotchkiss, J.P., Andrew Cochrane, James Barker, William Leslie, Denis Maxwell, Alexander B. McIntyre, Constantine O'Neill, J.P., Michael Donohoe, John Dempsey, Charles Kennedy, J.P., Bridget Dunion, Iain B. Nicolson, J.P., Anne Jarvis. Chief Executive Officer/Chief Officer, Environmental Services: C. Mallon; Director of Administration: R.L. McClelland; Director of Finance: D. Brant; Chief Officer, Housing: I. Laurie; Chief Officer, Planning Services: R. Dent; Chief Officer, Recreational Services: H. Barrow; Chief Officer, Technical Services: W.J. Hayes. District Council. Population of District: 88,000.

Strathspey Railway Association (1972), The Station, Boat of Garten, Inverness-shire, PH24 3BH. T.-Boat of Garten 692. Chairman: D.P. Rowland; Secretary: D.M. Norris. Supports the Strathspey Railway Company in the operation of trains between Aviemore and Boat of Garten; raises funds to operate a railway operated primarily by steam traction.

Structural Engineers, Institution of, Scottish Branch. Hon. Secretary: R. Robertson, 25 Craigendoran Avenue, Helensburgh, G84 7AZ. T.-041-889 5459, Ext. 422. Chairman: A.N. Tait. Learned society.

Sub Aqua Club, Scottish, 16 Royal Crescent, Glasgow, G3 7SL. T.-041-339 9291. Hon. Secretary: Alex. Tysen; Administrator: Elisabeth Brown.

Sunday Mail (1919), 40 Anderston Quay, Glasgow, G3 8DA. T.-041-248 7000. Editor: Endell Laird. National Sunday newspaper.

Sunday Post (1920), Courier Buildings, 2 Albert Square, Dundee, DD1 9QJ. T.-0382 23121. National Sunday newspaper.

Surgeons of Edinburgh, Royal College of (1505), Nicolson Street, Edinburgh. T.-031-556 6206. President: Sir James Fraser, Bt.; Vice Presidents: R. Myles Gibson, I.F. MacLaren; Secretary: Peter Edmond; Treasurer: A.B. MacGregor; Council: P.S. Boulter, Professor D.C. Carter, Professor G.D. Chisholm, Professor Alfred Cuschieri, A.C.B. Dean, Miss C.M. Doig, A.A. Gunn, Professor S.P.F. Hughes, D.W. Lamb, Professor James Lister, T.J. McNair, Dr A.G.D. Maran, W.A.T. Robb, J.W.W. Thomson, W.F. Walker; Convener of the Dental Council: L.D. Finch. Clerk to the College: Margaret Bean. Promotion and maintenance of standards in surgical training and practice.

Sutherland District Council (1974), District Offices, Golspie, Sutherland. T.-Golspie 3192. Chairman: Mrs L. Mackenzie; Members: J.K. Bell, Mrs M. Fielding, D. Gordon, W. Henderson, Mrs E.B.M. Jardine, J.O.F. Mackay, R.H. Mackay, I.M. MacAulay, N.G. McDonald, R.R. McDonald, A. Mackenzie, D.I. MacRae. Chief Executive and Director of Administration: D.W. Martin; Director of Finance: W. Sutherland: Director of Technical and Housing Services: G. Durrand; Director of Environmental Health: F. Hayward; District Amenities Officer: D. Munro. District Council. Population of District: 13,000.

Swimming Association, Scottish Amateur, Pathfoot Building, University of Stirling, Stirling. T.-Stirling 70544. Hon. General Secretary: W. Black. Director of Administration: R. Betteley, D.F.C.; Director of Swimming: H. Hamilton Smith.

T

Table Tennis Association, Scottish, 18 Ainslie Place, Edinburgh. T.-031-225 3020. General Secretary: Fiona Marchbanks; National Coach: G. Davies.

Tartans Museum, Scottish (1975), Comrie, Perthshire, PH6 2DW. T.-0764 70779. Director: Dr Micheil MacDonald; Curator: Penny Calder MacDonald. The Museum, founded by the Scottish Tartans Society, is situated in the Highland village of Comrie. It houses the most comprehensive collection of tartans and Highland dress in the world, and a unique archive of all known tartan setts. In its first year, it won the Museum of the Year Award for the Best Small Museum in Scotland.

Tartans Society, Scottish (1963), Comrie, Perthshire, PH6 2DW. T.-0764 70779. President: The Duke of Atholl; Chairman and Vice President: Dr D. Gordon; Vice Chairman: Angus Whitson; Hon. Treasurer: Ruairidh H. MacLeod. Preservation of Scotland's tradition of dress and tartan.

Tay River Purification Board (1975), 3 South Street, Perth, PH2 8NJ. T.-Perth 27989. Chairman: W.I. Malcolm, O.B.E., J.P. Director: J.A. Rangeley; Depute Director: D.F. Miller; Clerk: J.E.D. Cormie; Treasurer: H. Robertson. River pollution prevention and hydrometric authority for an area consisting of the catchment areas of the Rivers Earn, Eden, Lunan, Dighty Water, North Esk, South Esk, and Tay.

Tayside Community Relations Council (1973), 6 North Isla Street, Dundee. T.-0382 25802. Chairman: Dr S. Sarkar; Secretary: Mrs M.K. Faulkner. Community Relations Officer: H.R. Sanmugapalasooriar. To promote good community relations and equality of opportunity, especially in education, employment, and housing.

Tayside Health Board (1974), P.O. Box 75, Vernonholme, Riverside Drive, Dundee. T.-0382 645151. Chairman: D.B. Grant; Vice Chairman: J.W. Duncan; Members: Rev. J. Caldwell, E.W. Cameron, E.C. Lowson, J. Campbell-Smith, R.J. Croft, Professor P.D. Griffiths, Dr A.G.R. Law, Professor J. Swanson Beck, Mrs R. Bolton, Mrs L.V. Grewar, M.B. Kerr, Mrs S.D.R. Kydd, J.C. Macfarlane, J.T. Robb, Mrs A. Woore, Dr P.G. Aungle, J.S. Fair, B.W.M. Johnston, W. Stewart. Chief Administrative Medical Officer: Dr R.C. Graham; Chief Area Nursing Officer: Miss M.M. Shand; Treasurer: J.R. Hudson; Secretary: G.G. Savage. Provision of health service in Tayside.

Tayside Regional Council (1974), Tayside House, Crichton Street, Dundee. T.-0382 23281. Convener: Dr W.K. Fitzgerald, C.B.E., J.P.; Vice Convener: James A.O. Fordyce, J.P.; Members: Martha Munro, Peter Vettese, John Y. Allan, Sheila D.R. Kydd, Hugh MacPhail, William Johnston, M.B.E., J.P., James G. Findlay, O.B.E., J.P., Frances E. Duncan, Thomas M. Robertson,

J. Wallace Thom, Barbara Vaughan, Alexander Dollman, Gordon S. Watson, O.B.E., J.P., Bruce D. Mackie, J.P., Jean Thomson, Raymond A. Mennie, Ronald M. Tosh, J.P., James F. Doig, J.P., Ian D. Mackie, J.P., Joseph Barton, W. Ian Malcolm, O.B.E., J.P., William Derby, William Smith, George W. Buckman, J.P., Richard F. Black, John McAllion, Ian Borthwick, J.P., Allan Inglis, J.P., Dorothy Pattullo, The Hon. Mrs Gilbert Hendry, J.P., J. Greig Sandilands, Iain M. Young, Ian W. Stevenson, Norman K.P. Jamieson, James R. Dow, J.P., John S. Mackay, Alan Powrie, W. Scott Ferguson, T.D., Robert E. Buchan, Robert A. Pullar, Stewart O. Miller, Gavin L. McLuggage, Sir Alan Smith, C.B.E., D.F.C., J.P.
Chief Executive: John A. Wallace; Depute Chief Executive: A.G. Mitchell; Director of Finance: I.B. McIver; Director of Education: D.G. Robertson; Director of Architectural Services: R.J.A. Hopkins; Director of Social Work: S.J. Moxley; Director of Roads: A.R. Mollison; Director of Water Services: A.G. Cockburn; Director of Planning: H. Ramsay; Regional Assessor: J.R. McNab; Director of Public Transport: Neil Townend; Chief Constable: J.W. Bowman; Firemaster: D. Nicoll, M.B.E.; Regional Quantity Surveyor: R. Leslie; Reporter to Children's Panel: R.I. Meek; Director of Trading Standards: A.M. Mitchell; Public Analyst/Regional Chemist: R.A. Evans.
Local authority responsible for major services for 395,000 people in Scotland's fourth largest region. Political composition of the Council is:- Conservative, 26; Labour, 13; S.N.P., 4; Independent, 2.

Technical Education Council, Scottish (1973), 38 Queen Street, Glasgow, G1 3DY. T.-041-248 7900. Chairman: W. Nicol; Members: A.W. Clark, Dr P. Clarke, G. Craig, D. Dickson, T.M. Howie, A.B. Joiner, Dr D.A. Kennedy, T.S. Lansley, A. McAlpine, J.D. McWilliam, J. Meiklejohn, T. Murphy, J. Murray, J.M. Oliver, J. Pollock, J.W. Sellars, J.E. Whigham, Dr J.P. Wiltshire, J.B. Wright, Dr G.A.P. Wyllie. Chief Officer: D. Hemingway; Senior Education Officers: Dr I.H. Anderson, Dr S.A. McKellar. SCOTEC provides courses and awards for key personnel in manufacturing and service industries. The courses, which are offered at colleges of further education and central institutions, are designed to meet the needs of individuals and employers in engineering, science, construction, agriculture and food production, art and design, life science, and many other categories. Courses are open to those in employment as well as full-time students. Successful candidates are awarded certificates, diplomas, higher certificates, or higher diplomas depending on the level of their course.

Technology Group, British (1949), 87 St. Vincent Street, Glasgow, G2 5TF. T.-041-221 1820. Manager in Scotland: Colin Dale. Public sector organisation concerned with technology transfer. It provides finance and support to universities, central institutions, and other research establishments in Scotland, and can provide finance to private industry for innovative technology.

Television, Scottish (1957), Cowcaddens, Glasgow, G2 3PR. T.-041-332 9999. Directors: Sir Campbell Fraser (Chairman), William Brown, C.B.E. (Managing Director and Deputy Chairman), Sir Kenneth Alexander, Gavin Boyd, C.B.E., Bill Bryden, Rev. Robin D. Buchanan-Smith, Ferdinando Coia (Director of Facilities), Dorothy Dunnett, Charles A. Fraser, M.V.O., Hugh W. Henry (Director of Airtime International), David K. Johnstone (Director of Programmes), Alan L. Montgomery (Director of Finance and Administration), Jonathan F. Shier (Director of Sales and Marketing), Sir Iain M. Stewart. Controller of Personnel and Industrial Relations: Colin

Waters; Public Relations Manager: John Loch; Finance Controller and Company Secretary: Don Kinloch; Controller of Engineering: Shaun Clamp. Independent Television contractor for Central Scotland. S.T.V. makes an average of 11 hours of programmes per week, reflecting a wide aspect of Scottish life, to complement I.T.V.'s network output.

Telford College of Further Education, Crewe Toll, Edinburgh. T.-031-332 2491. Principal: Dr Michael A. Taylor; Registrar: John D. Grant. College of further education. Its student population exceeds 10,000, half of whom attend day classes.

Tertiary Education Advisory Council, Scottish (1984), Room 3/112, New St. Andrew's House, Edinburgh, EH1 3SY. T.-031-556 8400, Ext. 5473. Chairman: D.M. McCallum, C.B.E.; Vice Chairman: Dr T.R. Bone; Members: Dr H.G. Cuming, Dr Ethel Gray, C.B.E., Sir Alwyn Williams, T.N. Biggart, C.B.E., A.E. Harper, D.J. MacLeod, A.K. Smith, C.B.E. Secretary: N. MacLeod; Assistant Secretary: B. O'Connor.
The Council's terms of reference are to consider and report on the future strategy for higher education in Scotland, including the arrangements for providing institutions with financial support and the general principles which should govern relationships between universities and other institutions. The Council advises the Secretary of State for Scotland on such other matters as he remits to it, and collaborates as necessary with the University Grants Committee, the national advisory bodies for local authority higher education in England and Wales, the Manpower Services Commission, and other appropriate bodies.

Textiles, Scottish College of, Galashiels, Selkirkshire, TD1 3HF. T.-0896 3351. Chairman, Board of Governors: James Walker. Principal: J.C. Furniss; Vice Principal and Head of Department of Technology: Dr R.J. Harwood. Scottish Central Institution of higher education offering degree and diploma level courses leading to careers in industry, business, and the professions. Specialist interests lie in textile and clothing technology, applied chemistry, textile design, and business management.

Theatre Company, Scottish (1980), 37 Otago Street, Glasgow, G12 8JJ. T.-041-339 8777. Chairman, Board of Governors: Martin Reid-Foster; Members: Kirsty Adam, Robin Anderson, Iain Cuthbertson, Charles Hart, Robert Love, Professor Sir Kenneth Alexander, Alex. Clark, James F. Donald, Dr Jack Kane, Duncan MacLeod, Countess of Strathmore and Kinghorne. Artistic Director: Tom Fleming; Administrator: Ruari McNeill.
The Company's policy is to present the best of Scots and international drama, using a growing ensemble of Scottish actors and directors, and a group of distinguished guest designers, to evolve a distinctive style. Its productions have toured large and small theatres throughout Scotland and have been seen by more than 100,000 people since 1982.

Third Eye Centre, 350 Sauchiehall Street, Glasgow, G2 3JD. T.-041-332 7521. Chairman: Richard Clark. Director: Chris Carrell; Administrator: Erika King. Arts centre specialising in contemporary art. Studio theatre, bookshop, vegetarian cafe, and bar, as well as two main galleries.

Thistle Foundation (1944), 27A Walker Street, Edinburgh, EH3 7HX. T.-031-225 7282. Director: Philip Croft. The Foundation offers disabled men and women an alternative to life in hospital. It provides its residents with a home and nursing care at its village in Edinburgh. Both family houses and hostel accommodation for single disabled people are available.

Thurso Technical College (1959), Ormlie Road, Thurso, Caithness, KW14 7EE. T.-0847 66161. Principal: Colin M. MacLean; Depute Principal: William J. Donald. Built primarily to provide education and training for personnel at the Dounreay Experimental Reactor Establishment nearby. However, the College now provides a wider range of courses, including agriculture, business and secretarial studies, carpentry and joinery, catering, computing, electrical installation, health studies, modern languages, and motor vehicle work.

Tourist Board, Scottish (1969), 23 Ravelston Terrace, Edinburgh, EH4 3EU. T.-031-332 2433. Chairman: Alan R. Devereux, C.B.E.; Members: G. Susan Bell, Robert A. Fasken, C.B.E., Ian F.H. Grant, J.P., Sir Peter C. Hutchison, Bt., Graeme M. Simmers, O.B.E., Sir Alan Smith, C.B.E. Chief Executive: Dr D.A. Pattison; Director of Development: Dr J.G. Adams; Director Overseas Tourism: N.C. Chumley; Director Area Operations: D.J. MacIntyre; Director External Relations: J.A. Stuart; Director of Finance: J.M. Wallace; Head of U.K. Marketing: W.S. Legg.
The Board attracts holidaymakers to Scotland through a wide range of marketing activities, including advertising, exhibitions, workshops, and publications, and encourages the development of visitor facilities through its grants and loans scheme. It co-ordinates tourism interests within the country and co-operates closely with the network of local area tourist boards. The Board works closely in Scotland with the tourism industry and with the various statutory agencies whose activities affect tourism. Regular liaison is maintained with the British Tourist Authority on the promotion of Scotland in overseas markets.

Town Planning Institute, Royal, Scottish Branch (1914), 15 Rutland Square, Edinburgh, EH1 2BE. Hon. Secretary: William Amcotts (T.-031-337 3423). National organisation for planners. The Scottish Branch publishes the *Scottish Planner* and runs a programme of topical conferences and seminars, as well as supporting environmental education projects and four planning aid groups.

Trades Union Congress, Scottish (1897), 16 Woodlands Terrace, Glasgow, G3 6DF. T.-041-332 4946. Chairperson, General Council: T. Dougan; Vice Chairperson: H. Wyper; Treasurer: J. Morrell; Members: A. Barr, C. Binks, G. Bolton, W. Clydesdale, W. Cowan, R. Curran, H. D'Arcy, R. Devine, C. Gallacher, R. Gillespie, J. Langan, J.C. Lewis, D.C. Magregor, N.J. McIntosh, Mrs J. McKay, A.B. McLuckie, D. Paterson, J.D. Pollock, W. Queen, E. Reilly, R.R. Webster, Mrs M. Wilson, Miss G. Wood. General Secretary: J. Milne; Deputy General Secretary: J. Henry; Assistant Secretary Research: D. Harrison; Assistant Secretary: W. Speirs.
Association of trade unions which meets as an assembly of delegates at a five-day Annual Congress in April. More than 70 unions representing a million members, and 47 local Trades Councils, are directly affiliated to Congress. The S.T.U.C. plays an influential role in social, economic, and industrial issues.
The following are among the unions affiliated to the S.T.U.C. In most cases, the unions are British based, but the names and addresses given are those of the Scottish officials, and the membership figures relate to Scotland only.

Actors' Equity Association, British. Scottish Secretary: A. Clark, 65 Bath Street, Glasgow, G2 2BX. T.-041-332 1669. 1,700 members.

Banking, Insurance and Finance Union. Deputy General Secretary: D. Paterson, 7 Buchanan Street, Glasgow. T.-041-221 6475. 20,228 members.

Carpet Workers' Union, Scottish. Secretary: J. Deighan, 83 Carlton Place, Glasgow, G5 9TD. T.-041-429 5199. 1,073 members.

Civil and Public Servants, Society of. Scottish Officer: E. Reilly, 7 Royal Terrace, Edinburgh, EH7 5AB. T.-031-556 0407. 9,000 members.

Communication Workers, Union of. Scottish Secretary: R. Devine, U.C.W. Room, Head Post Office, Edinburgh. T.-031-550 8325. 15,667 members.

Construction, Allied Trades and Technicians, Union of. Scottish Secretary: J. McBride, 6 Fitzroy Place, Glasgow, G3 7RL. T.-041-221 4893. 30,313 members.

Educational Institute of Scotland. Secretary: J.D. Pollock, 46 Moray Place, Edinburgh, EH3 6BH. T.-031-225 6244. 45,665 members.

Electrical, Electronic, Telecommunication and Plumbing Union. Scottish Officer: A.B. McLuckie, Stanley House, 71 Hamilton Road, Motherwell, ML1 3DG. T.-Motherwell 69316. 35,000 members.

Engineering Workers, Amalgamated Union of. Engineering Section: Regional Officer: T. Dougan, 145-165 West Regent Street, Glasgow, G2 4RZ. T.-041-248 7131. 90,000 members.

Fire Brigades Union. Scottish Regional Secretary: J. Flockhart, 81 Carlton Place, Glasgow. T.-041-429 6688. 4,165 members.

Furniture, Timber and Allied Trades Union. Scottish Secretary: A. Izat, 46 Carlton Place, Glasgow, G5 9TQ. T.-041-429 5507. 2,638 members.

General, Municipal, Boilermakers & Allied Trades Union. Regional Secretary: J. Morrell, Fountain House, 1/3 Woodside Crescent, Glasgow, G3 7UJ. T.-041-332 8641. 101,368 members. Boilermakers Section: District Delegate: W. Clydesdale, 6 Lansdowne Crescent, Glasgow, G2 6NQ. T.-041-334 1141. 20,121 members.

Graphical and Allied Trades, Society of. Branch Secretary: R. Gillespie, 25 Newton Place, Glasgow, G3. T.-041-332 1501. 19,792 members.

Health Service Employees, Confederation of. Scottish Secretary: C. Binks, 28 Leonard Street, Perth. T.-0738 36143. 25,147 members.

Hosiery and Knitwear Workers, National Union of. Scottish Secretary: J. Robertson, 44 Kelvingrove Street, Glasgow, G3 7RZ. T.-041-333 0990. 4,045 members.

Iron and Steel Trades Confederation. Divisional Officer: J.C. Lewis, 8 Royal Crescent, Glasgow, G3 7SL. T.-041-332 8435. 8,000 members.

Locomotive Engineers and Firemen, Associated Society of. Scottish Secretary: J. Walker, 17 Almond Drive, Calderwood, East Kilbride, Glasgow. T.-East Kilbride 26930. 2,404 members.

Mineworkers, National Union of. Scottish Area Secretary: E. Clarke, 5 Hillside Crescent, Edinburgh, EH7 5DZ. T.-031-556 2323. 10,198 members.

Musicians' Union. Scottish District Organiser: J. Fagan, 135 Wellington Street, Glasgow, G2 2XD. T.-041-248 3723. 3,240 members.

National and Local Government Officers Association. District Secretary: C. Gallacher, Hellenic House, 87-97 Bath Street, Glasgow, G2 2ER. T.-041-332 0006. 78,647 members.

Post Office Engineering Union. N.M. Ross, Rooms 201, 8 Willison Street, Dundee. 10,853 members.

Prison Officers' Association, Scottish. Secretary: J.B. Renton, 21 Calder Road, Saughton, Edinburgh, EH11 3PF. T.-031-443 8105. 2,760 members.

Public Employees, National Union of. Scottish Secretary: R. Curran, 18 Albany Street, Edinburgh, EH1 3QB. T.-031-556 0922. 73,575 members.

Scientific, Technical and Managerial Staffs, Association of. National Officer: J. Langan, 1 Woodlands Terrace, Glasgow, G3 6DD. T.-041-331 1216. 30,000 members.

Seamen, National Union of. Scottish Secretary: L. Green, 9-15 James Watt Street, Glasgow, G2 8NF. T.-041-248 7534. 3,000 members.

Secondary Teachers' Association, Scottish. Secretary: A.A. Stanley, 15 Dundas Street, Edinburgh, EH3 6QG. T.-031-556 5919. 7,132 members.

Shop, Distributive and Allied Workers, Union of. Scottish Divisional Officer: W. Cowan, Muirfield, 342 Albert Drive, Glasgow, G41 5PG. T. 041-427 6561. 49,862 members.

Tailors and Garment Workers, National Union of. Scottish Secretary: F. Dickinson, Albany Chambers, 534 Sauchiehall Street, Glasgow, G2 3LX. T.-041-331 2747. 9,884 members.

Tobacco Workers' Union. Scottish Secretary: R.T. Brown, 180 West Regent Street, Glasgow, G2 4RW. T.-041-248 3118. 1,362 members.

Transport and General Workers' Union. Scottish Secretary: H. Wyper, 24 Park Circus, Glasgow, G3 6AR. T.-041-332 7321. 130,000 members.

Transport Salaried Staffs' Association. Scottish Secretary: R.S. King, 180 Hope Street, Glasgow, G2 4TB. T.-041-332 4698. 4,682 members.

Traffic Area, Scottish (1932), Department of Transport, 83 Princes Street, Edinburgh. T.-031-225 5494. Chairman of Traffic Commissioners and Licensing Authority: Hugh McNamara. Clerk to the Traffic Commissioners and Licensing Authority: Douglas W. McDiarmid; Senior Area Mechanical Engineer: Arthur White. Responsible for the licensing of P.S.V.s and goods vehicles and their drivers, under the Road Traffic Acts; taxi appeals; driving tests; annual car and vehicle testing, etc.

Tramway Museum Society, Scottish (1951), P.O. Box 78, Glasgow, G3 6ER. Chairman: Ian G. Stewart; Vice Chairman: Stuart M. Little; General Secretary: John G. Fender. Tramway preservation and research.

Transport Group, Scottish (1969), Carron House, 114-116 George Street, Edinburgh, EH2 4LX. T.-031-226 7491. Chairman: W.T. Stevenson; Managing Director: I.S. Irwin, C.B.E.; Secretary: John Stark. Manpower Executive: A. Douglas.
Public authority under The Transport Act 1968. Operates the principal bus network in Scotland through the companies of the Scottish Bus Group, the main sea ferry services in the Clyde and the Western Isles under the flag of Caledonian MacBrayne Ltd., and has associated interests in travel, insurance, and in transport marketing, advertising, and public relations.

Transport Users Consultative Committee for Scotland, 249 West George Street, Glasgow, G2 4QE. T.-041-221 7760. Chairman: Col. W.A. Dalziel, C.B.E., T.D., J.P.; Deputy Chairman: J.G. Watson, J.P.; Members: C.J.F. Hope, M. Macleod, J.P., D.A. Roser, L. Dall, W. Cowan, Commander I.T. Campbell, C.B.E., V.R.D., N.D. Smith, Mrs E.M. Sillars, M.B.E., J.P., Miss M.H. Mullen; Lt. Col. T.D.S. Bell, T.D. Set up by Parliament to help people who have complaints about either the train services and other facilities provided by British Railways or the shipping services provided by the Scottish Transport Group. The Committee also has a statutory duty to consider objections from users to any proposal by British Rail to withdraw a train service or close a station; or any proposal by the Scottish Transport Group to withdraw a shipping service or close a pier. It is then required to make its findings known to the Government.

Travelling People, Secretary of State's Advisory Committee on Scotland's (1971), St. Andrew's House, Edinburgh, EH1 3DD. T.-031-556 8501. Chairman: Rev. Murdo J. Nicolson, C.B.E.; Members: P.W. Collier, J.E.D. Cormie, C. Douglas, Councillor N.M. Faccenda, Councillor C. Gray, C. MacDonald, Mrs B.L.C. Moira, J. Pollock, A. Young. Secretary: G.T. Musselbrook. To advise particular local authorities on appropriate ways to secure adequate provision of sites for travelling people and resolve disputes that may arise over the details of such provision; to formulate objectives for site provision; and to advise the Secretary of State on these and related matters.

Traverse Theatre (1963), 112 West Bow, Grassmarket, Edinburgh, EH1 2PD. T.-031-226 2633. Chairman: Angela Wrapson; Vice Chairman: David Gerrard. Administrator: Vanessa Rawlings-Jackson; Artistic Director: Peter Lichtenfels. Consistently performs new plays by new playwrights, particularly young Scottish playwrights. Specialises in innovative work.

Tribunals, Council on, Scottish Committee (1959), 20 Walker Street, Edinburgh, EH3 7HR. T.-031-225 3236. Chairman: I.R. Guild; Members: Mrs E. Anderson, D. Bruce, Q.C., R.N.M. MacLean, Q.C., G.S. Peterkin, N. Robertson, R.B. Weatherstone, Sir Cecil Clothier, K.C.B., Q.C. (ex officio). Statutory consultative and advisory body which considers the machinery for administrative adjudication and addresses itself to general issues relating to the tribunals system.

Trust for Scotland, National (1931), 5 Charlotte Square, Edinburgh, EH2 4DU. T.-031-226 5922. President: The Earl of Wemyss and March, K.T., J.P.; Vice Presidents: The Duke of Atholl, Mrs Edward Denny, O.B.E., E.J. Ivory, A. Kennedy, A.S. Roger, M.B.E., J.P., The Marquess of Bute. Chairman of Council: William M. Cuthbert; Deputy Chairmen: Sir Robin MacLellan, C.B.E., Lord Ross of Marnock, M.B.E. Executive Committee: William M. Cuthbert (Chairman), the President and Vice Presidents (ex officio), Sir Robin MacLellan (Deputy Chairman), Mrs Alan Baxter, Frank Bracewell, Mrs Brodie of Lethen, N.W. Buchanan, G. Christie, R.G.M. Clow, Professor G. Donaldson, Mrs Angus Grossart, J. Douglas Hutchison, Mrs Robert MacDonald, Mrs Stephen Mackie, Kenneth Macrae, Sheriff W.R.M. Murdoch, Mrs Farquhar Ogilvie, The Hon. Sir Steven Runciman, Provost A.G. Sellar, I.H. Stuart Black, R.C. Tyrrell, Mrs A.G.O. Walker, R.J. Wheater. Director: Lester Borley; Director of Administration: J. Davie; Deputy Directors: D.S. Erskine, Findlay McQuarrie, M.D. Blacklock; Controller, Finance and Investment: A.F. McN. Paulin.
Established 'for the purposes of promoting the permanent preservation for the benefit of the nation of lands and buildings in Scotland of historic or national interest or natural beauty'. The Trust is an independent charity, supported by legacies, donations, and the subscriptions of its 120,000 members. It owns more than 90 properties which are open to the public and attract 1.5m. visitors annually. Listed below are brief details of the most popular of the Trust's properties. The number of visitors stated is for 1983.

Culzean Castle and Country Park, Ayrshire. Administrator: Michael L. Tebbutt. T.-065 56 274. No. of Visitors: 289,213.

Glencoe Visitor Centre, Lochaber. Representative: Peter MacNeill. T.-085 52 307. No. of Visitors: 108,925.

Inverewe Garden, Ross and Cromarty. Representative: J.G.B. Gibson. T.-044 586 200. No. of Visitors: 107,592.

Culloden Visitor Centre, Inverness. Representative: John MacRae. T.-0463 790607. No. of Visitors: 87,020.

Killiecrankie Visitor Centre, Perth and Kinross. Representatives: Mr and Mrs N. Reid. T.-0796 3233. No. of Visitors: 85,929.

Crathes Castle and Garden, Kincardine and Deeside. Representative: Anne Murray. T.-033 044 525. No of Visitors: 74,486.

Tuition of the Disabled, Scottish Centre for the (1979), Queen Margaret College, Clerwood Terrace, Edinburgh. T.-031-339 5408. Chairman: D. Dunsmuir; Scottish Organiser: Elizabeth Pearce; Lothian Organiser: Patricia Staniforth; Strathclyde Co-ordinator: Mirren Graham. Provides an information, advice, and voluntary tutorial service to disabled adults. Tuition can be provided in any subject or activity, ranging from work for examinations to craft skills and hobbies. It is given free.

Tweeddale District Council (1974), District Offices, Rosetta Road, Peebles, EH45 8HG. T.-0721 20153. Chairman: John P. Campbell, J.P.; Vice Chairman: Alexander Melrose; Members: Bryan C. Brockie, Alexander W. Walker, J.P., Ronald P.D. Runciman, J.P., Charles A. Thomson, John R. Meikle, Michael A.R. Maher, J.P., John A. Hogg, Nancy S. Thorburn. Chief Executive Officer: George Gardiner; Director of Finance: Vallance Cree; Director of Technical Services: John B. Forrest; Environment Health Officer: Robert J. Little. District Council. Population of District: 14,000.

Tweed River Purification Board (1975), Burnbrae, Mossilee Road, Galashiels, TD1 1NF. T.-Galashiels 2425; 4797. Chairman: Major D.J. Anderson. Director and River Inspector: J.C. Currie; Clerk: John D. Bell, P.O. Box 4, Council Chambers, Galashiels. The Board's principal duty is to promote the cleanliness of the rivers and other inland waters and all tidal waters, and to conserve as far as practicable the water resources of the area.

U

United Free Church of Scotland (1929), 11 Newton Place, Glasgow, G3 7PR. Senior Principal Clerk to General Assembly: Rev. Alexander Innes; Junior Principal Clerk to General Assembly: Rev. James Cassels; General Secretary: Isabel D. Baird; Moderator: Andrew K.M. Rankin. Presbyterian church.

Universities Research and Reactor Centre, Scottish (1963), East Kilbride, Glasgow, G75 OQU. T.-03552 20222. Director: Professor H.W. Wilson; Deputy Director: J.A. Izatt. Provision of research and teaching facilities in the reactor field, including radioisotopes, radiochemistry, neutron activation analysis, nuclear engineering, and reactor physics. Environmental radioactivity studies. Isotope geology, including dating of rocks and stable isotope measurements. Application of nuclear techniques to medicine and veterinary science.

University Teachers (Scotland), Association of (1922), c/o Dept. of Botany, The University, Glasgow, G12 8QQ. T.-041-339 8855, Ext. 448. Chairman: A. Young; Hon. Treasurer: R.P. Doig; Hon. Secretary: B.W. Ribbons. The advancement of university education and research in Scotland; regulation of relations between university teachers and their employers; promotion of common action by university teachers; safeguarding of the interests of the members (about 4,500 in the Scottish universities).

Veterinary Association, British (1923), c/o Veterinary Division, West of Scotland Agricultural College, Ayr, KA6 5AE. T.-0292 520468. President: W. Beswick; Secretary/Treasurer: C.L. Wright. To foster the interests of the veterinary profession in Scotland.

Volleyball Association, Scottish, Castlecliff Workshops, 25 Johnston Terrace, Edinburgh, EH1 2NH. General Secretary: Kevin Sewell; Technical Director: N. Moody; Executive Officer: Sheena Bell.

Voluntary Service, Aberdeen (1870), 38 Castle Street, Aberdeen, AB9 1AU. T.-0224 586395. Chairman: Colin W. Murray; Vice Chairman: Gordon Hardie. Secretary: William Howie; Deputy Secretary: Eleanor Palmer; Administrative Officer: Robert Bruce; Principal Social Worker: John Sullivan. Provides a range of direct services to people in need within the city, particularly the elderly and disabled, single parent families, and children at risk. Residential and day care facilities, and fieldwork services, are provided through seven component societies. The agency is also concerned with the general task of fostering voluntary effort in Aberdeen.

Voluntary Youth Organisations, Scottish Standing Conference of, Atholl House, 2 Canning Street, Edinburgh, EH3 8EG. T.-031-229 0339. General Secretary: John Knox.

W

War Blinded, Scottish National Institution for the, P.O. Box 500, Gillespie Crescent, Edinburgh, EH10 4HZ. T.-031-229 1456. Secretary and Treasurer: J.B.M. Munro. To provide rehabilitation, training, settlement, and after care for men and women blinded on service with the armed forces.

War on Want, Scottish, 143 Stockwell Street, Glasgow. T.-041-552 8357. Chairman: J. Stuart. Scottish National Officer: J. Boothman. Campaigns against the causes of poverty and underdevelopment; raises funds for development programmes overseas.

Water Pollution Control, Institute of (Scottish Branch), Burnbrae, Mossilee Road, Galashiels, TD1 1NF. T.-Galashiels 2425; 4797. Hon. Secretary: J.C. Currie. Professional body.

Water Ski Association, Scottish, 18 Ainslie Place, Edinburgh, EH3 6AU. T.-031-226 4401.

Waterways Board, British (1963), Canal House, Applecross Street, Glasgow, G4 9SP. T.-041-332 6936. Engineer (Scotland): R.B. Davenport; Estate Officer (Scotland): P. Coyne; Leisure Officer (Scotland): M.C. Lindsay. Responsibility for the overall management of 2,000 miles of inland waterways in Scotland, England, and Wales. The Board seeks to promote the use of the waterways for leisure, recreation and amenity, and freight transport, where appropriate. In Scotland, the Board's waterways are the Caledonian and Crinan Canals (both open to navigation), and the Forth and Clyde, Union, and Monkland Canals (all closed to navigation).

Weir Group PLC, The (1871), 149 Newlands Road, Glasgow, G44 4EX. T.-041-637 7111. Chairman: Viscount Weir; Managing Director: Ronald Garrick. Engineers. Turnover (1984): £119m.

Welfare of Children in Hospital (Scotland), National Association for the (1977), 94 Murrayfield Gardens, Edinburgh, EH12 6DJ. T.-031-337 6412. Chairman: Mrs D. Maclean; Co-ordinator: Mrs J. Millar; Administrator: Mrs M. Hall. Aims to persuade hospitals that parents have a necessary and practical part to play in the care of their sick child. Works through the branches to offer practical help in a variety of ways to enable the needs of sick children to be fully met.

Welfare of the Blind, Scottish National Federation for the (1917), 8 St. Leonard's Bank, Perth, PH2 8EB. T.-0738 26969. Hon. Secretary and Treasurer: J.N. Innes. To promote the well-being and protect the interests of the blind in Scotland by the co-operation and mutual assistance of various affiliated bodies.

Western Isles Health Board (1974), 37 South Beach Street, Stornoway, PA87 2BN. T.-0851 2997. Chairman: Mrs M.A. MacMillan; Members: M. Campbell, Captain J. MacIntyre, D.N. Kesting, D.W. MacLeod, A.D. Whiteford, A. Matheson, Dr W.M. Speirs, Dr N.R. Gillies, Mrs C. MacEachen, M.J. MacIver, I.D. Sutherland, M. MacLeod, J.H. Downie. Secretary: J.J. Glover; Treasurer: J.B. Dick; Chief Administrative Medical Officer: Dr D.B. Campbell; Chief Area Nursing Officer: Miss C. MacLean. Provision of health service in the Western Isles.

West Lothian College of Further Education, Marjoribanks Street, Bathgate, West Lothian, EH48 1QJ. T.-0506 634300. College of further education.

West Lothian District Council (1974), St. David House, South Bridge Street, Bathgate, West Lothian, EH48 1TT. T.-Bathgate 53631. Convener: D. McCauley; Vice Convener: R. Gamble; Members: William Cannon, James Clark, Terry Coleman, Joseph Cumming, Violet Cunningham, Shirley Davidson, Daniel Flannigan, Agnes H. Hamilton, Robert Lee, Aileen T. McCulloch, Alistair MacDonald, James McGinley, Allister Mackie, Daniel Main, William S.C. Renwick, William Russell, Marion C.W. Ryce, Mary Sharkey, James G.M. Sibbald, Donald Stavert, David Stenhouse, James Walker. Chief Executive Officer: D. Morrison; Director of Administration: W.N. Fordyce; Director of Finance: S.H. Stirton; Director of Housing Services: J. Spraggon; Director of Leisure and Recreation: R. Taylor; Director of Environmental Health: J. McIntyre; Director of Physical Planning: G. McNeill; Director of Architectural Services: G. Stenhouse; Chief Librarian: W.S. Walker. District Council. Population of District: 140,000.

West of Scotland Agricultural College (1899), Auchincruive, Ayr, KA6 5HW. T.-0292 520331. Chairman, Board of Governors: W. Watson Peat, C.B.E.; Vice Chairman: Robert J. Lennox, O.B.E., J.P. Principal: Professor J.M.M. Cunningham, C.B.E.; Depute Principal: Dr D.J. Martin; Secretary and Treasurer: E. Innes. Founded in Glasgow to combine the work of the Scottish Dairy Institute at Kilmarnock with that of the Agricultural Dept. of the Glasgow and West of Scotland Technical College. In 1927, the estate of Auchincruive was presented to the College and work was carried out both in Glasgow and Auchincruive until 1974, when the Glasgow centre was closed. Since 1974, the estate of Auchincruive has been developed as a centre for education, to provide a general and specialist advisory service for farmers and growers, and to carry out applied research and development work. Areas of special interest include the science, husbandry, and economics of milk, beef, and sheep production, milk utilisation, the treatment and use of farm waste, grass production and utilisation, and protected crop production.

West Sound (1981), Radio Ayrshire Ltd., Radio House, Holmston Road, Ayr, KA7 3BE. Managing Director: Joseph Campbell. Independent Local Radio station for Ayrshire.

Wholesale Druggists Association, Scottish (1933), 17 Smiths Place, Leith Walk, Edinburgh. T.-031-554 1551. Chairman: D.V. Mellstrom; Hon. Secretary: C.C. Cumming. Trade association.

Wigtown District Council (1974), District Offices, Sun Street, Stranraer, DG9 7JJ. T.-0776 2151. Chairman: D.R. Robinson; Members: R.E.B. McCaig, W. Service, A.D. Nelson, M. McHarrie, The Countess of Stair, W. Scobie, D. McHarg, J. Ward, Jean Hyslop, R.E. Caughie, I. Drape, S.F. Norris, J. Brown. Chief Executive and Director of Administration: A. Geddes; Depute Chief Executive and Director of Finance: B.W. Ward; Director of

Architectural Services: J.G. Sowerby; Director of Technical Services: S. Atkinson; Director of Environmental Health: J.H. McMillan. District Council. Population of District: 30,000.

Wigtown Rural Development Company Ltd. (1983), Royal Bank Building, 42 Victoria Street, Newton Stewart, Wigtownshire, DG8 6BT. T.-0671 3434. Managing Director: W. Phillips. Offers assistance to all sectors of the business community, including grants and loans, training, advice, premises, marketing, and financial guidance.

Wild Land Group, Scottish (1982), c/o 93 Queen Street, Alva, FK12 5AH. T.-0259 60102. Chairman: Roger Smith. Pressure group aiming to promote the conservation of wild land in Scotland by increasing public awareness of the problems, helping to co-ordinate the efforts of like-minded groups and individuals, and pressing for the adoption of planning policies which recognise conservation as a relevant factor.

Wildlife Trust, Scottish (1964), 25 Johnston Terrace, Edinburgh, EH1 2NH. T.-031-226 4602. President: Sir Charles G. Connell; Chairman of Council: George G. Stewart, C.B., M.C., T.D.; Vice Chairmen: Lt. Cdr. E.F.B. Spragge, H.A.P. Ingram, E. Gillett; Hon. Treasurer: K.G. Sutherland; Law Agent: D.G. Andrew. Chief Executive: Bernard Gilchrist, M.B.E.
Aims to conserve all types of wildlife and their habitats in Scotland. Activities include establishing wildlife reserves, carrying out surveys, providing information on wildlife conservation, and advising on land management for wildlife. The Trust has 8,000 members organised in 10 branches throughout Scotland. 65 reserves are managed, covering 38,000 acres of countryside.

Women Artists, Scottish Society of (1924), 13 Braehead Loan, Edinburgh, EH4 6BL. T.-031-339 6952. President: Louise Annand, M.B.E.; Secretary/ Treasurer: Pamela Snowdon. Aims to give encouragement and opportunity to women artists. Its policy is to maintain high standards and to admit to membership artists of every outlook. The Society holds an annual exhibition in the Royal Scottish Academy.

Women's Aid, Scottish (1975), 11 St. Colme Street, Edinburgh. T.-031-225 8011. Voluntary organisation which works with 28 local Women's Aid groups in Scotland providing advice, support, and refuge for battered women and their children. The national office concentrates on children, training, education and information, the law, and housing with regard to battered women.

Women's Amateur Athletic Association, Scottish (1930), 16 Royal Crescent, Glasgow, G3 7SL. T.-041-332 9304. President: Isabel Robertson; Hon. Secretary: Eleanor Gunstone. To foster and control athletics for women in Scotland.

Women's Bowling Association, Scottish. Secretary: Mrs A.G. Marden, 13 Marnock Terrace, Paisley, PA2 7JU. T.-041-889 6862.

Women's Hockey Association, Scottish, 18 Ainslie Place, Edinburgh, EH3 6AU. T.-031-226 4401. President: Wendy McLean; Hon. General Secretary: Ann Ferguson.

Women's Keep Fit Association, Scottish, 18 Ainslie Place, Edinburgh, EH3 6AU. T.-031-226 4401. Development Officer: Maureen E. Clowe.

Women's Royal Voluntary Service (1938), Scottish Headquarters, 19 Grosvenor Crescent, Edinburgh, EH12 5EL. T.-031-337 2261. Chairman Scotland: The Hon. Mrs Mary Corsar; Vice Chairmen, Scotland: Mrs S. Ballantine, Mrs E. Campbell, Mrs A. Whitefoord. To assist Government departments, local authorities, and voluntary bodies in organising and carrying out welfare and emergency work for the community on a nationwide network operated through local authority regions and districts and operating from 74 offices.

Women's Rural Institutes, Scottish (1917), 42 Heriot Row, Edinburgh, EH3 6ES. T.-031-225 1724. Chairman: Mrs I.D. MacKenzie; Vice Chairmen: Mrs M. Mackie, Mrs B. Kelly; Hon. Treasurer: Mrs N. Whamond. General Secretary: Mrs J.A. Noble; Handicrafts and Housewives Secretary: Mrs Nicol; Education Secretary: Miss H. Dennis.
Scottish Women's Rural Institutes are groups of women who meet together in centres throughout Scotland. The objects of the movement are to provide social, educational, and recreational opportunities for those who live and work in the country or are interested in country life.

Woollen Industry, Scottish (1984), 45 Moray Place, Edinburgh, EH3 6EQ. T.-031-225 3149. Chairman: J.A. Packer; Vice Chairman: R.F. Gray. Director: Fergus M. Wood; Training and Industrial Relations Officer: W.J.R. Ritchie; Promotions Manager: Anne Critchley. Formed from five organisations. Represents the weaving, spinning, and associated service companies in Scotland, and has as its principal role the corporate promotion of the industry. There are two main arms: a Training and Industrial Relations Council and a Publicity Council. In addition, a Technical Committee looks after the research and technical needs of the industry. There are 47 members with a total workforce of some 4,500.

Workers' Educational Association, The. West of Scotland District, 212 Bath Street, Glasgow, G2 4HW. T.-041-332 0176. Secretary: Jean Barr. North of Scotland District, 163 King Street, Aberdeen, AB2 3AE. T.-0224 642725. Secretary: Margaret Marshall. South East Scotland District: Riddles Court, 322 Lawnmarket, Edinburgh, EH1 2PG. T.-031-226 3456. Secretary: Colin Kirkwood. Provides and promotes adult education for all, particularly the educationally and socially disadvantaged.

Writers, Scottish Association of. Hon. Secretary: James Muir, 150 East Princes Street, Helensburgh, G84 7DN. T.-Helensburgh 3722. President: Robin Lloyd-Jones; Treasurer: Sandie Shaw. Exists to promote the art and craft of writing in all its forms. The Association organises conferences, competitions, and weekend schools for its members.

Writers to H.M. Signet, Society of (1594), Signet Library, Parliament Square, Edinburgh, EH1 1RF. T.-031-225 4923. Keeper of the Signet: Earl of Wemyss and March, K.T. Council: Peter C. Millar, Deputy Keeper; Ian T. Johnstone, Treasurer; David C. Fulton, Fiscal; Iain W. Noble, Professor of Conveyancing, Edinburgh University; D. John McNeil, Collector of the Dependants' Annuity Fund; and 21 other members of the Society. Clerk to the Society: Andrew M. Kerr.
Originally, the Signet was the private seal of the early Stuart kings, and the Writers to the Signet were those authorised to supervise its use and, later, to act as clerks to the Courts. The earliest recorded use of the Signet was in 1369, but the Society did not take definite shape until 1594, when the King's Secretary, as Keeper of the Signet, granted Commissions to a Deputy Keeper and 18 other writers. The function of the Society has changed much since then, but every summons initiating an action in the Court of Session still 'passes the Signet', meaning that it is stamped with the Royal seal. The present Signet was made by the Royal Mint in 1954. Today, the Society is consulted on many legal matters and is represented on the governing bodies of many organisations. There are about 850 members, most being solicitors in private practice in Edinburgh. The Society is particularly noted for its

ownership of the Signet Library, one of the finest Georgian buildings in the country. The Library contains about 63,000 books, of which almost half are legal.

Y

Yachting Association Scotland, Royal, 18 Ainslie Place, Edinburgh, EH3 6AU. T.-031-226 4401. Hon. Secretary: S. Glanvill.

Y.M.C.A.s, Scottish National Council of (1875), 11 Rutland Street, Edinburgh, EH1 2AE. T.-031-228 1464. President, Scottish National Union of Y.M.C.A.s: Robert B. Jack; Chairman, Scottish National Council of Y.M.C.A.s: Keith McIntosh. General Secretary: James C.B. Thomson; Secretary for Personnel and Training: Robert King; Secretary for Christian Education and Programme: Colin McAulay; Director of Sport and Recreation: George M. Ross; Regional Secretary, Strathclyde Federation of Y.M.C.A.s: Gilbert Dickson. Educational and physical activities based on the Christian ethic. Hostel management, hotels, conference centres, apartments for young homeless people; work with the community using the skills of the unemployed and youth training.

Young Enterprise Scotland, 41 Balgreen Road, Edinburgh, EH12 5TY. T.-031-337 1942. Director: Dundas Thorburn. Part of a U.K. scheme offering young people the opportunity of operating an industrial enterprise, a scale-model company, on a voluntary, part-time basis. The scheme caters primarily for young people who are still at school, giving them an understanding of industry.

Young Farmers' Clubs, Scottish Association of (1938), Young Farmers' Centre, Ingliston, Newbridge, Midlothian, EH28 8NE. T.-031-333 2445/6. Chairman: W.J. Davidson. Director: D.Y. Brown; National Field Officer: Miss M.R. Whiteford; National Administrative Officer: Miss H.S. Paton. An association of 140 young farmers' clubs with 6,500 members throughout Scotland. The Association provides a balanced programme of educational, recreational, cultural, competitive, and social activities, including international work.

Youth Clubs, Scottish Association of (1933), Balfour House, 17 Bonnington Grove, Edinburgh, EH6 4DP. T.-031-554 2561. Chairman: Allan F. Blacklaws, O.B.E.; Vice Chairmen: The Hon. E.D. Bruce, William G. Hawthorne, M.B.E.; Treasurer: Ian C. Lewis. Director: Audrey W. Milan; Youth Work Manager: Zander Jack. The Association's objective is to give young people opportunities for enjoyable and constructive leisure-time activities. It supports voluntary adult helpers, clubs, and area associations, carries out a programme of competitive and non-competitive sport, trains senior members and leaders, and arranges conferences for young people. Membership: 113,000 young people in 1,088 clubs, and 7,500 adults, mainly voluntary workers.

Youth Hostels Association, Scottish (1931), National Office, 7 Glebe Crescent, Stirling, FK8 2JA. T.-0786 72821. Chairman: J.P. Lawson. General

Secretary: J. Martin; Assistant Secretary: T. Muir Wright. The S.Y.H.A.'s main objective is to provide value for money accommodation in its 80 hostels across the country for the young and 'young at heart'. In addition, the Association offers a wide variety of summer and winter activity holidays, hostelling for all the family, and conference facilities.

Youth Orchestras, National Association of (1961), Ainslie House, 11 St. Colme Street, Edinburgh, EH3 6AG. T.-031-225 4606. Chairman: Michael Rose. Secretary/Co-ordinator: Carol Main. Represents youth orchestras and inter-school orchestras throughout the country and fosters their development. The Association has presented five successive Festivals of British Youth Orchestras during the Edinburgh International Festival.

Youth Theatre, Scottish (1977), 48 Albany Street, Edinburgh, EH1 3QR. T.-031-557 2224/0962. Chairman: Dr Tom Kinninmont; Vice Chairman: Andrew McCallum. Artistic Director: Robin Peoples; Administrator: Carolyn Lappin. Established to give young people aged between 12 and 21 the opportunity to be involved in theatre arts of a high standard, and in so doing to develop their artistic, social, and individual skills and interests. The S.Y.T.'s main activities include an annual summer festival, a national workshop programme, a young playwrights' festival, and a national television course.

Y.W.C.A. of Great Britain, Scottish National Council (1855), 7 Randolph Crescent, Edinburgh, EH3 7TH. T.-031-225 7592. President: Mrs R.A. Dingwall Smith; Convener of Scottish Executive: Mrs H. Birrell. General Secretary (Scotland): Miss S.A. Moyes; Assistant General Secretary: Mrs M. Dawson; Training Officer: Mrs E. Macdonald; Appeal Director: Mrs K. Steele. Membership of the Y.W.C.A. of Great Britain is open to girls and boys over the age of seven, and to women and men regardless of religion, race, or creed. The Y.W.C.A. provides a wide range of leisure activities and community services, and is involved with issues of concern, such as the environment, human rights, peace education, and health.

Z

Zoological Society of Glasgow and the West of Scotland (1936), Glasgow Zoo, Calderpark, Uddingston, Glasgow, G71 7RZ. T.-041-771 1185. President of Council: W.R.S. MacKenzie; Vice Presidents: Dr A. Young, T.D., J.B. MacWilliam. Director/Secretary: R.J.P. O'Grady; Curator: Lutz Kuschinski; Education Officer: Stephen Bostock. To develop and maintain zoological gardens worthy of the West of Scotland. The zoo was opened to the public in 1947; it attracts 150,000 visitors every year.

Zoological Society of Scotland, Royal (1913), Murrayfield, Edinburgh, EH12 6TS. T.-031-334 9171. President: Rt. Hon. Viscount of Arbuthnott, D.S.C.; Vice President and Hon. Treasurer: F. Wilson Horne, O.B.E., J.P.; Vice Presidents: Dr John Berry, C.B.E., Professor Sir Alexander Robertson, C.B.E.; Executive Committee: F. Wilson Horne (Chairman), Dr A.S. Clarke, Dr J.M. Deag, Margaret Elliot, H.W. Gillon, Dr R.A. Kille, K.A. McLellan, M.B.E., Dr Elizabeth Rogers, Professor J.C. Smyth. Director: R.J. Wheater; Curator of Animals: Miranda F. Stevenson.

To promote, facilitate, and encourage the study of zoology and kindred subjects, and to foster and develop an interest in and a knowledge of animal life. The Society has its own zoo, the Scottish National Zoological Park, promotes research into animal life, and conducts an extensive educational programme.

SCOTLAND'S PARLIAMENTARY CONSTITUENCIES

Results of the General Election of June 1983 in each of the Scottish Parliamentary constituencies are set out below. There have been no changes of representation in any of the Scottish constituencies since the General Election.

Aberdeen North. R. Hughes (Lab.) 19,262; C.S. Deans (S.D.P./All.) 10,118; Mrs G. Scanlan (Con.) 7,426; J.A. McGugan (S.N.P.) 3,790; Ms. M. Harty (Ecology) 367. Lab. Maj.: 9,144.

Aberdeen South. G. Malone (Con.) 15,393; R. Middleton (Lab.) 11,812; I.G. Philip (S.D.P./All.) 10,372; S. Coull (S.N.P.) 1,974. Con. Maj.: 3,581.

Angus East. P.L. Fraser (Con.) 19,218; A. Welsh (S.N.P.) 15,691; Miss P. Hammond (S.D.P./All.) 4,978; C. McConnell (Lab.) 3,497; Mrs P. Ross (Ecology) 239. Con. Maj.: 3,527.

Argyll and Bute. J. MacKay (Con.) 13,380; Mrs J.R. Michie (Lib./All.) 9,536; I. Smith (S.N.P.) 8,514; C. McCafferty (Lab.) 3,204. Con. Maj.: 3,844.

Ayr. G.K. Younger (Con.) 21,325; K. MacDonald (Lab.) 13,338; C. Brodie (Lib./All.) 12,740; I. Goldie (S.N.P.) 2,431. Con. Maj.: 7,987.

Banff and Buchan. A. McQuarrie (Con.) 16,072; D. Henderson (S.N.P.) 15,135; E. Needham (S.D.P./All.) 6,084; I.F.R. Lloyd (Lab.) 3,150. Con. Maj.: 937.

Caithness and Sutherland. R. Maclennan (S.D.P./All.) 12,119; A. Scouller (Con.) 5,276; D. Carrigan (Lab.) 3,325; J. Ingram (S.N.P.) 2,568. S.D.P./All. Maj.: 6,843.

Carrick, Cumnock and Doon Valley. G. Foulkes (Lab.) 21,394; J. McInnes (Con.) 10,024; R. Logan (S.D.P./All.) 7,421; R. Wyllie (S.N.P.) 2,694. Lab. Maj.: 11,370.

Clackmannan. M. O'Neill (Lab.) 16,478; Mrs J. Jones (S.N.P.) 6,839; C. Hendry (Con.) 6,490; Mrs H. Campbell (S.D.P./All.) 6,205. Lab. Maj.: 9,639.

Clydebank & Milngavie. H. McCartney (Lab.) 17,288; J. Gourlay (S.D.P./All.) 9,573; R. Graham (Con.) 7,852; A. Aitken (S.N.P.) 3,566; J. Bollan (Communist) 308. Lab. Maj.: 7,715.

Clydesdale. Dame J. Hart (Lab.) 17,873; P. Bainbridge (Con.) 13,007; Miss M. Craig (S.D.P./All.) 9,908; T. McAlpine (S.N.P.) 5,271. Lab. Maj.: 4,866.

Cumbernauld and Kilsyth. N. Hogg (Lab.) 16,629; D. Herbison (S.D.P./All.) 6,701; G. Murray (S.N.P.) 5,875; Mrs A. Thompson (Con.) 4,590. Lab. Maj.: 9,928.

Cunninghame North. J. Corrie (Con.) 15,557; J.N. Carson (Lab.) 13,920; R. Leishman (S.D.P./All.) 7,268; C. Cameron (S.N.P.) 3,460. Con. Maj.: 1,637.

Cunninghame South. D. Lambie (Lab.) 19,344; P. Gallie (Con.) 7,576; J. Boss (Lib./All.) 6,370; Mrs K. Ullrich (S.N.P.) 2,451. Lab. Maj.: 11,768.

Dumbarton. I. Campbell (Lab.) 15,810; I. Lawson (Con.) 13,695; R. Sawyer (S.D.P./All.) 9,813; I. Bayne (S.N.P.) 3,768. Lab. Maj.: 2,115.

Dumfries. Sir H. Monro (Con.) 18,730; J. McCall (S.D.P./All.) 10,036; T. McAughtrie (Lab.) 8,764; E. Gibson (S.N.P.) 4,527. Con. Maj.: 8,694.

Dundee East. G. Wilson (S.N.P.) 20,276; C. Bowman (Lab.) 15,260; Mrs B. Vaughan (Con.) 7,172; S. Rottger (Lib./All.) 3,546. S.N.P. Maj.: 5,016.

Dundee West. E. Ross (Lab.) 20,288; D. Senior (Con.) 10,138; Mrs E. Dick (S.D.P./All.) 7,976; J. Lynch (S.N.P.) 7,973; P. Marks (Ecology) 302. Lab. Maj.: 10,150.

Dunfermline East. G. Brown (Lab.) 18,515; D. Harcus (Lib./All.) 7,214; C. Shenton (Con.) 6,764; G. Hunter (S.N.P.) 2,573; A. Maxwell (Communist) 864. Lab. Maj.: 11,301.

Dunfermline West. R. Douglas (Lab.) 12,998; Dr P. Davison (Con.) 10,524; F. Moyes (S.D.P./All.) 9,434; J. Fairlie (S.N.P.) 2,798; S. Dobson (Ecology) 321. Lab. Maj.: 2,474.

East Kilbride. Dr M.S. Miller (Lab.) 17,535; D. Sullivan (S.D.P./All.) 13,199; R. Dalkeith (Con.) 11,483; D. Urquhart (S.N.P.) 4,795; W. Doolan (Communist) 256. Lab. Maj.: 4,336.

East Lothian. J. Home Robertson (Lab.) 20,934; M. Fry (Con.) 14,693; M. Kibby (Lib./All.) 9,950; R. Knox (S.N.P.) 2,083. Lab. Maj.: 6,241.

Eastwood. A. Stewart (Con.) 21,072; J. Pickett (S.D.P./All.) 12,477; J. McGuire (Lab.) 9,083; Ms J. Herriot (S.N.P.) 2,618. Con. Maj.: 8,595.

Edinburgh Central. A. Fletcher (Con.) 14,095; R. Kelley (Lab.) 11,529; Dr M. Macleod (S.D.P./All.) 9,498; R. Halliday (S.N.P.) 1,810; D. Carson (Communist) 119. Con. Maj.: 2,566.

Edinburgh East. G. Strang (Lab.) 16,169; P. Martin (Con.) 10,303; R. Macleod (Lib./All.) 7,570; P. Scott (S.N.P.) 1,976. Lab. Maj.: 5,866.

Edinburgh Leith. R. Brown (Lab.) 16,177; D. Graham (S.D.P./All.) 11,204; B. Cooklin (Con.) 10,706; J. Young (S.N.P.) 2,646. Lab. Maj.: 4,973.

Edinburgh Pentlands. M. Rifkind (Con.) 17,051; K. Smith (S.D.P./All.) 12,742; E. Milligan (Lab.) 10,390; N. MacCormick (S.N.P.) 2,642; A. Nicol-Smith (Ecology) 687. Con. Maj.: 4,309.

Edinburgh South. M. Ancram (Con.) 16,485; J. Godfrey (S.D.P./All.) 12,830; R. McCreadie (Lab.) 12,824; N. MacCallum (S.N.P.) 2,256; Mrs L. Hendry (Ecology) 450. Con. Maj.: 3,655.

Edinburgh West. Lord J. Douglas-Hamilton (Con.) 17,646; D. King (Lib./All.) 17,148; A. Wood (Lab.) 9,313; J. Nicoll (S.N.P.) 2,126. Con. Maj.: 498.

Falkirk East. H. Ewing (Lab.) 17,956; D. Masterton (Con.) 7,895; A. Wedderburn (S.D.P./All.) 6,967; J. MacGregor (S.N.P.) 4,490; Miss F. McGregor (Communist) 334. Lab. Maj.: 10,061.

Falkirk West. D. Canavan (Lab.) 16,668; I. Mitchell (Con.) 7,690; M. Harris (Lib./All.) 7,477; B. Cochrane (S.N.P.) 4,739. Lab. Maj.: 8,978.

Fife Central. W.W. Hamilton (Lab.) 17,008; Mrs T. Little (Lib./All.) 9,214; D. Mason (Con.) 8,863; J. Taggart (S.N.P.) 4,039; D. Allison (Ecology) 297. Lab. Maj.: 7,794.

Fife North East. J.S.B. Henderson (Con.) 17,129; M. Campbell (Lib./All.) 14,944; Dr J.K.M. Hulbert (S.N.P.) 2,442; D. Caldwell (Lab.) 2,429; T.G. Flinn (Ecology) 242. Con. Maj.: 2,185.

Galloway and Upper Nithsdale. I. Lang (Con.) 17,579; G. Thompson (S.N.P.) 12,118; G. Douglas (Lib./All.) 5,129; M.B. Miller (Lab.) 4,464. Con. Maj.: 5,461.

Glasgow Cathcart. J. Maxton (Lab.) 16,037; D. May (Con.) 11,807; K. Bloomer (S.D.P./All.) 8,710; W. Steven (S.N.P.) 2,151. Lab. Maj.: 4,230.

Glasgow Central. R. McTaggart (Lab.) 17,066; W. Harvey (Con.) 6,104; Mrs I. Nelson (Lib./All.) 5,366; P. Mallan (S.N.P.) 3,300; J. McGoldrick (Communist) 347. Lab. Maj.: 10,962.

Glasgow Garscadden. D. Dewar (Lab.) 19,635; W. Lyden (S.D.P./All.) 6,161; K. Macleod (Con.) 5,368; N. MacLeod (S.N.P.) 3,566; S.A. Barr (Communist) 218. Lab. Maj.: 13,474.

Glasgow Govan. B. Millan (Lab.) 20,370; I. McDonald (S.D.P./All.) 7,313; A. Mackenzie (Con.) 7,180; P. Kindlen (S.N.P.) 2,207. Lab. Maj.: 13,057.

Glasgow Hillhead. R. Jenkins (S.D.P./All.) 14,856; N. Carmichael (Lab.) 13,692; M. Tosh (Con.) 9,638; G. Leslie (S.N.P.) 2,203; J. Davidson (Independent Conservative) 249; A. Whitelaw (Ecology) 239; J. Robins (A.V.), 139. S.D.P./All. Maj.: 1,164.

Glasgow Maryhill. J. Craigen (Lab.) 18,724; Ms E. Attwooll (Lib./All.) 7,521; J. Gibbs (Con.) 5,014; I. Morrison (S.N.P.) 2,408; P. Smith (Communist) 274. Lab. Maj.: 11,203.

Glasgow Pollok. J. White (Lab.) 18,973; J. Carlaw (Con.) 7,441; G. McKell (Lib./All.) 6,308; F. Hannigan (S.N.P.) 3,585. Lab. Maj.: 11,532.

Glasgow Provan. H.D. Brown (Lab.) 20,040; A. Heron (S.D.P./All.) 4,655; Miss S. Gordon (Con.) 3,374; Ms P. Kennedy (S.N.P.) 2,737; I. Jackson (Communist) 294. Lab. Maj.: 15,385.

Glasgow Rutherglen. J.G. Mackenzie (Lab.) 21,510; R. Brown (Lib./All.) 12,384; Mrs H. Hodgins (Con.) 8,017; K. Fee (S.N.P.) 2,438; C. Corrigan (Workers' Revolutionary Party) 148. Lab. Maj.: 9,126.

Glasgow Shettleston. D. Marshall (Lab.) 19,203; I. Henderson (Con.) 6,787; S. Strachen (Lib./All.) 6,568; D. Hood (S.N.P.) 2,801; K. Hill (British National Party) 103. Lab. Maj.: 12,416.

Glasgow Springburn. M.J. Martin (Lab.) 22,481; J. Kelly (Lib./All.) 4,882; D. Tweedie (Con.) 4,565; J. McLaughlin (S.N.P.) 2,804. Lab. Maj.: 17,599.

Gordon. M. Bruce (Lib./All.) 20,134; J. Cran (Con.) 19,284; G. Grant (Lab.) 3,899; K. Guild (S.N.P.) 2,636. Lib./All. Maj.: 850.

Greenock and Port Glasgow. N.A. Godman (Lab.) 20,650; A. Blair (Lib./All.) 16,025; C. Crichton (Con.) 4,314; A. Clayton (S.N.P.) 2,989; G. McKinlay (Workers' Revolutionary Party) 114. Lab. Maj.: 4,625.

Hamilton. G. Robertson (Lab.) 24,384; S. Donaldson (Lib./All.) 9,365; Mrs M. Scott (Con.) 8,940; Mrs M. Whitehead (S.N.P.) 3,816. Lab. Maj.: 15,019.

Inverness, Nairn and Lochaber. R. Johnston (Lib./All.) 20,671; D.G. Maclean (Con.) 13,373; D. MacMillan (Lab.) 6,448; H. Vernal (S.N.P.) 4,395. Lib./All. Maj.: 7,298.

Kilmarnock and Loudoun. W. McKelvey (Lab.) 20,250; R. Leckie (Con.) 11,450; A. Ross (S.D.P./All.) 10,545; C. Calman (S.N.P.) 4,165. Lab. Maj.: 8,800.

Kincardine and Deeside. A. Buchanan-Smith (Con.) 20,293; S. Waugh (Lib./All.) 12,497; Mrs M. Morell (Lab.) 6,472; A. Tuttle (S.N.P.) 3,297. Con. Maj.: 7,796.

Kirkcaldy. H. Gourlay (Lab.) 15,380; I. Walker (Con.) 10,049; M. Black (S.D.P./All.) 9,724; D. Wood (S.N.P.) 3,452. Lab. Maj.: 5,331.

Linlithgow. T. Dalyell (Lab.) 19,694; C. Jones (Con.) 8,333; D. Ramsay (S.N.P.) 8,026; P. Cockcroft (S.D.P./All.) 7,432; Dr M. Parnell (Communist) 199. Lab. Maj.: 11,361.

Livingston. R. Cook (Lab.) 14,255; A. Henderson (Lib./All.) 9,304; J. Campbell (Con.) 9,129; K. MacAskill (S.N.P.) 5,090. Lab. Maj.: 4,951.

Midlothian. A. Eadie (Lab.) 19,401; A. Dewar (S.D.P./All.) 13,245; D. Menzies (Con.) 9,922; Mrs M. Hird (S.N.P.) 2,826. Lab. Maj.: 6,156.

Monklands East. J. Smith (Lab.) 18,358; J. Love (Con.) 8,559; A. Rennie (Lib./All.) 5,721; T. Johnston (S.N.P.) 3,185. Lab. Maj.: 9,799.

Monklands West. T. Clarke (Lab.) 20,642; L. Cameron (Con.) 8,378; R. Ackland (S.D.P./All.) 6,605; A. Lyon (S.N.P.) 2,473. Lab. Maj.: 12,264.

Moray. A. Pollock (Con.) 16,944; H. Watt (S.N.P.) 15,231; M. Burnett (Lib./All.) 7,901; J. Kiddie (Lab.) 3,139. Con. Maj.: 1,713.

Motherwell North. J. Hamilton (Lab.) 24,483; R. Hargrave (Con.) 6,589; G. Whitelaw (Lib./All.) 5,970; R. Lyle (S.N.P.) 5,333. Lab. Maj.: 17,894.

Motherwell South. J. Bray (Lab.) 19,939; P. Walker (Con.) 7,590; B. Ashley (Lib./All.) 6,754; J. Wright (S.N.P.) 3,743. Lab. Maj.: 12,349.

Orkney and Shetland. J. Wallace (Lib./All.) 9,374; D. Myles (Con.) 5,224; Mrs W. Ewing (S.N.P.) 3,147; Ms R. Goodlad (Lab.) 2,665. Lib./All. Maj.: 4,150.

Paisley North. A. Adams (Lab.) 15,782; Miss A. McCartin (S.D.P./All.) 8,195; B. Townsend (Con.) 7,425; H. Morrell (S.N.P.) 2,783; Dr N. Carlaw (Ecology) 439. Lab. Maj.: 7,587.

Paisley South. N. Buchan (Lab.) 15,633; Mrs E. Buchanan (Lib./All.) 9,104; J. Knox (Con.) 7,819; J. Mitchell (S.N.P.) 4,918; D. Mellor (Ecology) 271. Lab. Maj.: 6,529.

Perth and Kinross. N. Fairbairn (Con.) 17,888; D. Crawford (S.N.P.) 11,155; B. Coutts (Lib./All.) 10,997; A.J. Stuart (Lab.) 4,414. Con. Maj.: 6,733.

Renfrew West and Inverclyde. Mrs A. McCurley (Con.) 13,669; J.D. Mabon (S.D.P./All.) 12,347; G. Doherty (Lab.) 12,139; W. Taylor (S.N.P.) 3,653. Con. Maj.: 1,322.

Ross, Cromarty and Skye. C. Kennedy (S.D.P./All.) 13,528; H. Gray (Con.) 11,824; M. Elder (Lab.) 4,901; Miss K. Matheson (S.N.P.) 4,863. S.D.P./ All. Maj.: 1,704.

Roxburgh and Berwickshire. A. Kirkwood (Lib./All.) 15,920; I. Sproat (Con.) 12,524; D.A. Briggs (Lab.) 2,326; R. Shirley (S.N.P.) 852. Lib./All. Maj.: 3,396.

Stirling. M. Forsyth (Con.) 17,039; M. Connarty (Lab.) 11,906; R. Finnie (Lib./All.) 10,174; W. Houston (S.N.P.) 3,488. Con. Maj.: 5,133.

Strathkelvin and Bearsden. M. Hirst (Con.) 17,501; R. Waddell (Lib./All.) 13,801; A.P. Ingram (Lab.) 12,308; Mrs M. Bain (S.N.P.) 4,408. Con. Maj.: 3,700.

Tayside North. W.C. Walker (Con.) 19,269; A. Morgan (S.N.P.) 9,170; D. Skene (Lib./All.) 7,255; N. Wylie (Lab.) 2,057. Con. Maj.: 10,099.

Tweeddale, Ettrick and Lauderdale. D.L. Steel (Lib./All.) 16,868; A. Ballantine (Con.) 8,329; M. Saren (Lab.) 2,200; A. Macartney (S.N.P.) 1,455. Lib./All. Maj.: 8,539.

Western Isles. D.J. Stewart (S.N.P.) 8,272; B.D.H. Wilson (Lab.) 4,560; M. Morrison (Con.) 1,460; N. McLeod (Lib./All.) 876. S.N.P. Maj.: 3,712.

APPENDIX I

Chronology of Scottish Institutions

The following institutions, with their year of foundation, are among the oldest surviving in Scotland, all being at least 200 years old.

University of St. Andrews 1410
University of Glasgow 1451
University of Aberdeen 1495
Royal College of Surgeons of Edinburgh 1505
Faculty of Advocates 1532*
University of Edinburgh 1583
Society of Writers to H.M. Signet 1594
Royal College of Physicians and Surgeons of Glasgow 1599
Royal College of Physicians of Edinburgh 1681
Bank of Scotland 1695
Royal Bank of Scotland 1727
Royal and Ancient Golf Club 1745
British Linen Bank 1746
Society of Antiquaries of Scotland 1780
National Museum of Antiquities of Scotland 1781
Glasgow Herald 1782
Glasgow Chamber of Commerce 1783
Royal Society of Edinburgh 1783
Royal Highland and Agricultural Society of Scotland 1784
Society of Solicitors in the Supreme Courts of Scotland 1784

*approximate date

APPENDIX II

Glossary of Abbreviations

The following is a list of abbreviations used for a selected number of the organisations listed in the A to Z section.

A.C.A.S. .... Advisory Conciliation and Arbitration Service
A.F.R.C. .... Agricultural Food Research Centre
C.A.B. ....Citizens Advice Bureau
C.B.I. ....Confederation of British Industry
C. of S. .... Church of Scotland
C.O.S.L.A. .... Convention of Scottish Local Authorities
E.I.S. .... Educational Institute of Scotland
H.I.D.B. .... Highlands and Islands Development Board
I.B.A. .... Independent Broadcasting Authority
M.S.C. .... Manpower Services Commission
N.C.B. ....National Coal Board
N.F.U. ....National Farmers' Union of Scotland
R. & A. .... Royal and Ancient Golf Club
R.I.A.S. .... Royal Incorporation of Architects in Scotland
R.I.C.S. .... Royal Institution of Chartered Surveyors
R.o.S.P.A. .... Royal Society for the Prevention of Accidents
R.S.A. .... Royal Scottish Academy
R.S.A.M.D. ....Royal Scottish Academy of Music and Drama
R.S.P.B. ....Royal Society for the Protection of Birds
R.S.S.P.C.C. .... Royal Scottish Society for Prevention of Cruelty to Children
S.A.B.E.U. .... Scottish Adult Basic Education Unit
S.A.C. .... Scottish Arts Council
S.A.C.R.O. .... Scottish Association for the Care and Resettlement of
Offenders
S.A.I. ....Scottish Agricultural Industries
S.C.C.L. ....Scottish Council for Civil Liberties
S.C.D.A. .... Scottish Community Drama Association
SCOTBEC ....Scottish Business Education Council
SCOTBIC ....Scottish Business in the Community
SCOTEC .... Scottish Technical Education Council
S.C.R.A.M. .... Scottish Campaign to Resist the Atomic Menace
S.C.P. .... Scottish Conservation Projects Trust
S.D.A. .... Scottish Development Agency
S.E.D. ....Scotttish Education Department
S.F.A. .... Scottish Football Association
S.M.T.A. .... Scottish Motor Trade Association
S.N.O. .... Scottish National Orchestra
S.N.P. .... Scottish National Party
S.S.H.A. ....Scottish Special Housing Association
S.S.P. ....Scottish Society of Playwrights
S.S.P.C.A. .... Scottish Society for Prevention of Cruelty to Animals
S.S.T.A. ....Scottish Secondary Teachers' Association
S.T.U.C. .... Scottish Trades Union Congress
S.T.V. .... Scottish Television
S.W.R.I. ....Scottish Women's Rural Institutes
S.Y.H.A. .... Scottish Youth Hostels Association

W.E.A. .... The Workers' Educational Association
W.R.V.S. ....Women's Royal Voluntary Service
Y.M.C.A.s .... Young Men's Christian Associations
Y.W.C.A. .... Young Women's Christian Association

APPENDIX III

Useful Telephone Numbers

The following is a list of the telephone numbers of 100 prominent organisations whose full entries may be consulted in the A to Z section.

Aberdeen District Council	0224 642121
University of Aberdeen	0224 40241
Royal Scottish Academy	031-225 6671
Department of Agriculture and Fisheries for Scotland	031-443 4020
Bank of Scotland	031-229 2555
B.B.C. Scotland	041-339 8844
Borders Regional Council	0835 23301
Confederation of British Industry (Scotland)	041-332 8661
British Rail (Scottish Region)	041-332 9811
British Telecom Scotland	031-229 2525
Central Regional Council	0786 73111
Institute of Chartered Accountants of Scotland	031-225 5673
Church of Scotland	031-225 5722
Citizens' Theatre, Glasgow	041-429 5560
Scottish Civic Trust	041-221 1466
Clydesdale Bank	041-248 7070
Comhairle nan Eilean (Western Isles Islands Council)	0851 3773
Scottish Conservative Party	031-226 4426
Scottish Consumer Council	041-226 5261
Countryside Commission for Scotland	0738 27921
Court of Session	031-225 2595
Crofters Commission	0463 237231
Crown Office	031-557 3800
Scottish Development Agency	041-248 2700
Scottish Development Department	031-556 8400
The Distillers Company plc	031-337 7373
Dumfries and Galloway Regional Council	0387 53141
Dundee District Council	0382 23141
University of Dundee	0382 23181
Edinburgh District Council	031-225 2424
Edinburgh Festival Society	031-226 4001
University of Edinburgh	031-667 1011
Educational Institute of Scotland	031-225 6244
Scottish Education Department	031-556 8400
South of Scotland Electricity Board	041-637 7177
Scottish Examination Board	031-663 6601
National Farmers Union of Scotland	031-337 4333
Fife Regional Council	0592 754411
Forestry Commission	031-334 0303
National Galleries of Scotland	031-556 8921
Scottish Gas	031-559 5000
General Accident Fire & Life Assurance Corporation plc	0738 21202
General Register Office for Scotland	031-556 3952
General Teaching Council for Scotland	031-556 0072
Glasgow District Council	041-221 9600
Glasgow Herald	041-552 6255

University of Glasgow 041-339 8855
Grampian Regional Council 0224 682222
Grampian Television 0224 646464
Heriot-Watt University 031-225 8432
Royal Highland and Agricultural Society of Scotland 031-333 2444
Highland Regional Council 0463 234121
Highlands and Islands Development Board 0463 234171
Historic Buildings Council for Scotland 031-226 3611
Scottish Home and Health Department 031-556 8501
Industry Department for Scotland 031-556 8400
Labour Party, Scottish Council 041-332 8946
Scottish Law Commission 031-668 2131
Law Society of Scotland 031-226 7411
Scottish Liberal Party 031-337 2314
National Library of Scotland 031-226 4531
Convention of Scottish Local Authorities 031-225 1626
Lothian Regional Council 031-229 9292
British Medical Association 031-225 7184
Scottish Milk Marketing Board 041-887 1234
Royal Scottish Museum 031-225 7534
Scottish National Party 031-226 3661
North of Scotland Hydro-Electric Board 031-225 1361
Scottish Opera 041-332 3321
Scottish National Orchestra 041-332 7244
Orkney Islands Council 0856 3535
Parole Board for Scotland 031-661 6181
Pitlochry Festival Theatre 0796 3054
Scottish Postal Board 031-228 7200
Scottish Society for Prevention of Cruelty to Animals 031-225 6418
Royal Scottish Society for Preventionof Cruelty to Children 031-337 8539
Roman Catholic Church 041-221 1168
Royal and Ancient Golf Club 0334 72112
Royal Bank of Scotland 031-556 8555
The Saltire Society 031-228 6621
The Scotsman 031-225 2468
Scottish Council (Development and Industry) 031-225 7911
Scottish Office 031-556 8400
Sea Fish Industry Authority 031-225 2515
Shetland Islands Council 0595 3535
Scottish Council for Spastics 031-337 9876
Scottish Special Housing Association 031-225 1281
Scottish Sports Council 031-225 8411
University of St. Andrews 0334 76161
University of Stirling 0786 73171
Strathclyde Regional Council 041-204 2900
University of Strathclyde 041-552 4400
Tayside Regional Council 0382 23281
Scottish Television 041-332 9999
Scottish Tourist Board 031-332 2433
Scottish Trades Union Congress 041-332 4946
Scottish Transport Group 031-226 7491
National Trust for Scotland 031-226 5922
Scottish Wildlife Trust 031-226 4602
Scottish Women's Rural Institutes 031-225 1724

INDEX

Agriculture and Fisheries

Armed Services

Artistic and Cultural Organisations

174   The Scottish Companion

Consumer Organisations

Countryside Interests

Development Corporations

Educational Bodies

Health and Medicine

International Interests

Legal and Judicial Bodies

Learned Societies

Local Authorities

Major Companies

Newspapers and Broadcasting Organisations

Political Parties and Pressure Groups

Professional Organisations

Recreation and Leisure

Research Institutes

River and Port Authorities

Sports Organisations

Tourist Organisations

Voluntary and Charitable Organisations

Women's Organisations

Youth Organisations